Gunship: *Spect...* ...

Henry Zeybel is a ...   ...e U.S.
Air Force. He ser...   ...l the
Silver Star, eight l
nineteen Air Medals.

Also by **Henry Zeybel** in Pan Books

The First Ace

Henry Zeybel

Gunship:

Spectre of Death

Pan Books
London, Sydney and Auckland

This novel is a work of fiction. Names, characters, places and
incidents are either the product of the author's imagination or
are used fictitiously. Any resemblance to actual events or locales
or persons, living or dead, is entirely coincidental.

First published in the USA 1987 by Pocket Books,
Simon & Schuster, Inc. 1230 Avenue of the Americas, New York, 10020
First published in Great Britain by Pan Books Ltd,
Cavaye Place, London SW10 9PG
9 8 7 6 5 4 3 2 1
© Henry Zeybel 1987
All rights reserved
ISBN 0 330 30472 0
Printed and bound in Great Britain by
Richard Clay Ltd, Bungay, Suffolk

To Karen

Who would not want to be the angel, high
Over the enemy's cities with wings
Broad as the foreshadow of death? What boy
Cannot recall from his pitiless dreams
That carnage laid about him in his bed. . . .

—Robley Wilson, Jr.

To a long and happy war!

—Joy Kauffman

Prologue

Is it possible Steel Tiger was a fantasy land?

Did we egotistically take credit for the technoviolence generated by machines, attribute to ourselves personalities that matched their power?

But machines lacked imagination. We were there to provide a spirit of victory.

Chapter 1

Come Together

THE SEASON I flew combat with the AC-130 Spectre gunships turned out to be like playing in the Super Bowl six nights a week and never losing. There were nights when the outcome was in doubt to the final minute, however, and I was happy to finish with a tie. Where Spectre played, over Laos, one loss put a team out of competition forever.

The AC-130 Spectre gunship was the final word in a line of weapon systems that evolved from the AC-47 Spooky through the AC-119 Stinger. Converted from cargo planes, gunships were designed to orbit slowly at low altitudes and to destroy targets with side-firing machine guns and cannons. The orbiting tactic was conceived by a brilliant young major after he read about small planes that delivered and picked up mail at jungle outposts by flying a tight pylon turn over a clearing and lowering a container on a rope. The major replaced the rope with a line of gunfire and a new weapon system was born. Among gunships, the four-engine AC-130 was the largest and carried the heaviest firepower and most sophisticated sensors for locating targets in darkness.

Spectre, officially designated the Sixteenth Special Operations Squadron (SOS), was an exclusive club. It owned the only twelve AC-130s in the air force inventory and manned them with eighteen crews. As a thirty-seven-year-old major who was returning to Southeast Asia (SEA) for a second time, I was given my choice of airplanes. Fulfilling a voluntary returnee's preference was the Air Force Personnel Center's way of rewarding madness. I chose Spectre.

During my previous SEA tour in 1967–1968, I had navigated a C-130 Hercules around South Vietnam and felt no desire to repeat that drudgery. I had my fill of being shot at; this time I wanted to shoot back.

I was qualified as a Strategic Air Command B-52 navigator-bombardier, but the idea of dumping iron bombs on the jungles of Laos and Cambodia from six miles up didn't satisfy me. Atari made games that were more exciting. And F-4 Phantom jet fighters, "fast movers" in air force talk, had a limited appeal for me. For a pilot, driving an F-4 was like being the image straight off an enlistment poster. However, from the F-4 back seat at Mach 2, twice the speed of sound, a navigator viewed the war as a series of strobe-light productions. He caught glimpses of action but never saw the entire picture.

Spectre fitted my needs perfectly. The AC-130 gunship was the only attack airplane in which navigators—five in each gunship—ran the war from front-row seats. A "table" navigator, who sat on the flight deck with the pilots and engineer, directed the course of the gunship, was in control until the sensor team found a target.

Four navigators made up a sensor team. They sat in the belly of the gunship, in a small room called "the booth," an artificial technoviolent world where they were as isolated as if in a space capsule orbiting and searching a planet of which they were no part. From among the crew of thirteen, they were the only men who couldn't see outside with the naked eye; yet they were the ones who viewed and controlled the killing. The electronic wizardry of their passive, unblinking sensors—low-light-level television (TV), side-looking infrared (IR), and an electro-magnetic radiation detector called the Black Crow (BC)—made them into icy gods who saw in the dark, granted them a touch of destructive magic.

In gunship nomenclature there was no difference between man and machine. "Sensor" and "TV" and "IR" and "BC" signified both the equipment and the men who operated that equipment.

I was a TV.

Basically, the AC-130 reduced the pilot to a puppet who depended upon navigators to lead him in battle. He followed the table nav's directions until the sensors found a target. At that point, he rolled into a thirty-degree left bank and circled the target. Then, by lining up a pair of electronic symbols on a computer display, he refined his orbit and thereby aimed the fixed side-firing guns at exactly where the sensor crosshairs were centered. When the computer symbols were aligned, he fired the guns. He depended upon the sensors to inform him of the results.

Spectre was a navigator's dream, a perfect toy.

As a bonus, the squadron operated out of Ubon Air Force Base in beautiful Thailand.

I returned to SEA in style. I flew commercial air to San Francisco, took a limo to Travis Air Force Base, and there boarded a chartered commercial airliner that carried me to Bangkok.

I planned the trip so that I spent a night in Frisco. Almost every GI did. They roamed the streets, got drunk, maybe picked up some stranger or got found by a hooker. I looked up a friend whom I hadn't seen since two years before on my way home. She had a batch of ambivalent feelings. To her, war was crazy and I was an asshole for going back, but she respected and admired anyone who willingly faced the danger.

We stuffed ourselves with green enchiladas, took in half a porno double bill *(The L.A. Ten Writhe Again)*, smoked some hash, then fucked each other to sleep. I did the hash only because it was a special time; I was never a pothead. Hell, I didn't even smoke cigarettes. Air force troops are damn straight. But that night in Frisco carried importance: last touch of the Real World, round eyes, and all that. Building Memory City. It was what made Tony Bennett's "I Left My Heart in San Francisco" a hit. When that number played overseas, a lot of guys got a dreamy look and spent a little time remembering whatever good happened to them on that last night.

There was plenty of thinking time between Travis and Bangkok. I remembered my last flight to SEA, my first trip to war . . .

I was amazed to recall that the first time I'd left for Southeast Asia I had actually cried. My wife and daughters had accompanied me to the airport. The farewell before boarding was not much different from a farewell if I'd been headed to work for the day. Earlier in the week June, my wife, had said, "You certainly are relaxed. If I was in your shoes, I'd be worried. You're going where you could get killed. I think about that. I wonder if you do. You don't seem to care that you're going." I'd taken being alive for granted until I was seated and waiting for the airliner to taxi. Then I was struck by the idea that my life was not my own. Was I a pawn of society? Was I being forced to go to war and to possible death? Anguish and self-pity suddenly became the orders of the day. Tears filled my eyes, rolled down my cheeks. I could hardly breathe. I unfastened my seatbelt, stood, and for several seconds mentally debated running off the airplane, saying fuck it to the air force.

As I headed into the unknown, my feelings warned me that I was doomed never again to see my two daughters, who would grow up fatherless; my wife would live the remainder of her life without me. Twelve thousand miles with misty vision!

I hated the memory of being so goddamn human.

This time there was no remorse. I was happy to be going back to war.

As it turned out, my first-time feelings had been exactly right. June divorced me a year later, right after I returned to the States. During that first tour I quickly tired of reading about the new social science teacher, the broken lawn mower, the car tune-up, the home insurance dividend, and the other mundane bullshit that June detailed in page after page after page. Somewhere along the way I decided that none of it related to me. By the end of the year I had a desk drawer filled with unopened and unanswered letters. The cruncher

5

came when I refused to meet her for R & R in Hawaii but later went to Bangkok and Hong Kong alone.

Being halfway around the world from ex-wives—Yes, I'd chalked up a second nuptial failure *(that* four-month escapade would have made the Marquis de Sade jump for joy) between the first divorce and the second SEA departure. Anyhow . . . being halfway around the world from ex-wives gave a man a hassle-free contentment that was impossible to find when only a phone call away.

Even the air force differed overseas, in a combat zone. For flyers, bullshit paperwork and arbitrary rules were waived or, at squadron level, ignored. At crew level, the average man's philosophy was simple: "I'm here for a year of flying, fighting, and fucking. Everything else sucks." I loved that attitude. The sad part about it was that too many men forgot that they enjoyed living that way when the war ended. They forgot the freedom that combat provided.

I bypassed the Philippines en route because I had completed jungle survival training at Clark Air Base my last time over. It was no loss. Missing a night in Angeles City, the slum outside Clark's main gate, was like missing clap. On my last trip I'd seen Huk machine gunners blow away three local politicians in front of my hotel, before breakfast. It was all I could do to eat my brains and eggs afterward. In lighter moments I'd watched the live fuck shows in the Angeles nightclubs. A classy town. When we overflew it, even from thirty thousand feet, I thought I smelled its rankness.

Upon reaching Bangkok, the good deal ended. Travel up-country to Ubon Royal Thai Air Force Base was by C-47, the old Goon. I decided to R & R in Bangkok for a few days before risking my life in one of those ancient birds. Bangkok's Don Muang Airport was still being modernized. In the two years since I last had seen it, the airport construction had proceeded unhampered by progress. I guessed the Thai builders planned to have the terminal ready for use in some future life, like sometime in the fourth millennium. By the time I found my A-3 and B-4 bags, I was sweating freely. I had forgotten how heavy the climate was. Both temperature and humidity were near one hundred.

It was the beginning of October 1970 and nearing the end of the rainy season. I waited through a downpour and thought about starting a rent-an-aqualung franchise. The rain washed the air, but in minutes the dense traffic refilled it with oil, gas, and benzene fumes. The blare of horns had never diminished. On the wet streets, the taxi ride to downtown was above average: *absolutely* terrifying. I was proud that I didn't shut my eyes and hold my breath but twice.

At the Florida Hotel I found a new crop of little golden maidens working the top floor. Along with jet lag, they took care of three days in Bangkok. A few of those girls were so tiny and sweet that a man could slip one on in the morning and wear her around all day.

Ubon Royal Thai Air Force Base was located on the eastern plains of Thailand, thirty-five miles from the Laotian border. Southwest of the base was Ubon Ratchatani; combined with Warin Chamrap, its smaller sister city south across the Mae Nam Muo, it claimed a population of forty thousand, a total that included five thousand registered prostitutes. The Mae Nam Muo flooded once a year and a major fire leveled a significant number of buildings about two of every three years; the disasters produced most of the urban development.

Upon attempting to deplane from the C-47 at Ubon, I was rammed in the chest and driven back aboard by a wild-eyed first lieutenant carrying a live turkey that pecked at my face. "Get that fucking bird off me," I shouted.

"Major . . ."—the wild-eyed lieutenant looked at my name tag—". . . Zorn, this isn't a fucking bird; this is Herky the Turkey. I'm Danny Dashout. Welcome to Ubon." He squeezed my hand and pushed by me. "Lieutenant Hamilton aboard?" he shouted.

The turkey gobbled insanely, loudly, while frantically flapping its wings and lunging about. Dashout managed to hold one skinny drumstick. Partially airborne, the bird pecked and fired streams of shit in several directions. Trapped in the small passenger compartment, the new arrivals took hits and fired curses in reply.

"Sorry 'bout that," Dashout shouted. "The poor bastard

7

can't tell one airplane from another. He's been messed up in the head since his fifteenth mission in a gunship. Hey, Hamilton!"

"Yo," a tall, neatly groomed lieutenant answered from the front of the passenger compartment.

By wrapping his arms around the turkey's wings, Dashout gained control of the bird and pushed his way toward Hamilton. "Glad to see you." He grinned. "I outrank you by two days, which makes you the junior officer in the squadron. I've checked and double-checked. Therefore, it's my pleasure to inform you that as of immediately you are assigned additional duty as Sixteenth Special Operations Squadron TCO—Turkey Control Officer—Keeper of the King Canary." He held out the bird.

"No way," Hamilton protested.

"No way, my ass." Dashout launched the bird into Hamilton's arms and it shit down the shirtfront of its new keeper. Hamilton turned red, muttered, and roughly wrapped a hand around the bird's neck. "Whoa!" Dashout warned. "Anything happens to Herky, man, it's your ass." He settled Herky into Hamilton's arms, patted both creatures on the head. "You'll learn to love him," he said, then turned and shouted, "Anybody assigned to Spec, Sixteenth SOS, follow me." He ran through the airplane, leaped from the cargo door, and skipped to a jeep that was hooked to a roofed trailer painted to resemble a carrousel. A loudspeaker on the trailer blared out "Ghost Riders in the Sky," the Spectre fight song.

"Major Z! Up front in the jeep," Dashout yelled at me. "You're ranking man this trip."

The kid was weak on military bearing but high on enthusiasm. I told him, "You can call me Hal, Lieutenant Dashout."

He nodded, then smiled. "That new guy better understand that Herky is *the* mascot on base. The Night Owls once had a cute little gray owl. At a dining-in, the chef carried a covered platter to the head table, lifted the lid, and—presto—owl, one each, fricasseed. The wing commander went ape laughing and everybody else sat around like they'd taken a fifty-seven magnum up the ass." Dashout scowled. "Anybody fries Herky, Hamilton dies." By then, Hamilton and Herky, the other new Spectres, and our bags were on the trailer; Dashout drove away from the passenger terminal, an enormous tin Quonset hut.

We passed a sign that read: "Welcome to the 8th Tac Fighter Wing." Along with Spectre, Ubon housed two squadrons of Phantom jets, the 433rd and 435th. Half in humor and half in honor, the fighter jocks called the gunship "The Fabulous Four Engine Fighter." A detachment of Nail Forward Air Controller (Nail FAC) OV-10 Broncos, down from Nakhon Phanom, also operated out of Ubon.

On two sides, jungle bordered the base; an ever-increasing number of restaurants, tailor shops, jewelry stores, custom shoe shops, and massage parlors stacked up against the opposite sides, hustling for the GI dollars. "Great security setup," I said. "A sapper could order lunch, then stroll in and blow up a couple planes while he's waiting to be served."

Dashout rolled down his lower lip. "That happened once, last year. Somehow the Thais got it across to the NVA that it was a real no-no. Since then things have been pretty calm."

Dashout followed the scenic route and we passed down the flight line. I got my first look at the only AC-130 Spectre gunships in the United States Air Force. The dozen black bastards sat pressed to the ramp, awaiting the dry season, when with muffled roars from their turbo-prop engines they would slip away at nightfall and head to Laos. The sight of that latent death and destruction practically gave me a hard-on. Guns mounted side by side projected from the left of the fuselages: each airplane carried two 20-mm Vulcan cannons, dual 7.62-mm machine gun modules, and a pair of 40-mm Bofors cannons. The Twenties and machine guns were six-barrel Gatling guns: shredders. The Forties were blasters. I knew what they could do. For two months at Lockbourne AFB, Ohio, I had been taught gunship procedures and tactics in AC-119 Stingers. I could hardly wait to bring it all together.

The base was a compact little country club. Living quarters surrounded the facilities, which were crammed into nine square blocks: BX outlets, theater, bowling alley, gym, clubs—there was even a swimming pool. Most of the buildings were mustard colored, frame, one or two story, World War II design. What looked like the newest structures were cinder block, painted blue. That stuff was nothing but frosting. The flight line was the only place that mattered.

Dashout stopped in front of the BOQ. "The other officers from your—from Major Holcomb's crew got here earlier in the week," he said.

"I fucked off in Bangkok a few days."

Dashout smiled as if the confession pleased him.

A fast scrub and rub, I thought, and I'd be ready for war.

Chapter 2

Paint It Black

SPECTRE AIRCREWS AFFECTIONATELY called the AC-130 gunship "Turkey" because, like that largest of North American game birds, it was high winged and ponderous in flight, with a large aft opening. Best of all, however, it was hard to hit, harder yet to knock down.

With four huge propellers on four big engines hung from straight wings, the AC-130 had the squat, squarish, primitive look of an aged cargo plane. The gunship had little choice as to its profile. Its skeleton was a C-130 Hercules, the ancient but reliable Trash Hauler.

Spectre's paint job made the plane extraordinary. The airframe was covered with the filmy, dull, shadowless black of a moonless night. *Black lightning*, I thought. However, painted prominently on the left side of the fuselage directly below the pilot's side window was the Sixteenth SOS emblem: a gray skeleton draped in green shrouds standing in front of a yellow crescent and cradling a blazing Gatling gun in its arms. The plane's other touches of color were less obvious. Each propeller blade was tipped with yellow. And, high on the vertical stabilizer, the unit designator letters, "FT," were stenciled in gray. Spectre weapon handlers, the gunners, said the letters stood for "Fuckin' Tough."

Upon closer examination the AC-130 proved itself to be a machine ingeniously designed for selectively dealing death

11

and destruction in the dark. Reminiscent of a marauding pirate sailing ship, the left side of the fuselage was lined with gun ports and protruding weapons. Two 20-mm Vulcan cannons, each capable of firing twenty-five hundred rounds per minute, stuck out from slightly ahead of the left main wheel well. Above the wheel well were a pair of 7.62-mm machine-gun modules that had two rates of fire. Low speed was three thousand rounds per minute; high was six thousand. The four Gatling guns fed themselves from enormous drums filled with belted ammunition. The line-up of weapons was completed by two 40-mm Bofors cannons located aft of the wheel well and capable of firing one hundred rounds per minute in short, rapid bursts. Cone-type flash suppressors on the muzzles of the 40-mm guns added a "professional" touch. The Forty was the primary weapon for killing.

My first walk through the AC-130 was like a walk through the imagination of an executioner. Every instrument was technologically perfect, focused on death. All those super-clever Anglo-Saxon minds hadn't designed all the super-deadly weapons to use against other Anglo-Saxons, I thought. Wouldn't future history books prove me right?

The gunship was boarded from beneath its high tail by stepping up approximately two feet onto the lowered cargo ramp, which was the width of the fuselage. The ramp was raised for flight to produce a streamlined airframe. An overhead cargo door, hinged at the rear, lowered to meet the lip of the ramp and thus close the cargo compartment. On combat missions, the cargo door remained open and provided a panoramic view behind the airplane.

Within the gunship, in what used to be the cargo compartment, recessed red bulbs glowed dimly. Like shrouds, weighty gray flak curtains draped the bulkheads, muffling reflections. What wasn't covered by the felt ballistic curtains was painted nonreflective gray. Light wasn't important. The gunners who worked here were flawlessly drilled, could perform their tasks by touch alone.

Forward from the ramp, multiple rows of 40-mm ammunition storage racks were located immediately to the right. Cannons and machine guns, of course, were to the left.

Halfway down the cargo compartment, off-center to the

right, was the fourteen-foot-long by seven-foot-wide and high booth—the "brain" of the gunship, or no less than the cerebrum. There, inputs from the "eyes" and "ears" of the gunship were received. There, life-and-death decisions were made, both logically and emotionally.

Entered from a door in the rear, the booth contained four massive consoles with a comfortably cushioned seat before each. A fourteen-inch television monitor with an eight-inch monitor above it was centered in each console and surrounded by control panels and indicators.

The low-light-level television (TV) console occupied the right-rear quadrant of the booth, and the side-looking infrared detector (IR) console filled the left-front quadrant. The passive detectors which fed information to these positions were the "eyes" of the airship.

The TV console received a standard black-and-white television picture from wide-angle and narrow-angle television cameras that amplified light sixty thousand times and turned night to day. For situations when there was insufficient ambient light, a 2KW searchlight installed aft of the 40-mm guns supplemented the cameras with either white light or infrared illumination. When shaded by dense filters the cameras were usable in daylight. The narrow-angle picture was magnified five times larger than the wide. TV cameras hung from a gyro-stabilized platform and looked out the left side of the gunship through an opening slightly forward of the 20-mm cannons. With a hand control, a joystick mounted on the TV console, the platform could be aimed from the horizon to a minus seventy degrees in elevation and sixty-five degrees both fore and aft in azimuth. Mounted on the bottom of the platform and aligned with the cameras was a laser to provide a pulsed beam of energy for guiding sensor-headed bombs.

The IR console received its picture from a globular detecting unit that protruded from the wheel well below where the 7.62-mm guns were mounted. The unit sensed infrared energy radiated from an object, depending upon the temperature of the object and its emissivity. The unit converted the infrared energy to electrical signals and fed them to an amplifier which produced a stylized picture of the object for

13

display on a monitor. The presentation strongly resembled a black-and-white television picture. Warm objects or parts of objects appeared light colored; cooler objects ranged from shades of gray to black. For example, an operating truck engine bloomed out startlingly white; if the truck was moving, the wheels also were white; the remainder of the truck appeared as various shades of gray against a dark roadway. With a hand control on the IR console, the gimbal-mounted, gyro-stabilized detecting unit could be aimed from above the horizon to a minus seventy-five degrees in elevation and from ninety degrees forward to sixty aft in azimuth; therefore, the IR had a field of search approximately twenty per cent larger than the TV. The IR had both "search" and "track" modes of viewing (roughly equivalent to the wide- and narrow-angle TV cameras) with four-power magnification in track. Both the IR and TV pictures centered around electronic crosshairs.

The console in the right front of the booth monitored the "ears" of the gunship, the Black Crow (BC) sensor. The BC picked up electro-magnetic radiations from internal combustion engines and displayed them as skittish green dot clusters on a grid-faced cathode-ray tube, thereby indicating the azimuth and range to the sources of the signals. The BC console also had a joystick for aiming the sensor. The sensing unit was mounted under a fiberglass radome near the left side of the gunship's nose and had a field of search far wider than both the IR and TV. The BC console also contained radar homing and warning (RHAW) gear: equipment for detecting radar scanning and tracking by antiaircraft artillery (AAA, commonly called "triple-A") and the more dangerous surface-to-air missile (SAM) sites.

The remaining console, in the left rear of the booth across the narrow center aisle from the TV, was the fire-control officer (FCO) station. Its one unique piece of equipment was a bomb damage assessment (BDA) recorder, which captured on videotape the imagery from the TV or IR, whichever was displayed on the FCO's master monitor. The videotape also recorded conversations from the main interphone.

The booth's four consoles were linked by remote control, switching, and slaving units. Therefore, each console could display any sensor image on either monitor. Furthermore, each console had dials which showed the absolute and relative sighting angles of all sensors. Finally, each sensor could be "slavcd" to any other sensor to follow its line of sight automatically. The four consoles were also linked by a private interphone system that was independent of the aircraft's main interphone.

If the booth was the cerebrum of the gunship, then the navigator's station was the cerebellum. From there the aircraft's position in space and its future movements were determined. The navigator's station was reached by continuing forward around the left side of the booth (avoiding the Bofors, machine guns, and Vulcans) to the forward bulkhead of the cargo compartment and then climbing the few rungs of a chest-high ladder to the flight deck.

The navigator's console spread across the right rear quarter of the deck and contained doppler, mapping radar, altimeters, compasses, LORAN C and D computer, gyroscopes, inertial measurement unit, two navigation computers, airspeed and ground-speed indicators, clock, temperature indicator, ADF, VOR, TACAN, and a sextant. The console also housed the fire-control computer, which, after being fed variables such as wind and boresight alignment corrections, converted sensor sighting data into steering and firing guidance for the pilot's electronic gunsight. It was as much equipment as one man could operate effectively.

A chain-smoking navigator described his season with Spectre by saying, "During the war I found time to light two cigarettes, and I actually managed to finish one of them."

The front half of the flight deck was filled with the pilot's seat, instrument panels, and controls to the left; the copilot's seat to the right; and, between them but slightly to the rear, the flight engineer's seat. The Spectre cockpit was the same as a Hercules cockpit except that off to the left of the pilot's seat was an electronic gunsight called a fire-control display. In daylight, fixed reticles on its one-foot-square transparent viewing screen served as gunsight rings for visual firing. In the dark, electronic symbols projected onto the viewing screen provided information from the navigator's fire-control computer, which told the pilot how to maneuver the airplane in order to aim the guns where the sensors were sighting.

GUNSHIP

The gunship was manned by a crew of thirteen: seven officers and six enlisted men. The gunners claimed the ratio was set at that level in case a life-or-death decision ever came to a vote. The officers were the pilot (he was the aircraft commander even if outranked by another officer), the copilot, the navigator, and the four-man sensor team.

The enlisted men were the flight engineer, four gunners, and a rear scanner. The flight engineer was an extra brain for the pilot. Usually a former ground-crew chief, he knew everything there was to know about the systems that controlled the flight of the airplane. The gunners were primarily muscle. They hand loaded clips of four rounds into the 40-mm guns, shoveled spent cartridges away from the Gatling guns, and prevented or repaired in-flight gun malfunctions. The gunners also took turns sitting before an open hatch directly in front of the booth and warning the pilot of antiaircraft fire from the right while he was engrossed with the gunsight to his left. In a like manner, the rear scanner hung out the open cargo door and acted as an extra set of eyes in the back of the pilot's head.

Enlisted men were volunteers who believed "If you ain't Spectre, you ain't shit."

Chapter 3

The Long and Winding Road

SPECTRE'S MISSION WAS to interdict the Ho Chi Minh Trail, the supply route that linked North Vietnam to South Vietnam and Cambodia. The trail was actually a network of dirt and log-covered roads, footpaths, and waterways that the North Vietnamese Army constantly broadened in an effort to avoid interdiction. From North Vietnam, the trail entered eastern Laos through several passes in the Annamese Cordillera, then snaked southward across the Laotian panhandle's heavily forested hills.

The trail was passable only from November to May, a period known as the "dry season" in Laos, Cambodia, and Thailand. During that time, monsoons prevailed from the northeast and rain was dissipated on the eastern slopes before the winds crossed the Annamese Cordillera and reached Laos. During the other months, the wet season, southwestern monsoons dumped flooding rains on the trail. Mud, washouts, and landslides closed most roads. Fords, key points in the network, became swollen and impassable. The few bridges, pontoon types made of bamboo and hinged to be pulled parallel to the riverbank and camouflaged when not in use, were washed away. In general, the trail was a mess.

During the dry season, however, the trail was maintained in a state nearing perfection by the North Vietnamese Army's

559th Transportation Group, which controlled supply operations. Around the clock, crews instantly repaired damage to roads and vehicles. It was imperative to keep traffic flowing: a year's worth of supplies had to be moved in six months. Movements were made primarily by trucks which traveled singly, or in small convoys of about five, or in large convoys of about fifteen. Whichever, the trucks moved by stages. As a result, Laos was dotted with storage areas as well as rest and repair areas. Naturally, traffic moved predominantly at night, when aerial interdiction was hampered by lack of visibility.

By the late sixties the U.S. Air Force had been tailored so that there were few airplanes suited for roadway and truck interdiction. Although B-52s frequently closed a pass or obliterated a crossroads, planners agreed that a formation of three B-52s, each dropping sixty-seven thousand pounds of bombs, was overkill against a truck. One was too much. Even in daylight, fast-moving jet fighters had trouble finding and hitting small mobile targets, such as single trucks. Night or day, however, it was not cost effective to risk a ten-million-dollar fighter three or four times on low-level passes in order to kill a ten-thousand-dollar truck. But we did it.

The AC-130 Spectre gunship was the air force's solution to the truck-killing problem: the airplane had enough fuel to loiter in the target area for up to four hours, it carried great quantities of inexpensive munitions of a size reasonable for the task, and it hunted discriminatingly.

For the 1970–1971 dry season, Spectre had a surprise package for the NVA: twice as many airplanes armed with pairs of 40-mm cannons capable of firing two-pound shells at a rate of one hundred per minute. The heavier firepower permitted the gunship to operate from a higher altitude and to increase its probability of survival. Altitude was the gunship's primary defense: the higher the airplane, the more time its pilot had to react to avoid antiaircraft artillery fire. Spectre faced a tough schedule. Every game was in the enemy's arena, the southern part of the Laotian panhandle code-named Steel Tiger. The playing field was the 50- by 150-mile section of Laos contiguous to South Vietnam. The NVA set up a zone defense and Spectre had to penetrate it.

Each season the zone toughened: the size and the number of antiaircraft guns increased. The battle of Spectre versus AAA was a long series of trade-offs.

During their first two seasons of combat, 1968–1969 and 1969–1970, armed with four 20-mm cannons and four 7.62-mm machine guns, six AC-130 gunships initially operated over Steel Tiger at 5000 feet. That altitude kept them beyond the range of small-arms ground fire, which constituted the principal threat. The NVA introduced 23-mm AAA into Steel Tiger and the trade-offs commenced.

The 23-mm had an *effective* range of 6600 feet (which meant the gun could be *accurately aimed and fired* to that altitude; the projectile actually traveled to an *absolute* altitude of 8000 feet before running out of energy and falling earthward). In moving beyond the effective range of 23-mm AAA, Spectre forfeited the use of its machine guns: from 6000 feet altitude the 7.62-mm rounds were spent by the time they reached the target.

When Spectre climbed higher, the NVA deployed 37-mm guns with an effective range of 8200 feet (the shell carried to 13,000). Spectre pilots opted to work from 7500 feet altitude, a distance within range of the new threat, because from higher the gunship's 20-mm cannon rounds tumbled in flight near the end of their trajectory and fewer than half detonated upon impact.

To permit Spectre to move outside the effective 37-mm range, the USAF Aerospace Systems Development laboratory modified the 40-mm Bofors for gunship use in the 1970–1971 dry season. The heavier firepower enabled Spectre to climb to 8500 feet.

When the NVA deployed 57-mm guns effective to 13,100 feet (the shell carried to the moon if it missed), trade-offs ended. Spectre pilots were trapped inside an operational ceiling of 10,000 feet for three reasons.

First, beyond that altitude, the accuracy of the 40-mm cannons deteriorated and lengthened the time required to kill something, which, in turn, increased crew exposure to ground fire.

Second, oxygen, or rather the lack of oxygen, became a factor. AC-130s had no supplemental oxygen system. Men needed oxygen to survive. Half of earth's oxygen was below 10,000 feet. Above that height, men did not perform well for long periods; therefore . . . Flight altitude was determined by the distance above the target. For example, when attacking a truck on a road with an elevation of 3000 feet, a gunship operating at 10,000 feet actually flew at 13,000. In the rarified air at that altitude, during rapid feeding of twenty-pound clips into the 40-mm loader assembly, gunners easily overexerted, developed hypoxia, and often passed out. "Man down back here" became a common report from the loading crew. The pilot usually replied, "Tell me when he's on his feet." The unconscious gunner was dragged off to the side. After he awakened and felt rested, he returned to humping ammo. Passing out was an accepted side effect of the trade. A gunner once asked me, "You think, passing out like that, there's chance of brain damage?" I told him, "First, you gotta have a brain." He grinned at me: "Then I wouldn't be a gunner."

The third and most important factor that limited the gunship to 10,000 feet was sensor resolution. That altitude was the greatest range from which the sensors could effectively detect and discriminate targets. If it gave up its ability to hunt, the gunship surrendered the tactical capability for which it was designed. In that case, it was time to return the bird to trash-hauling duty.

Debates on the cat-and-mouse theories regarding altitudes and millimeters came to a screeching halt whenever the NVA troops lugged a gun to the top of a piece of high ground, such as a jutting four-thousand-foot chunk of karst. While working over a truck that was deep down in one of the valleys, a gunship crew suddenly found itself eyeball to eyeball with the crew of such a weapon. In that situation, any size gun was a son of a bitch.

Spectre started the 1970–1971 season on the back side of the power curve, hiding in the open. There was no place to go to escape 57-mm AAA. A pilot's final choice was to say "Fuck it" and remain where he was or go back down to a lower altitude and shoot it out. Like all combat, the situation finally evolved into what was quaintly called "nut cuttin' time."

Triple-A was the nemesis and the fascination. The experts on trip-A were the rear scanners. Their task was to face it and to evaluate it. Other crewmen stood or sat within the gunship's airframe, behind the protection of armor plating which ran the length of the left side of the fuselage. (My roomie, Major Dick Kaulbach, who was our crew's table nav, laughed uproariously the day he peeled back one of the ballistic felt curtains that lined the interior of the cargo compartment and, on a thick ceramic armor plate which was expected to stop the wrecking-ball impact of a 57-mm shell, read the stenciled words "DO NOT DROP.") The rear scanner stretched out on his stomach and hung head downward out the open cargo door, exposed to the chilling slipstream, and for hour after hour watched the fire that streamed up at the gunship. He had no heater at his position and there was no respite from duties. It took tremendous willpower and stamina to perform well during the last hour on target, when body heat was sapped and muscles ached. Of course, that was how the men who filled that position wanted it to be. Among themselves, they doted over the physical strain and the cold and the danger.

A rear scanner knew the importance of being that "extra set of eyes in the back of the pilot's head." A scanner mentally predicted the trajectory of every antiaircraft shell and, when he saw the need, informed the pilot to alter course to avoid the accurate ones. By stretching far over the lip of the ramp and putting his trust in a thin steel safety cable, he had a 360-degree field of vision below the aircraft. Despite the fact that there also was a right scanner, a job at which the gunners took turns, pilots relied primarily upon the rear scanner to protect them from unseen threats. He was the pro.

Scanners had a fixation about the fire from triple-A. A man who was generally quiet and seemingly inarticulate, a man like our crew's rear scanner, Master Sergeant Otis Birdwhistle, who was lean and relaxed from the hills of Tennessee, even he had a fixation and spouted a litany describing antiaircraft fire: "You're hangin' off the ramp," he told me, "and the wind is flowin' and blowin' and you're eyeballin' the night and then that stuff starts comin' up out of nowhere. First rounds on a night remind me of our anthem . . . rocket red glare, bomb burstin' in air . . . ya know. That stuff is beautiful. Muzzle flashes you can hardly see—wink! wink! wink!—and the tracers ignite and are so damn *orange,* so orange against the black. There's not a light in sight. Then wink! The tracers zip out of nowhere. Watching that stuff come up is . . ." He shook his head in awe, couldn't find the proper word. "You know it's Death with a capital D, but all the same it's pretty when it explodes in your face." Bird-whistle stared hard at the ground. "Pretty. And excitin'." He set his jaw, paused for a couple deep breaths, then said, "I never told anybody because it sounds like braggin', but regular trip-A is easy to outguess. The rounds are like slow motion. You have all the time in the world to move out of the way. Now magnum rounds—zing-bang! they're on you. Dodgin' them is pure knee jerk. And tracerless is definitely somethin' else. It goes off in your face with no warnin', makes your heart just *leap.* I think there ought to be a rule in the Geneva Conventions against usin' tracerless." He chuckled. "Still, it sure is pretty."

Pilots preferred rear scanners who were fearless. A touch of craziness made a man unflinching in the face of heavy and accurate gunfire. The most popular rear scanner was spit-and-polish Master Sergeant Dynamite Dixon, who flew more gunship missions than anyone in the history of the United States Air Force. Dixon was dazzling. His combat boots were mirror bright. To impress newcomers, he touched up his hair by looking at his reflection in a boot toe. His flight suits were starched, then pressed with military creases sharp enough to slice bread. He had his hair cut and his fingernails manicured twice a week. The fact that his manicurist gave blow jobs in a back room of the barber shop partially accounted for Dixon's excellent grooming. He shaved to a closeness that made his skin translucent. Then, he drenched himself in Old Spice aftershave lotion. A heavy aroma announced his approach before he entered a room. Up close he was eye-watering.

The lotion was a necessity. Without it Dixon reeked of booze. He was saturated with alcohol. He drank from the time he landed after one mission until it was time to report for the next mission. His roommates repeatedly were amazed when Dixon arose from what appeared to be the sleep of the dead, with unopened eyes unerringly hit the refrigerator, then chugged two or three beers before crashing back onto his rack. Occasionally his roommates bet that Dixon couldn't find, let alone climb on, the correct airplane. However, once Dixon boarded the gunship, he was in his milieu and, for practical purposes, he was sober.

Dixon called antiaircraft fire with an ease and accuracy that was unmatched. His talent was a gift. He chattered in a soft and rolling voice much like that of an infielder or catcher who talked only to his pitcher. Dixon smoothly spoke through conversations of others without disturbing them. He spoke for only the pilot's ears: "All right, sir, here come four, from six o'clock—accurate—but not accurate enough. Hold what you have and keep firing. You're shooting good tonight, sir, shooting real good. And, easy does it, they miss." Four rounds of triple-A flashed by the tail, no more than ten feet away. "Fine. Good flying, sir. Three more rounds from that same gun—seven o'clock—can't touch us. Not even close. Ahhhhh, *accurate,* five o'clock. Roll level, *now!* Dynamite move, sir, dynamite. And—they miss." Four rounds sped through the airspace where the gunship would have been had not Dixon ordered the course alteration. "Log four, accurate, BC. We're in control, sir. Looking good, looking real good. They'll never touch *you,* sir."

One evening after a stretch in which he flew ninety-six missions in a hundred days, Dixon arrived at the airplane as his usual shining self; his eyes, however, were somewhere beyond Betelgeuse. Because he was flying with a new crew, nobody noticed anything unusual until, while taxiing prior to takeoff, Dixon donned his combat gear, stretched out on the ramp, and in his own calm style described the antiaircraft fire that only he saw: "Four rounds, sir, and they're accurate. Going to be close. Hold what you have. And they miss. Dynamite flying, sir." The airplane was still on the ground and the new pilot thought Dixon's performance grew funnier and funnier as Dixon described closer and closer and even closer streams of gunfire. Then Dixon screamingly announced that they were hit and bailed out spread-eagled onto the concrete taxiway.

The medics dried him out and weeks later Dixon voluntarily returned to flying. For his first stone-cold-sober mission some of the spit was where the polish should have been. The boots and flying suit were flawless. The haircut was new, but the fingernails were chewed to the quick. The shave was as close as ever except that Dixon had missed a tuft below his nose and had cut himself in several places. Band-Aids and scabs spotted his face. In the air, he said nothing. Antiaircraft fire flew up from everywhere while Dixon remained mute and bug-eyed. The following day he turned in his wings. The squadron operations officer summed it up: "Regardless what everybody says now, I was never sure he drank until the first time I saw him sober."

Spectre legend often spoke of when Whale, a Gargantuan black sergeant, fell overboard while attempting to visually follow an interesting stream of tracer fire to its burnout point somewhere above the gunship's altitude. The night he went overboard, dangling by his lifeline in the slipstream, Whale called on interphone, "Pilot, nine o'clock, accurate, three rounds. If they miss, request permission to come aboard."

"I see 'em. No sweat," the pilot said. "Whale, what the hell're you doing? I can hardly hear you. Where are you?"

"About an arm's length and a half beyond the end of the ramp, sir. Request permission to come aboard."

The gunners who rushed aft and hauled him to safety swore that Whale was hanging by his lifeline with his arms stretched forward, palms and head slanted slightly upward, in the style of Superman. His first words after being dragged onto the ramp were: "They mount some guns on this old Whale and he'll zoom out here and do this dirty work himself."

Chapter 4

Here Comes the Sun

THE DRY SEASON officially started in November. The frequent daily rains didn't stop all at once. Instead, in late October they grew farther and farther apart until one day early in November it rained only once and then the next day was completely clear.

Similarly, bumper-to-bumper traffic didn't explode out of the passes and sweep southward through Steel Tiger. The 559th Transportation Group took weeks to gin up its operation: waited for the ground to firm, cleared away landslides, put down new logs, lashed bamboo together, and moved in more guns.

Our crew's first two missions were like Stateside training sorties. Steel Tiger was divided into ten sections and a gunship normally was assigned to cover one or more of them for a four-hour period. On those first two flights, however, we were permitted to wander the length of Steel Tiger and get the lay of the land. We didn't see a hostile round and we didn't locate a thing of value. Nevertheless, we fired out our ammo. Like a kid with a BB gun, a crew could always find something to shoot: logs floating in streams, sandbars, road intersections, suspicious-looking foliage . . . Our IR operator, Captain Lee Schmidt, claimed a secondary explosion from one particularly hostile-looking clump of trees, but nobody agreed with him.

Schmidt had spent part of 1967 in Southeast Asia with the Spectre prototype. I saw that he was going to be a problem. He believed everything should be shot off guidance from the IR, his sensor; it was what he was used to—the prototype had no TV. Of course, I preferred to shoot off the TV, my sensor. After years in bombers and transports, I knew that a good crew was a team and, at times, as close as a family. Dick Kaulbach jokingly made the point: "The crew that flies together dies together. And there goes my job as squadron morale officer." On a good crew, the role of leader shifted from man to man as the mission progressed and as the situation dictated. In crises the leadership was conceded to the man with the greatest expertise for the situation, regardless of rank. Mutual trust and mutual respect turned the other men into willing subordinates.

On a Spectre gunship, the sensor operators controlled the tempo of the attack. When hunting trucks, half of the finds were made by the BC. The targets then were relayed to the IR or TV for tracking and providing firing guidance to the pilot. The capabilities of the two were nearly equal. Schmidt believed that we should rely primarily on the IR because of his previous experience. However, pilots agreed that the TV gave a steadier picture and was slightly easier to follow in the fire-control display. At night a pilot never saw a target unless it blew up or burned. In the final analysis of who was best qualified to lead, there was one other factor to be considered: I was senior to everybody on the crew, including the aircraft commander, Major Ed Holcomb, and on a day-to-day basis I wasn't going to sit on my thumb and watch a goddamn captain run the show.

Our crew was heavy with combat experience. Ed Holcomb had spent 1968 flying around South Vietnam in C-130s, same as I had. He too had faced the Tet Offensive, resupply missions to Khe Sanh when it was under siege, and a deadly fiasco in the A Shau Valley during Operation Delaware. We had logged our fair share of being shot at, in the air and on the ground. "Clay pigeons," Ed called us. Now was our time to get even.

Dick Kaulbach had returned to Ubon to be with a Thai lady he met while there on his first combat tour with Blind Bat.

Dick was divorced, once, recently. Just as I'd gone down the tubes twice, Schmidt was also a two-time loser but both times with the same woman. Dick told him, "That counts as only once and a half."

"I got lonesome and wanted to visit my old furniture for a while," Schmidt explained.

When I heard that, like me, Schmidt had two daughters, I raised both hands as if to stop traffic and said, "Don't show me their picture." Schmidt popped a glower-grin: "Don't have one." Neither did I. We laughed together. Our alienation was our bond.

Dick had experience over Steel Tiger and the northern part of Laos, the "pan," code-named Barrel Roll. On our first mission he gave us a detailed tour of Steel Tiger and a fast look in the Barrel. Like a Spectre Lowell Thomas, he pointed out spots of interest and reminisced aloud: "See that narrow little valley inside that horseshoe-shaped mountain line? One night I was FACing two navy fighters on trucks parked in there. The first plane made its pass down the valley, got too low, and flew into the mountainside. Airplane splattered everywhere." Dick sighed. "I told him it was a dead end! The second fighter was still on the perch. After about a minute, the second pilot said, 'I'm rolling in now, but don't expect too much. That's a hard act to follow.' Now, over there . . ."

Major Jim Ballard on BC and Captain Juan Sueno as FCO filled up the booth: they looked all right; each found his correct seat on the first try. They claimed to be happily married men (as if that were possible). Ballard still was married to his college sweetheart, was father to two sons and a daughter. Sueno was childless. By the way, Ed Holcomb was married too. Was he ever! Six sons. No wonder he volunteered to return to war. I would have asked for kamikazes.

Our copilot was Lieutenant Steve Tyler, a bachelor Texan and a rookie flyer who wanted to be wearing cowboy boots and a white silk scarf and Maching around in Phantom jets. He spent more time trying to look cool than he did paying attention to what was happening. He was lucky to be sent to gunships. In charge of anything faster, he would have killed himself. Fuck him. Major Ed Holcomb was so good that he could have done it without a co. Ed flew like an American eagle.

And Ed Holcomb could shoot. Of course, those abilities went together. If a man couldn't fly the airplane, he couldn't shoot. On the other hand, there were pilots who could fly like crazy but still were lousy shots. On our two free rides, Holcomb showed us what a natural he was. With the 40-mm he had a cadence of fire that indicated he was in his groove. One round punched off, there was a one-second pause, then three rounds followed as rapidly as the cannon fired. After two seconds of silence, the pattern of fire repeated. One. One-two-three. Pause. One. One-two-three. Over and over and over. His rhythm was so perfect that we could have danced to it.

The 40-mm shells impacted practically on top of each other. The Spectre expression that described his performance was "He could've driven nails." As far as Ed's shooting was concerned, for the boys in the booth it was love at first flight.

Many men desired to be on Holcomb's crew. His popularity was predicated upon his flawless flying, which meant he could line up a computer display and hold a gunline on target better than anyone in Spectre. That ability qualified him as the squadron's best shooter, the man who scored kills quickest and in the greatest number.

Being the best shooter was like being heavyweight boxing champion. Lesser beings sought to be part of the champ's entourage, to bask in the aura of his power and potency, hoped that miraculously some of his magic might rub off on them.

Before again entering and proving himself in combat, however, Holcomb arranged to have Kaulbach, Schmidt, and me assigned to his crew. Because we'd been shot at before, he viewed us as hardened professionals, his highest accolade.

Within a crew, a man was judged by what he had done and what he continued to do on a day-in, day-out basis. Potential wasn't worth shit in a fight. I saw we had a tough bunch of hitters. Murderers Row? Although on only their first tours, Ballard and Sueno had asked for Spectre. Except for the young copilots, almost all of the officers in Spec had sought the assignment. They understood the mission: Destroy. I never saw or heard one of them suffer a case of conscience that lasted more than a few seconds.

Our third mission started with a bang. We got our first taste of triple-A. Actually it was more like a force-fed banquet. Shortly after we entered Steel Tiger, Holcomb decided to run a boresight alignment check on a road intersection out in the middle of nowhere. The check verified that the guns were hitting somewhere near where the sensors were looking. The 40-mms were new and not always true. Normally a crew boresighted on the first target of the night; however, Ed said, "Not that busy out here. May as well warm up slowly." It was perfectly clear. There wasn't a vehicle in sight. Lee had the IR crosshairs on the center of the empty crossroads. Ed fired four 40-mm rounds: *ka-pung . . . ka-pung, ka-pung, ka-pung.* That was how it sounded from inside the booth: the gun coughed loudly, *ka*, and then the spent casing ejected into a metal barrel, *pung.* Double syllable of death. Ed fired a second burst. In response, the jungle came alive with antiaircraft guns. The scanners called out triple-A rounds in groups of five and ten and ". . . a dozen, maybe fifteen." Ed banked sharply out of orbit and headed west. "Let's go back and start over," he said.

"Good grief," Jim Ballard said. "We weren't hurting anything."

Lee Schmidt told him, "Those fuckers've been saving up all summer."

Juan Sueno said, "If that's an indication of what's to come—" He looked across the narrow center aisle toward me and smiled. "Is it too late to sign up with the NVA?"

That was the excitement for the night. We clawed through the weeds for hours but couldn't find a thing and ended up shut out again.

A first truck kill is a lot like a first piece: it ends almost before it begins, it produces thrills that live beyond the spastic moment, and it inspires dreams of doing it again and again and again.

The first truck kill scored by our crew was textbook perfect. Shortly before midnight, with the constellation of mighty

Orion the Hunter looming dominantly in the newly cleared nighttime sky, we crossed the Mekong River near Pak Se, then headed northeast into Steel Tiger and intercepted the Ho Chi Minh Trail where roads climb toward the Bolovens Plateau.

Spec's hunting technique was simple. Using the LORAN computer and 1:250,000 charts, the table nav directed the pilot along a course that paralleled a main road. When the nav wanted to be exact, he flipped to a 1:50,000 chart and pinpointed a position. The LORAN was accurate to within one hundred feet. Heading down the road, the sensor operators randomly scanned the terrain. If they decided to concentrate on a portion of road or wanted to investigate a side road, they ordered the pilot to circle in a shallow left bank. The tactic was called "road recce." Broadly speaking, with our sensors, we found anything that reflected light, radiated heat, or made noise.

We were on our fourth mission and were heading down a road with BC and IR searching as far forward as possible. Schmidt was working his ass into a lather, trying to look everywhere at once, straining to be first to find a truck. From my vantage point in the right rear quadrant of the booth, I viewed the back of his helmeted head and pictured him drooling in anticipation.

Schmidt was the perfect mesomorph: five-nine (a couple inches shorter than me), a solid one-eighty (he had twenty pounds on me), pure muscle and appetite. He wore his dark brown hair in a tall crew cut above dark brown eyebrows that arched together above brown eyes. He had a constant five o'clock shadow. Thick, curly brown hair covered his forearms and chest and ringed his neck below where he shaved it in a circular line. He appeared menacing. His dark, low profile reminded me of some type of badger, a wolverine.

When he smiled, his brows contracted and he looked sinister rather than pleased. Thais treated him cautiously. He found their reactions amusing. The more he smiled to reassure them, the more cautious they became toward him. Schmidt didn't understand the Asiatic belief that body hair indicated strength and virility. The point had been driven home to me in a Hong Kong theater during the showing of the seemingly endless, although cleverly and expensively made, motion picture commercials which preceded the feature movie. In one commercial a Chinaman in a swimming pool raised his arms overhead and revealed large clumps of underarm hair. The otherwise sedate packed house cheered and applauded in a spontaneous outburst of admiration. A woman seated next to me pretended to swoon with delight.

One afternoon, Juan Sueno and I met Schmidt in downtown Ubon and we decided to share a taxi back to the base. I halfheartedly bargained with the Thai driver but quickly agreed on a price that was exorbitant. Juan and I climbed into the rear of the tiny taxi. Schmidt sat next to the driver and said nothing during the ride. The driver glanced at him more and more frequently. Schmidt finally realized that the driver was openly staring at him; his brows contracted and he gave his misunderstood smile in reply. The driver bowed his head, then stared straight ahead for the remainder of the trip. At the base, the driver refused payment. Schmidt didn't understand any of it.

Anyhow . . . there we were on our fourth mission to Steel Tiger. I was growing irritated. The TV couldn't see as far forward as either BC or IR. Frustrated, I allowed the cameras to settle to the "dead nuts" position, staring forty-five degrees downward and straight off the left wing. Stretching to my left, I looked around my console to see what Jim Ballard was doing on BC.

Ballard was a rangy six-and-a-half footer who walked with a lithe, frictionless gait. When seated, his long, thin, sloping shoulders drew together much like those of a chastised dog. A loyal and devoted expression usually filled his dark, round eyes. Often I felt an urge to pat his head. Indeed, Ballard did resemble a dog, a pointer, because of the way he concentrated on his console for hours on end. Later, during missions when action slowed, Schmidt and I would grow bored, distracted, even catnap. But Ballard's head never bowed. Always he was wide awake, intelligently alert. Of course, his job was to show the way, to point the targets. From there, TV or IR made the kill.

Now, on the BC console, the empty oscilloscope face glowed blankly in ghostly green silence.

When I looked back at my console, there on the TV screen a truck topped a rise along a stretch of exposed road. From my perspective, the darkened vehicle appeared to emerge blindly from beyond the curvature of the earth, appeared to be wandering in search of me as listlessly as I had been searching for it. My pulse accelerated. *Like finding money in the street,* I thought. A flash earlier I would have been too early; a flash later, too late. In that proper intervening flash the truck became mine.

Punching the narrow-angle camera picture onto my fourteen-inch monitor, I magnified the vehicle by five, then centered and held thin white electronic crosshairs on its hood. "TV has a mover," I said breathlessly. "TV tracking." From the corner of my eye I saw Schmidt look back at me, but I pretended I didn't. I felt a hundred feet tall, invincible. "He's headed toward us. Nine o'clock," I said. On my eight-inch monitor I had the IR punched up and I saw that Schmidt had slaved to the target. The computer-enhanced infrared image of the truck was as detailed as the low-light-level television picture.

"Fuel truck," FCO Juan Sueno said. He too had TV on his monitor. "Southbound." The NVA transported fuel in standard three-compartment, eighty-one-hundred-gallon tanker trucks. The direction of travel indicated the truck probably was loaded.

Dick Kaulbach said, "TV in, pilot. You're clear to fire." His call informed the pilot that TV was providing guidance to his illuminated fire-control display through the fire-control computer and also verified that the target was in enemy territory.

"Jesus, he turned on his lights," I blurted out. It was the first and last truck I saw with lights.

"Dumb ass," said Schmidt.

Atop a knoll, the truck was moving no more than ten miles an hour. The upper halves of its headlights were hooded, but to the light-sensitive television cameras the lower portions stood out like earthly half moons. Moonbeams undulated slowly as the truck groped its way toward us.

"I want a Twenty on the line," Holcomb said.

"You got it, sir," the chief gunner, Technical Sergeant Rusty Brown, said.

The truck slowed to a walking pace. Ed Holcomb found a tangent on the firing circle, rolled into a thirty-degree left bank, and circled the prey, reducing destruction to a geometric solution.

The truck stopped. I milked the TV joystick, glided crosshairs from truck hood to center of tanker trailer. Drift was killed perfectly. The crosshairs hovered motionless in space.

In that moment, I was forever linked to Ed Holcomb. From my mind, my body, my grasping hand, physical and mental energy flowed through the gunship's system. Without me, Holcomb was helpless; without him, I was incomplete. We became one, the same. Together, we were Death.

In his illuminated gunsight, Holcomb delicately maneuvered the gunship until an electronic diamond that represented the fixed gunline moved into coincidence with an electronic circle, the target. With symbols superposed, using his left thumb, Holcomb depressed the trigger mounted on the pilot's control wheel, held it down for three seconds. One hundred twenty-five high-explosive incendiary rounds streamed from the Vulcan's muzzle with the whirring buzz of a gigantic chain saw. Twenty-eight pounds of explosive steel at thirty-four hundred feet per second!

Holcomb's flying was precise. The rounds impacted on the tanker within a seven-foot circle.

For a second or two it appeared as if a glittering sequined blanket had been spread atop the vehicle. Flashing stars danced in sparkles. Then the tanker exploded with astonishing suddenness. One moment it was sitting quietly on the knoll; a heartbeat later it was a raging ball of fire. Thick smoke bunched skyward; flames darted up its column and vanished into the night. All I thought to say was "You have a blower and a burner."

"I see it," Holcomb said. Only when a target exploded or burned was a pilot able to view destruction.

"You sure put out his lights," Jim Ballard said softly.

Lee Schmidt shook a raised fist.

GUNSHIP

I found myself on the edge of my seat. My mouth was dry. Was it over? My thumping heart slowed. Ended already? That easily? I felt an urge to shoot the truck again. I wanted to start over, to make it last longer. I wanted to shoot the truck again, do it a thousand times. Reason told me that such a definitive act shouldn't end so swiftly. It was irrational that such an act had been performed virtually at leisure, while seated in the foam-cushion comfort of a climate-controlled capsule.

We watched the vehicle burn. My nervous system beat counterpoint to logic. Inwardly I blazed with a fever of omnipotence, felt transformed, became master of the night. Fleetingly I thought of the truck driver. Had the man escaped? For a moment I wasn't certain if I wanted the driver safe or dead. Then it didn't matter. The tanker erupted anew as flames spread to an adjoining fuel compartment.

The havoc was gratifyingly beautiful.

Chapter 5

Around and Around

THE NVA DIDN'T put trucks on the road in great numbers and "truck busting" didn't become a full-time occupation until December. Because of the light November traffic, Spectre sent up only eight sorties a day. Our crew went out every second or third night and destroyed or damaged one, or two, or three vehicles. Lee and I took more time arguing over who was going to track a target than Ed took to hit it. Our problem was compounded by my hatred for triple-A.

It was gospel that an airplane did not duel with an antiaircraft gun. Instructors at Lockbourne and a few Spectre hands left over from the end of the previous dry season preached it: An airplane could not win a shoot-out with AAA. They cited example after example in which jet fighters were blown out of the sky going nose to nose with trip-A. Yankee stubbornness had led to the death of many good pilots, they said (as if the navigators in the backseats hadn't died along with the pilots). If a *jet fighter* couldn't do it . . .

In the solitude of our tiny air-conditioned room, Dick and I discussed the matter. In none of the examples did an airplane have the ability to loiter and fight back with a 40-mm cannon, the way an AC-130 did. The rate of fire of our 40-mm was slightly less than a 37-mm antiaircraft gun but slightly more than a 57-mm. We fired from a moving platform; AAA sites were stationary targets. Our gunfire was guided by sensors and computers; in Steel Tiger, AAA was aimed visually, in the dark. We held the advantage of the high ground. Deciding that the facts favored us, Dick and I rewrote the unwritten law. We convinced Ed that there was no more danger in circling and trading fire with an antiaircraft gun than there was in circling a truck while that same gun shot at us from nearby.

I had independently reached that conclusion before Dick and I opened our discussion. Fuck historical precedent. I didn't want those Dink bastards taking potshots at me without fear of being hammered into the ground. I had sort of a toughest-kid-on-the-block syndrome about the subject. It helped to have Dick on my side. The crew recognized that Dick thought the world operated on logic. I *knew* that it turned on emotions.

Toward the end of November, the conflict over TV or IR and my hatred of AAA brought issues to a temporary resolution after we found our first convoy. Jim Ballard announced the initial contact: "BC has movers!" Green dot clusters swarmed across the etched grid of his cathode-ray tube. "Sixty right, about seven miles. Looks like a bunch." The BC azimuth scan and range went well beyond those of the other sensors. Lee and I frantically searched as far forward as possible while Ed followed BC guidance. "Three miles," Jim said. "They're about—"

"I have eight, nine, ten, eleven trucks," Lee shouted. His monitor bloomed with bright white IR returns.

"Who has eleven trucks?" Ed asked. He was being a prick and acting like a schoolmaster because, in the excitement of seeing that many trucks, Lee had forgotten to identify himself by position when making his interphone call. It was a bullshit hassle because Ed recognized our voices. He did it to make his point: We were professionals, not hot dogs.

"I do," Lee said. "I mean IR."

"TV has three more, along the spur." The trucks looked super hot on infrared, parked with their engines running. We probably caught them preparing to move out.

"IR tracking . . ."

"I am," I corrected—couldn't resist the pun. "TV also tracking," I said hurriedly. Although Lee had locked onto the trucks first, there was always the chance that Ed might select TV for firing.

". . . the big one in front of the line," Lee finished.

"Put IR in the computer," Ed ordered. "Give me a Forty."

"IR's in. You're clear to fire," Dick said.

"You have a gun," the chief gunner reported. The gunners controlled the safing and arming switches, which cut guns in and out of the firing circuitry.

The rear scanner warned: "Nine o'clock. Inaccurate. Five rounds. And five more. Hold what you got." Antiaircraft tracer rounds detonated near the gunship's altitude.

The gun firing at us was aft of dead nuts. On wide-angle TV I saw the muzzle flash of its first burst and pinpointed the gunpit on narrow angle when it fired the second time. "TV found him. TV tracking that gun."

"Put TV in," Ed said.

Lee said, "Let's get the trucks."

"TV in. You're clear," Dick said.

While Ed recentered our orbit around the gunsite, I squeezed the deadman's switch on the tracking handle and gently milked the crosshairs to keep them centered on the hole that housed the gun. Ed pumped out four-round bursts right on the bull's-eye. On TV a 40-mm shell exploded with a short-lived flash that produced a puff of smoke which quickly dissipated. On IR a 40-mm round showed briefly as a very white hot spot, then rapidly faded and disappeared. Now, on TV flashes appeared around and inside the gunpit. "You hit all over him," I said. The light wasn't quite right, and TV resolution wasn't good enough to see if men were still operating the gun. Although the gun had not answered our fire, I urged, "Kill that son of a bitch."

"Hose him again," Juan Sueno said. Ed fired more bursts. Flashes walked across the hole.

"That shut him up," Lee said. "Now let's get the trucks. IR tracking."

"Fuckin' trucks aren't going anywhere."

"Put IR in," Ed ordered.

"IR in. Clear."

Ed depressed the trigger and nothing happened. He shouted, "Gunners, I need a gun."

"Number one loader jammed, sir. Just a—"

"Gimme a g—"

"Number two Forty on the line, sir."

Ed blasted away, then asked, "Can you repair number one?"

Rounds impacted on the road ahead of the lead truck, and Lee called the center of the pattern: "Two mils forward." By plotting miss distances, the FCO determined windage as well as boresight alignment corrections to feed into the fire-control computer. A one-mil error equaled one foot from a distance of one thousand feet. From our altitude of seventy-five hundred feet, two mils equaled fifteen feet. We worked strictly in mils, which eliminated the need to convert. The sensor crosshairs were crosshatched with mil marks and the fire control computer read mils. Ed tapped off more rounds and Lee reported, "Four low." We already had boresighted the number one Forty; when we switched to the second gun, we had to rework the problem.

Juan Sueno, who held a degree in mathematics from Southern Cal, had an intuitive understanding of ballistics and weapon accuracy. He was the only FCO who ignored the graphs and resolved firing errors in his head. Before Ed fired again, Juan told Dick to feed a minute correction into the computer.

"You're shooting good tight patterns, Ed," I said to remind him that I was still available.

"Can you repair number one?" Ed Holcomb snapped.

"Yes, sir. It's cleared already."

"Good show, gunners. Put it back on the line," Ed said. He began firing four-round bursts. He was in his groove. Shells impacted practically atop one another.

"Hit him," Lee said. "Again, right on him. He's burning." On IR the truck signature disappeared in a growing ball of white, the signal produced by the heat of the fire.

"Destroyed?" Ed asked.

"Affirmative. IR tracking the last . . ."

"Look at that son of a bitch burn!" The truck flared like a torch. On TV dark smoke rolled upward and momentarily hid the other trucks.

". . . truck in line," Lee said. Operational procedures

dictated that a crew first disable the lead and the last vehicles in a convoy to block the road. The trapped vehicles were then attacked at will.

Juan Sueno said, "Look at that." The burning truck's cargo ignited and the fire tripled in size. Flames leaped across the road and reached the vehicle behind the burner. "Goddamn! It set fire to the truck behind it. Make that two destroyed." The burning vehicles merged into one raging fire. "The whole line's gonna go in a minute," Juan said.

"Three o'clock, four rounds, inaccurate," the right scanner called.

Ed Holcomb rhythmically fired four-round bursts at the last truck in line. "You hit him," Lee said. "Again. And again." Rounds punched into the cabin and body of the truck.

"He won't burn, dammit!" Before the introduction of the 40-mm gun, a vehicle had to blow up or burn in order to be considered destroyed. Now, a truck was classified as destroyed if merely struck by a 40-mm shell. Crews still tried for a blower or burner, however; the result was much more positive.

"We hit him enough?" Ed asked.

"Affirm. Must be full of rice. Let's—"

"Accurate. Break right, break right," Otis Birdwhistle shouted from the ramp. Ed Holcomb rolled the aircraft into a steep right bank and four 37-mm tracer rounds flashed by the left side of the gunship. He immediately rolled back to the standard left orbit. The antiaircraft gun fired again.

"TV got that gun. Let's hose his ass."

Lee said, "Fuck his ass. Let's kill trucks."

"Fuckin' trucks don't shoot back."

"Hey, fuck, Hal—"

"Hey, fuck you, Lee."

"Hey . . ." Lee snapped his head around, glared at me. I rose halfway out of my seat, but he turned back to his IR.

"Dick, please put somebody in the computer," Ed said. A minute later he resumed firing. Another truck exploded in flames.

By the time we finished, the road was ablaze with flaming vehicles. Burning fuel from tanker trucks ran down the roadside ditches. Tankers erupted anew and fires grew in intensity as they spread from one fuel cell to another. Ammunition trucks exploded when heat detonated their cargo; exploding tracer rounds pinwheeled into the air but fell back into the holocaust. It seemed as if nothing could escape the flames. It was sensational. On such a night it was almost satisfying to be merely a spectator.

As a result of that night, Ed Holcomb volunteered us to fly the daily daylight mission to Commando Basket, the code name for Cambodia, in support of friendly forces fighting the Khmer Rouge. Ed was the aircraft commander and had the final say in what we did. When he made a decision he reminded me of a bull elephant: No more thinking—charge! He was the size of a small elephant (neither fat nor muscular, just a beefy man) and had an emotional hide as thick as elephant skin. I admired the fact that he had the courage of his convictions. Had he been Calley's commander, there would have been no My Lai investigation. Ed would have cold-eyed the critics and said, "I ordered it," and they would have wilted. I was a little surprised that our bickering got to him.

We went into the Basket every day for a week. In daylight there was no need for the sensor operators to be along, but we went. Small-arms fire constituted the ground-fire threat. The first day was laughable. In a classic skirmish-line situation, a friendly squad was pinned down along a dirt road by a superior number of hostiles who were in an elevated tree line across a small, parched field. The hostiles ignored the gunship's arrival. Master Sergeant Stan Briscoe, our flight engineer, who was hanging over Ed's shoulder, said, "Probably think we're a trash hauler bringing supplies."

"For that big fuckin' war?" I said. "Right, Stan, there must be all of thirty guys down there."

After two loose orbits during which Ed talked over the situation with the friendly commander, the hostiles opened fire on the gunship. The interlaced streams of small-arms tracers described harmless short arcs at the tops of their trajectories, which were a thousand or more feet below our altitude of fifty-five hundred. Ed studied from whence the ground fire came, discussed it with Briscoe, then asked the

friendly commander, "Are all your people west of the road?"
When he got an affirmative reply, he descended five hundred
feet and tightened his orbit. Tracers continued to arc harmlessly below us.

Briscoe said, "Those Commie motherfuckers should know
better."

On the next time around Ed opened up with a 7.62-mm
minigun: *brrrrrrrrrrat*. At a rate of six thousand rounds per
minute, he sprayed ten-second bursts back and forth across
the portion of tree line from where the ground fire originated.
When he ran out of machine-gun ammo, he switched to the
20-mm cannons and fired those dry. A vulgar display of
overkill. No hostiles made a run for it. The attack was like the
Battle of the Little Bighorn. The gunship played the part of
the circling Indians. By the time Ed emptied the guns, the
trees were shattered, some shaved to ground level. There
wasn't a thing moving. Ed orbited the scene and told Briscoe,
"They know better now." Unopposed, the friendly squad
moved out across the dusty field.

Juan threw in his bid: "I'll take a pair of ears, if they can
find a pair."

The remainder of the week was much the same. In the
booth we did nothing but grow more bored and more restless.
I guessed it was Ed's method for teaching us to live with each
other. When involved with troops on the ground, the gunship
was under the direction of the friendly forces commander. He
and the pilot ran the show. On our next to last day out, we
were working near a village and the ground commander
asked, "You see the long building? The big one with the red
tile roof."

"Tell him we don't have color TV yet," I said. I felt
punchy. By then, Ed had made his point. A week was more
overkill. I thought about the red-tiled roofs in Saigon, all over
South Vietnam. In my opinion the French had done a good
job of building. They knew how to run a colony. They weren't
as good as the Brits, of course, when the Brits cared. I had
envied the French "Imperialists" after seeing the earth-tone
stucco, heavily tiled, well-maintained houses of the rubber
plantation owners in Vietnam. Meanwhile, in the cities, the
buildings were crumbling because of shitty maintenance by

the Vietnamese. The little fuckers needed constant supervision to preserve anything that wasn't made from bamboo. There wasn't a doubt in my mind that white Westerners deserved to control the people and the resources of Asia. And Africa. And South America. And Central America. That fuckin' Lenin . . . I laughed inwardly. The United States could have supported the French effort in Indochina, but the pols had no balls . . . exactly like now. A couple hundred B-52 strikes over the North . . . back to the Stone Age. *Wrong!* I thought. My mind was turning to fish sauce. That was no longer the American way. Our politicians never permitted our military forces to kick in the face of an opponent who was down. Otherwise, the Vietnam War would have ended in 1968. The North blew its load in the opening months of that year with the Tet Offensive, an act of desperation, a one-shot gamble that failed. Bombing had made the North a shambles, unable to support itself, let alone forces in the South. During 1968's spring and summer, the South was as quiet as Miami Beach. That was when we stopped bombing the North and let it recover. At that point, B-52 raids could have produced floods and famines which would have killed most of the North's population. The few survivors would have ended up back in caves. In Southeast Asia, back to the Stone Age was a short trip. In parts of Laos they still fucked in the trees. "Right, Johnny," I said, "in the trees?"

"Whatever you say, Z," Sueno agreed without asking the subject. He was half-asleep. Weren't we all?

By then Ed had found the building that the ground commander had designated. Ed may as well have been solo, I thought. He had volunteered for the goddamn daylight missions to put Lee and me in our places. He didn't need sensor guidance in daylight. The aircraft was equipped with backup metal crosshairs for visual firing by the pilot.

"That used to be a schoolhouse," the ground commander said. "The bad guys are using it for a hospital. Hit it!"

"We break every taboo at once," Jim Ballard said.

"Go back to sleep," I told him. "Ed'll ring if he needs you."

"Find a school bus so we at least get a vehicle out of this," Dick said.

"Knock off the chatter," Ed ordered. "Gun, give me a Twenty."

"Ed, why not put *both* Twenties on the line," Juan mumbled. Off interphone he said to me, "Get rid of the ammo that much faster; then we can go home."

"How about both Twenties and a Forty?" I said at once.

After a short time obviously spent thinking about our suggestions, Ed asked, "Chief, can we do that?"

"Don't matter shit-all to me, sir," chief gunner Rusty Brown replied. "It's your air machine."

"All right, do it."

"You got 'em, sir."

Ed Holcomb fired three ten-second twin streams of 20-mm cannon rounds at a rate of twenty-five hundred per minute per gun and punctuated them with sixty rounds from the 40-mm cannon. In the booth we laughed like idiots. From there the 20-mm and 7.62-mm Gatling guns sounded like monotoned elephant farts, a low-pitched and a high-pitched asshole. With both Twenties grinding and the Forty coughing and spitting brass it was bedlam. The booth reeked with the pungent odor of burnt gunpowder.

The long 20-mm bursts formed solid streams of fire from the gunship to the building. The roof and walls disintegrated. Because Ed saw the target and the impacting shells, few rounds missed. He simply held the crude metal crosshairs on the aim point and flew a pylon turn. Computer and tracking errors were eliminated. It was the most accurate firing technique. However, on the first burst Ed discovered one new correction he had to kick into the rudder. The concentrated recoil from three guns firing simultaneously caused the aft end of the plane to yaw and wiggle wildly. Each time Ed resumed firing, Juan Sueno shouted, "Cha, cha, cha."

"That's some meat grinder you have there," the ground commander said. "Work over the whole area. Hit those buildings south of the big one. And water that tree line across the road."

"Roger that," Ed said. He systematically smashed in the

tile roofs of the buildings. He switched to the miniguns and sprayed the tree line, then walked rounds across the heavily damaged buildings until he was out of 7.62-mm ammunition.

"You did a whole afternoon's work for us," the ground commander said happily. "That's all we have for today, big buddy. You can claim one hundred killed by air."

"Bullshit!" I hollered at Ed. "Nobody's down there."

"Thanks much, sir," Ed answered the ground commander, "but we'd prefer, when you move in over there, you make a count and forward the KBA through channels."

"We might not get over there until tomorrow or the day after," the ground commander said. "The bad guys'll have everything swept up by then. Why not claim seventy-five KBA?"

"Affirmative. Thank you," Ed told the man. Over aircraft interphone he said to Dick and Juan, "Report it as seven buildings destroyed, KBA unobserved. If they're dead, that's all that counts. The number doesn't matter. Let's go to Freedom Fire and use up the rest of the ammo."

Freedom Fire was the section of Cambodia east of Tonle Sap. It was a shooting gallery. Detailed rules of engagement (ROE) spelled out the who, what, when, and where in regard to attacking targets. For example, in Steel Tiger gunships were permitted to attack motorized vehicles at night on roads outside of villages. In Freedom Fire anybody was permitted to attack anything, anytime, anywhere—man or machine, day or night, off or on a line of communication, inside or outside of a village. All was fair. The removal of ROEs was intended to sterilize the area and deny its use to hostiles.

That afternoon in Freedom Fire, taking guidance from IR, Ed destroyed our only vehicle of the week. Jim Ballard picked up the engine noise on BC and Schmidt, the vulture, latched onto the target. Nodding over the TV, I raised one eyelid of stone to see that they'd found a motorcycle. Its rider was making slow progress across a drained rice field. His muddy track reminded me of a snail's trail.

Hurriedly Holcomb maneuvered the gunship into firing geometry. Or did the gunship maneuver the crew? Then Holcomb and gunship vented daylight frustration with a single prolonged burst from a Twenty, a burst long enough to form a solid stream of shells stretching from gunship to ground—a stream of shells that anchored gunship to ground, chained weapon to victim, linked men above to man below.

The second after the gun cut loose, the cyclist looked up. Had he heard the growl of the beast that consumed him? The moment sent a shiver along my spine. Was I asleep or awake? What had the cyclist felt in that pulverizing instant? "Perfect fucking lead," I said.

"He wasn't going very fast," Lee admitted.

I yawned. Nobody had remembered to start the videotape recorder. As a result the act took on the significance of a dream, became more surreal than real. The cyclist's image slithered into a dead-end channel of my mind, away from the network of normal recall. Had the man truly existed?

The long burst of gunfire had used the last of our ammo.

The seventh day in the Basket, we didn't see a thing. The friendlies hardly talked to us. It was probably Buddha's birthday or something and they'd postponed the war but had forgotten to pass the word. We bored hours of holes through the sky. At one point, Jim Ballard said, "Maybe whoever we're fighting got the word about the Turkey Bird . . ."

Juan Sueno muttered, "The Bird Is the Word. Rivingtons. Sixty-three."

". . . and are afraid to show their heads when we're around."

"Who asked you, Jim?" I said.

"BCs're all alike," Juan said. "Fuckin' know-it-alls."

Lee sneered: "Yeah. Who asked you, Jim?"

Self-assured Jim tuned us out.

I had the TV cameras aimed inside the airplane and a gunner was acting out some asinine charade for my enjoyment. I had already guessed the word "spring." On TV the gunner was crouched and was moving his arms back and forth in front of his chest. I said, "Shove, shove—push—get away! No. Push—shovel? Push in, push in—load!" The gunner tapped his nose. "Load. Right? Load! Spring-load . . ." The gunner pretended to be holding his penis in both hands. "Jack off," I said. "No? Clap? Clap Hands Here Comes Charley. No." Using one hand, the gunner pretended to aim his penis downward. "Come," I said. "Come? Drip? Piss?" The gunner grinned and touched his nose. "Piss. Spring-load piss . . ." I snapped my fingers and pointed at the screen. "Spring-loaded to the pissed-off position," I shouted. On TV the gunner touched a finger to his nose and applauded. *How appropriate,* I thought. An old air force term that meant perpetually short-tempered. Smart-ass gunner.

Another gunner who had his flying suit down around his ankles shuffled into the TV picture and bared his ass to the camera. "Moon over Miami," Lee said without inflection.

I stepped forward and switched off the TV picture on Lee's eight-inch monitor. "My game," I told him. He laughed. Grabbing Ballard's shoulder, I said from the corner of my mouth, "Play 'Melancholy Baby' on your BC and we'll see if John can name *that* tune."

"But I don't know 'Melancholy Baby,' " Jim Ballard said, willingly playing the straight man.

I didn't bother to deliver the punch line. Instead, I threw back my head, staggered backward, and fell into my seat. This was not what I had volunteered for! I clutched my head in both hands and screamed, "Fuck!" Grinning, Lee watched my performance. I raised one eyebrow, told him, "Nevah—in the history of wahfare—has combat been so boring. I'm going crazy."

Lee shouted, "The man's nuts! Grab 'em."

The outcome of the week was that Lee and I stopped arguing over interphone. Instead, we shouted across the booth at each other. Juan and Jim joined us and, from then on, most of the booth's business was conducted that way. We had a private interphone network over which only we could talk. However, Ed was able to listen to what we said over it. Shouting cut him out completely. The showdown sort of ended in a draw. Earlier, we had enjoyed a great laugh at Ed's expense.

As part of the learning process, we shot whatever else we had found besides trucks: leveled a few huts, sank a pair of barges, and "partially damaged" a huge boat along the Se Kong River. On one of our early missions, I had seen the boat first, bigger than life: wide-beamed, eighty feet long, with an oblong house centered aboard it. The boat was against the riverbank. Around it, there was no sign of life. "Definitely looks hostile," Juan Sueno said.

"What do you have?" Ed asked.

"Stand by," I told him. "Anybody know how long's a cubit?"

"A yard," Lee stated.

"If that was so, they wouldn't have named a yard 'a yard,'" Juan said.

"Makes sense," Lee agreed. "A cubit must be two feet. Maybe four feet."

"Four feet is a horse," Dick threw in from up front.

Jim Ballard said, "I think it varied, like the king's foot originally did. I think a cubit had something to do with the length of the forearm, around eighteen inches."

"Eighteen inches?" I said. "They named it after my cock. One swinging cubit!"

"Dream on," Lee said.

"Would you believe—half a cubit?" I asked.

Ed Holcomb butted in: "What do you have down there, Noah's ark?"

"You named it," Juan told him.

I described the size and shape of the boat, then added, "It has a high railing all the way around the outside edge of the deck. The boat looks like it's made completely out of wood." I had trouble believing that such a large target had escaped destruction until then. The boat obviously was aged.

"What do you want to do with it?" Ed asked.

I looked at Juan, who made a vague gesture.

"Fuck it. Hit it," Lee said.

Jim Ballard said, "Maybe we ought to—"

"Let's go down and put the Twenties all over it," Lee suggested.

And we did. From five thousand feet, with TV tracking, Ed emptied both 20-mm cannons into the boat. Every round appeared to hit and punch out a separate hole. By the time we finished, it looked like a colander.

"I'll bet when the owner sees that, he's going to be pissed," Ballard said. "I can't believe it didn't burn."

"Me either," said Juan.

In the back of my mind, that had been bothering me too. I said, "It didn't even sink any." The boat must have already been aground, I realized. Then it dawned on me: we had shot up an abandoned hulk. Hiding my mouth behind one hand, I laughed until my shoulders were shaking. Juan punched me on the arm. I looked across the aisle and saw he was grinning stupidly. "Call it 'partially damaged'?" I managed to say for Ed's benefit.

"Sounds about right," Juan said. He rolled his eyes.

"Do you want to put a Forty on it?" Ed asked. Juan and I convulsed with laughter. Ed said, "Don't you think maybe we did a little more than *partially* damage it?"

"You didn't make it burn," I managed to say before a burst of laughter overtook me.

"You didn't make it sink even one inch," Juan said; then laughter grabbed him.

"Ed," I said solemnly, "I'm afraid . . ." It took the last of my self-control to finish. ". . . 'partially damaged' is the best we can give you." By then, Ballard and Schmidt also had it figured out. We delighted in our stupidity, then vowed never to tell Ed.

Throughout the remainder of the dry season, we saw the hulk often and each time it looked more and more beat up. Every sensor team in Spectre probably hit it at least once, but nobody ever confessed to doing it.

Chapter 6

Get Off My Cloud

IN SPECTRE A man's first allegiance was to his crew, those men he accompanied into the wild black yonder. Within a crew, allegiances were further defined. Navigators, for example, tended to side with other navigators, then with pilots, who as fellow officers came before the enlisted crewmen. In a like manner, gunners' first loyalty was to other gunners, then other enlisted men, then pilots and navigators.

Beyond a crew, a man's first allegiance was to his squadron, but with similar priorities: navigators favored fellow navs; pilots, fellow pilots; and so forth. Nevertheless, squadron esprit de corps was a dynamic force, a point around which to rally. A Spectre officer, for example, backed a Spectre enlisted man in any situation involving a person from another squadron, regardless of the outsider's rank. Other squadrons were considered to be rivals, especially among flying units.

There were a few indistinct allegiances beyond the squadron, however. F-4 pilots, for example, felt a bond with other air force F-4 pilots. At Ubon, men of the 433rd and 435th Tactical Fighter Squadrons were friendly competitors. F-4 pilots then extended their camaraderie to fighter pilots in general. RF-4 pilots, who flew an unarmed reconnaissance version of the Phantom, were probably the next kin of F-4 jocks, albeit bastards.

Because the U.S. Air Force had no other AC-130 squadron, Spectre was an entity. Spectre's closest relative was a weaker half-brother, the AC-119 Stinger squadron stationed at Da Nang. The Stingers flew close support for U.S. and ARVN forces in South Vietnam. We seldom exchanged visits with Stinger. Spectre crewmen repeatedly insisted, "If you ain't Spectre, you ain't shit."

Bearing true faith and allegiance to one's crewmates was a self-protective reaction. To be a Fucking New Guy (FNG) in an established flying squadron was traumatic, especially when the squadron was engaged in combat. A man was expected to prove his ability before he was accepted. FNGs were ignored by old-timers, men who had flown at least fifteen combat missions and earned an Air Medal. Therefore, FNGs turned to other FNGs and, in particular, to crewmates for friendship. The needs for belonging and esteem were initially satisfied within one's crew structure. After a crew developed a reputation within the squadron, then men beyond the aircraft commander were individually recognized. I was known as "Holcomb's TV" long before I was recognized as Major Hal Zorn.

In a combat environment, efforts to fulfill the needs of belonging and of esteem were distorted because the lowest need, survival, was constantly jeopardized. In Spectre, Death waited thirty-five miles away across the Mekong River.

The complexities of being an FNG are best seen by examining the case of a hypothetical Lieutenant Colonel Smith, an IR sensor operator. Rank alone gave him relatively high esteem in the air force hierarchy, but as an FNG he was nameless. His identity was predicated upon his pilot, who, not unrealistically, could have been a captain. Thus, Lieutenant Colonel Smith became "Captain Doe's IR." From there, his reputation was determined by the crew's success. Within the squadron, a crew was judged by what it had done and what it could be depended upon to do day after day. If the crew clicked in short order, everything was fine. However, if the crew failed to get its shit together, Doe became Mud and Lieutenant Colonel Smith was known as "the IR on that jerk-off Doe's crew."

A man in Colonel Smith's predicament usually reacted

predictably. Generally, he suffered in silence and found an outlet in booze, or sex, or both. He "put in his year" by "counting the days" until he "returned to the Real World," where he was "somebody." Frequently, a man with such a problem schemed his way off a crew and into a staff or administrative position. As a result, he flew as seldom as possible or just enough to qualify for flight and combat pay. Occasionally such a man denied the problem and considered the judges to be wrong. In such a case, the crew continued with its methods, flew when scheduled and generally did what was asked of it, produced lackluster results month after month, and, not surprisingly, eventually gained acceptance. Very rarely, the man faced the problem from the start, took command of the situation after a power struggle, kicked asses, and otherwise did his best to organize the crew in the manner expected. If that effort failed, he had no choice but to take the most dramatic course of action and demand reassignment to a better crew.

In Vietnam, I saw a noteworthy, unpredictable reaction to being an FNG, the exception to the norm. A senior major navigator locked himself in his room for two weeks when he failed to hack it with his crew. He had no one else to turn to. His retreat coincided with the cataclysmic onset of the 1968 Tet Offensive. No esteem, no belonging, no safety, threatened survival: it was too much for him and he hid. The dumb ass was more likely to be killed on the ground by one of the frequent mortar and rocket bombardments than he was to be shot out of the air; however, on the ground in the privacy of his room, he could die without risking further rejection by his peers. Picture it: the Hercules plummeting earthward in flames and the pilot turns to him and says, "In seconds we're going to die, Leo, but, before that happens, I want you to know I still think you're a shitty navigator." *Splat!* But maybe not. When Death came, it came with a rush. One sunny afternoon long after Tet, I saw a single 122-mm rocket flash across the Tan Son Nhut runways, slice through a wall of the passenger terminal, and impact on a buck sergeant sitting alone in a corner. After a year in Nam, he had been thirty minutes from boarding his Freedom Flight to the Real World. Not another person was as much as scratched.

When that major navigator finally emerged from his room, he was treated like a ghost. Ignored by the other flyers, he was not scheduled for duty. Only two persons spoke to him: the squadron navigator, who was an alcoholic but at least flew his share of missions, and a Vietnamese housegirl who knew about fifty words of English. In limbo, the major returned to his room for a year. I thought the son of a bitch should be dragged out and shot, but it wasn't my decision to make.

New crews were strange beasties . . .

Within Spectre a newly formed aircrew of thirteen men resembled a grotesquely deformed baby, a thirteen-headed infant struggling to attain a recognizable shape and single direction. Like a baby, a crew grew and matured while developing outward appearances and inner drives. Combat pressures accelerated growth and exaggerated group dynamics. In most cases, strong personalities with extremist philosophies banded together or fought each other and thereby influenced the middle-of-the-roaders in establishing a crew image. Frequently a crew adopted or was labeled with a name to match that image. Sometimes one man was influential and powerful enough to control and give direction to an entire crew. The best crews were those in which the strong man happened to be the aircraft commander, the appointed leader. Our crew fit in that category. Although we generally could be classified as opinionated individualists, we accepted Ed Holcomb's direction because we respected his single-mindedness and competence in reaching what we recognized as a common goal: killing everything we found. At heart we were no different from other red-white-and-blue-blooded fighting men throughout history.

As was the case in individual personality development, a few crew personalities grew deviant. An old crew could become the strangest beastie . . .

Within Spectre, one of the more colorful crews was Los Borrachos led by Benny "El Indio" Aguilar. The crewmen prided themselves on their ability to drink great quantities of tequila—and rum—and gin. Aguilar was the sole Mexican, but his officers answered to the names of Mexican Revolutionists: Madero, Orozco, Villa, Zapata, Diaz, and Serdan. I never understood how they remembered who was who. But they did. They remembered even when they were knee walking. But at those times they forgot their real names. They wore moustaches à la Frank Zappa and grew their hair as long as regulations permitted, and then some. Real middle-aged hoods. They killed a lot of trucks, around a thousand, nearly as many as we did.

Lieutenant Colonel Pizza Pete Angelino led a perverse bunch of navigators who thought he was a mother hen and, therefore, did everything he didn't want them to do, which included calling him Pizza Pete. With reverse psychology Pete got them to do everything he wanted them to do. Until they decided Pete was proud of their image, they wore their heads shaved and had skull-and-crossbones shoulder patches that read "Yankee Air Pirates." When the men figured out that Pete was manipulating them, they refused to do anything and changed their name to "Lazy Dogs."

Major Rabbit Ripple's crew was manic. It took after its leader, who was notorious for his "Tablecloth Trick." Whenever Rabbit entered a crowded Officers' Club where he was unknown, he strode to the center of the dining room and selected a table with four people. Before the surprised diners reacted, Rabbit lifted two corners of the tablecloth and held them above the centerpiece with his fingertips. He then graciously introduced himself and with a line of merry patter persuaded the people at the table to hand him the other two corners of the cloth. Not a dish was disturbed. Lightly holding the four corners of the cloth in his fingertips, he suddenly raised his free hand toward the ceiling and loudly announced, "And now—the Rabbit Ripple—World Famous—Tablecloth Trick!" In one swift, continuous movement, he snatched the four corners of the cloth in both hands, whipped the cloth with the dishes inside it into the air, swung it in a wide circle above his head, then smashed the sacked china down onto the center of the table. He leaped back with arms raised triumphantly. A stunned spectator always said something like "I don't believe he did that" and Rabbit replied, "*That,* sir, is the trick." Rabbit also performed the feat in his own home. Afterward, he climbed onto the table with an upright sweeper and vacuumed up the breakage. He dared to do anything, and nobody on his crew could match him. Rabbit once rode a bicycle into the Ubon O-Club bar while buck naked, stopped for a few drinks (everyone, including bartender and waitress, refused him the satisfaction of recognizing his nudity), then pedaled back home to his room. Manic!

Rory Hansen's Razorbacks had three boisterous University of Arkansas graduates who at the slightest provocation bellowed out the same long-winded hog call to indicate delight or displeasure. When they let loose in the O-Club dining room, the Thai waitresses covered their ears with their hands or ran into the kitchen.

There was little love lost among crews. At most they tolerated one another's behavior.

The Sixteenth Special Operations Squadron was authorized eighteen crews for twelve Spectre gunships. The actual manning was strange: an abundance of pilots and copilots, two dozen or more of each; the minimum number of navigators, or barely enough to go around; enlisted men somewhere between in number. Therefore, only eighteen pilots were assigned crews; the other pilots filled staff positions and shared. After December, when the war got serious, pilots averaged four missions a week; navigators, six. Seventh Air Force Headquarters wanted a sortie rate of one, each airplane in the air each night. When trail traffic grew heavy, Seventh asked for as many as eighteen sorties daily; on those nights, every navigator flew.

I had been in the air force for fifteen years and there had been a shortage of navigators the entire time. I decided that air force leaders deliberately failed to train a sufficient number of navs. In that way, the few navs who existed remained in the cockpits and left the command positions open for the gaggles of pilots.

Spectre's scheduling officers (pilots, naturally) didn't enforce the regulation which limited the monthly flying hours per man. Their concern was names to fill positions. They scheduled Dynamite Dixon (he challenged their heartlessness by telling one of them: "The game's war, sir, fuck the rules.") until he bailed out on the taxiway. Because of the system, Holcomb and Tex Tyler flew only with our crew. Our sensor team flew with everybody. We tried to remain together. Often, however, we filled in alone with other crews. Nights when I wasn't scheduled, I quickly learned that some TV operator always was willing to go downtown for a scrub and rub if I offered to fill his seat. The way I looked at it, the season was five months (December through April) and I wanted to play in as many games as possible in that limited time. Why else had I volunteered? Like the fucking animals did, I needed to get as much as I could while things were in heat. Juan Sueno had the same urge. Holcomb and Tyler didn't know the thrills they missed by not flying with the hoi polloi.

The first time Juan flew with Rory's Razorbacks, he reported: "That is a circus gone amok. At the crew briefing, Rory wears a coolie's hat that's painted red. The co wears a Chinese skullcap with a long black pigtail. The navigator has a Porky Pig mask, and that asshole went to Cornell. And the IR and TV wear hats that look like boars' heads. Those two want to be called the Swine Brothers. They have these big rubber stamps, and they stamp big red pigs on everything. My flying suit is ruined! All of them snort and grunt on interphone, and—Jesus!—they throw food in the booth, I mean, a real food fight. I'll never fly with those fuckin' pigs again."

The men who flew on Chase's Chaste quietly flaunted their collective faithfulness to their wives. After a mission with them I had all I could take. I stomped into the room, slammed the door, and threw my hat against the wall. "That worthless fuck," I said to Dick.

We had a ritual. Following mandatory debriefings and informal crew discussions, Dick and I conducted a final critique of each mission in the privacy of our room. We talked far into the morning about gunship tactics and military strategy. Dick was a West Point grad. He lit a cigarette while his pale blue eyes twinkled and his laugh lines deepened. "Have trouble?" he asked.

I said, "We got zero trucks and ya know why?"

Dick shook his head. "But I'll bet you're going to tell me."

I laughed through my anger. Kaulbach affected me that way. He was an even-tempered little shit, about five-six, one-eighty. A little Buddha: bull neck, chunky torso, short legs, and heavy arms with sledgehammer fists. A bowling ball. A pulling guard. A fireplug. Nobody to fuck with. And he had more brains than any three navigators put together, which was no big deal. Navigator brains sold for a dollar a pound. On the other hand, pilot brains were priced at fifty dollars an ounce. The reason was that hundreds of pilots had to be slaughtered to find an ounce of brains.

I sat on my bed and unzipped my boots. "That supreme asshole Bill Chase would not attack. We were over in Nam, below the DMZ. We found ten trucks, parked. And that sis wouldn't attack."

"He think they were friendlies?"

"No. They were on the border. Sweet Billy thought it was a flak trap." A flak trap was a location where a lucrative target was set in the open amidst hidden, heavily concentrated antiaircraft guns. The objective of the trap was to lure aircraft to their destruction.

"Whaaaaat?"

"That asshole. All of Laos is a fucking flak trap."

"For sure."

"Billy said he wasn't going to risk an airplane for only ten trucks."

"Take any triple-A?"

"Not one round. I'm freezing my ass off on the NOD and he's hanging a loose orbit for thirty minutes. I suggested we try it and if the flak is heavy we leave."

"Where did he get the idea of a flak trap?"

I shook my head and shrugged. "Probably read an Intelligence report for the first time in his life and it was something new to him. I wanted to go up and stick my thirty-eight in his ear and tell him to attack or die. Shit! The trucks were on the fucking border, waiting to cross over. You know how we decided that destroying them close to destination is best. I talked about that while we were in orbit and explained how you negate all the manpower and supplies that were used to get the trucks that far." I caught my breath, then added, "Nobody else said a word." I leaned back against my pillow. "Billy-boy was positive it was a flak trap and decided he wasn't falling for it. He flew off down south, over the mountains east of the Bolovens. You can't walk there, let alone drive a truck. We bored holes until it was time to RTB."

"He goes home the end of this month."

"I know. They all do, his whole crew. Fuckin' virgins."

"He must've decided he doesn't want to get shot at any more." Dick lit another cigarette. "That's a shame. He shouldn't fly."

"None of them should. We didn't fire one fucking round!"

"He doesn't have enough courage to attack," Dick said, "and it'd take more courage to admit it."

"The worst part is that they've probably been operating that way for the whole year." Flying with other crews made me appreciate our crew more and more.

When a pilot entered the fire-control display, eased the electronic diamond over the circle, then pressed the trigger, a crew reached the moment of truth. Its image was at stake. Planning, searching, and tracking meant nothing if the pilot couldn't make the kill.

The proof of proficiency was on videotape. Pictures of blowers and burners left no doubt as to a crew's ability. After a night of wreaking unbridled devastation a crew exuded an aura of success. Whether a man was a member of a regular crew or merely part of a pickup gang, his ego swelled when the group displayed extraordinary competence. The feeling was similar to being on a championship team, only beyond that. There was the element of having whipped Death as well as an opponent.

With a weak shooter in the left seat, a sensor team was forced to stick to the criteria. According to Seventh Air Force Headquarters, a single direct hit with a 40-mm shell was enough to classify a truck as destroyed. A hit less than ten feet in front (one mil low) was adequate to call a vehicle damaged. With a hit that close, shrapnel remained concentrated enough to knock the truck out of commission for an indefinite period. With a weak shooter, trying for blowers or burners often resulted in spending an hour or more on one or two trucks. From my experience, weak shooters lacked a killer instinct. They were satisfied to fill a square the easiest way. Once they hit on or close to a truck, they were contented and their concentration flagged until they were presented with a new target.

A good shooter like Ed, or Rabbit Ripple, Benny Aguilar, Dave Wine, or Billy Killeen, was willing to work for an explosion or fire: a positive kill. One direct hit whetted his appetite for more direct hits. If he failed to get a blower or burner, the multiple hits he scored created a category of destroyed well beyond the designated minimum. A good shooter possessed finely honed flying skills and a compulsion to line up the fire-control display perfectly. Close wasn't good enough. For him, the 40-mm cannon was a high powered rifle that required perfect sighting. He tried to hit the bull's-eye with every round. Because of a good shooter's ability to fly the airplane precisely, his rounds were concentrated on one spot and he "drove nails," or frequently scored multiple hits with one burst. A poor flyer's rounds "walked," a pattern of hits in which one or two rounds were low, then one on target, then one or two high.

According to the air force, an AC-130 pilot learned to shoot during training at Lockbourne. In an AC-119, he flew half a dozen daylight missions over Lake Erie. The sensor operators threw down a buoyant flare marker as a target to track, and the pilot killed fish until the guns were empty. The AC-119 had only machine guns and 20-mm cannons, scatterguns. It was tough to miss the lake.

A pilot flew the AC-130 and fired the Forties only after reaching Ubon. Therefore, previous C-130 flying experience greatly reduced the AC-130 firing problems because basically the pilot flew instruments when firing guns. He saw most targets only if they blew up or burned. Shooting wasn't easy. The physical strain was as demanding as the mental. The pilot sat hunched close to the control wheel, half-turned, looking over his left shoulder at the fire-control display. The position was uncomfortable. The over-the-shoulder view was perpetuated because that was the way it had been done before: Spooky and Stinger gunships had fixed visual sights mounted in that location long before there were sensors to guide the pilots. A Spectre joke claimed that chairs in one row of the base theater were to be turned ninety degrees to the right so that pilots could also enjoy the movies. From his contorted position the pilot refined his aim by rolling, yawing, and pitching the gunship, after establishing altitude, airspeed, and a thirty-degree left bank around the target.

Shooting was hard work, yet navigators did not sympathize with pilots who failed to fly well enough to score direct hits consistently. At best they tolerated such performers. Day after day navigators trusted their lives to pilots, and they wanted men larger than life—godlike, infallible figures.

It was fun to fly with a spastic once in a while and experience the chillingly unexpected. Such flights were another spectacular form of cheating Death and a source of anecdotes to share with fellow navigators. I flew one time in a B-47 with Captain Vern Herman, who, on landing approach, flared while still a hundred feet in the air. The flare maneuver normally was made the instant before contact with the ground. At that critical point, the pilot leveled the aircraft, simultaneously reduced power, and transitioned smoothly from the steadily descending glide path to the ground run and rollout. From one hundred feet in the air, the bomber sailed and sailed and sailed while Vern repeatedly asked the copilot, "Are we down yet?" Seated far forward in the nose of the bomber and unable to see outside, with power reduced, I heard air rushing over the aircraft's skin. It was an eerie effect. Then the plane sank, like an elevator! The main landing gear hit the runway, the six-engine jet bomber porpoised, the gear hit again, and the bomber bounced high a second time. About fifty feet back in the air, Vern said, "Fuck it," chopped all power, and told the copilot, "Gimme the chute." The copilot released the huge drag chute designed to brake the plane during rollout. That big silk son of a bitch popped and just stopped us in midbounce. The airplane slammed down with a force that snapped amplifiers out of their racks. In the nose, I experienced the ultimate game of crack-the-whip. My nuts ended up in my socks. "We're down," Vern announced. I asked, "How you want that logged? Two landings for you and one for the copilot?" Later I described the experience to Vern's regular navigator, a kind of shaky guy, and he said, "Sounds like a normal landing to me." I remembered the words of Amelia Earhart: "Any touchdown the pilot can walk away from is a good landing." Vern Herman gave me a greater appreciation for the pilot with whom I normally flew—about a hundred times greater.

Ed Holcomb Appreciation Night occurred every time we flew with a weak shooter. The basic problem was that some pilots had too little time in the C-130 and couldn't control the AC-130 precisely enough to keep the electronic symbols lined up in the fire-control display. A few other pilots came to Spectre from desk jobs and were rusty, out of practice. The AC-119 training had not been adequate for those men. Occasionally Ed flew with a pilot who was having problems and gave him pointers from the copilot's seat. Tex Tyler stayed home and probably spent the night flogging off into a white scarf while dreaming about stroking the control stick of an F-4 jet. Meanwhile, Ed was training pilots under combat conditions, which I thought was preposterous.

Our crew was merciless toward an incompetent pilot. After one major rolled and yawed and pitched the gunship for ten minutes without getting off a shot (and there was no antiaircraft fire) Lee asked, "You have this much trouble trying to come?"

Juan said, "They're not shooting at us because they're waiting for us to self-destruct."

Lee said, "They're probably laughing too hard to aim."

To keep peace, Ed gave the weak dicks one hour in the saddle before he took over and got the job done.

On the return leg to Ubon during a mission when we had been especially abusive, the object of our wrath, a husky captain about my size, barged into the booth. "You the mouths who know everything?" he asked and looked down at Juan and me. That was his second mistake.

Entering the booth uninvited was a no-no. In flight, the booth was the sanctum sanctorum of the sensor team. Excepting general officers, sensor operators were totally unreasonable toward anyone who entered without being asked. Gunners knocked before requesting permission to enter. An uninvited air force captain who programmed war games at the

Pentagon once rode in our booth and was ignored until he mentioned that he was cold. Lee told him, "Your hands should be warm. You're not doing anything but standing around with your finger up your ass." When Ed maneuvered the gunship through the sky to avoid ground fire, the captain stated that he was airsick. I told him, "Get out. Go throw up in the trash can." The captain asked the can's location and Juan said, "Find your own barf space. We're fighting a war." Our crew was no different from any other. The booth belonged to the navigators.

Now, Juan and I looked up at the captain, who pointed a finger at my nose and asked, "You Major Know-it-all?" Mentally I gave him credit for not picking on Johnny, who was smaller.

I stood and Juan stood up across from me. "I know you can't fly for shit," I said. "Now get out of the booth."

Setting himself in the cramped aisle, the captain said, "Make me." I lunged an instant before Juan. My shoulder rammed the captain's chest and knocked him off balance. Juan's weight hit me from behind and drove us through the booth door. The three of us fell to the deck. On top of the captain, with Juan on my back, I grabbed his throat. He offered no resistance. My rush of anger faded and I found myself questioning our sanity. The captain had to have felt my anger ebb, my grip loosen. He said, "Easy. I was only joking. What's wrong with you two? Can't you take a joke?"

Juan said, "Bullshit, man." He reached around me and jabbed the captain's shoulder. "You were looking for trouble."

"Get off me, Juan," I said.

"You two can't take a joke. Screw you."

"Bullshit," Juan said.

Puzzled gunners helped the three of us to our feet. "You all right?" the captain asked me. He held the booth door. "You two always so touchy?"

By then even Juan had nothing to say. The captain worked at being polite and making us look and feel stupid. After I thought it over, I was dissatisfied with the outcome. I couldn't decide who had been right.

Back in the room I told Dick about it. He chuckled on and off for half an hour. One good thing came of it. For a week Lee agreed with everything I said.

We eased up a little after that. Following another mission with an FNG who couldn't hit, Dick and I talked it over in private. Dejectedly I said, "Nothing, absolutely nothing beats on-the-job combat training." The major with whom we had flown had used twenty-four orbits (Juan and I counted them out loud, but not over interphone) on one truck. "A major— a senior pilot—he never hit within twenty feet. We gave it to him. We just called it damaged."

"But he never missed by more than fifty," Dick said. He took a beer from our small refrigerator, opened it, and drank half. "Flat," he said. Carbonated drinks went through numerous extreme temperature changes on their journey from the States and half of them didn't survive.

"He plowed a trench all the way around the truck, like a moat. Honest to Christ. When he finished . . ."

Dick said, "Can you picture the repair crew . . ."

". . . the truck was on a little mesa."

". . . building a bridge to get to the truck?" Dick laughed at his own humor, sagged back into the room's lone chair, and finished the beer. "Really flat." He twisted the empty can down to the size and shape of a hockey puck. "Trouble is, the new guys rush. If they took their time, they'd be faster."

I said, "If you can't fly . . . Ed—he can fly. He's so smooth. It's like being home in front of the TV." I yawned and stretched out on my bed.

Dick caught the yawn, then said, "I heard. Juan said you propped up your feet and went to sleep the other night."

"I got bored. Ed was shooting everything off the IR. Fuck that. I ate about a hundred of those little cookies Johnny carries. That captain who flew the first hour . . ." I took off a boot and threw it in a corner. "Jesus . . ."

"We could have dumped the ammo off the ramp and been as effective."

"A perfect example of what I always say. Even his landing was shitty."

"It wake you?"

"Yeah." We laughed together. I chucked my other boot into the corner and crawled under the covers wearing my flying suit. The sun was up and it was time for sleep. Before I went out, I decided that I'd think of it tomorrow. After all, tomorrow was another day.

Chapter 7

Street-Fighting Man

FLYING WITH OTHER crews gave me time on the NOD (night observation device), a starlight scope. The NOD had preceded the TV as a tracking sensor and four gunships were stuck with it for the current dry season because of inadequate air force funding. The NOD didn't guide as smoothly as the TV and, for that reason, Holcomb disliked it. His luck kept him from being assigned NOD birds. With other pilots I ended up on the NOD about half the time.

The NOD amplified light treble umpteen thousand times and turned darkness into a green-glowing twelve-inch circular picture. It did not enlarge the view. The picture had superimposed crosshairs and, the same as other sensors, fed sighting angles to the fire-control computer.

The NOD was a character builder.

The NOD stood swivel-mounted in the opening that formerly served as the Hercules entrance door, where the TV cameras later were hung. Slightly aft of the aircraft's nose, the NOD protruded into the wind blast of the chilling slipstream, exposing the operator to nature's elements and to the threatening reality of what arose from below. Like the rear scanner, the NOD operator had no heater to counteract the slipstream's chill and his duties produced other prolonged physical discomforts.

The NOD operator stood behind the device, shuffled side

to side in a cramped few feet of floor space while bent in a back-breaking crouch, and manhandled the heavy three-foot-long scope with two pistol grips attached to a crossbeam that extended beyond shoulder width. From inside the gunship, anyone who viewed the NOD operator silhouetted against the star-filled sky could have imagined he was struggling with a cross.

Unlike other sensors, the NOD had no mechanical boost. The operator's strength and endurance determined the smoothness with which the NOD tracked a target. While straining to overpower the forces of the universe that united and conspired during rocking and rolling through antiaircraft fire, I sometimes felt that the NOD came alive, that I was trapped in a knuckle lock with a futuristic mechanical wrestler.

The position of the NOD, two steps away from the number one Twenty, added to the hardships. When that six-barrel cannon ripped loose, screamed with tongues of fire, an operator needed frozen nerves not to flinch. The gun's breath was thick with cordite fumes that surrounded the NOD operator, stung his eyes, permeated his clothes, and seeped into his pores. In a perverse way I learned to love that odor. I associated it with power and the sight of fire and destruction.

I also loved the freedom the NOD offered. The feat of standing in the open doorway and leaning out of the gunship was better than flying in a small open-cockpit airplane, a thrill I'd experienced years before. What made the gunship better was that when orbiting in a steep left pylon turn around a target I was face downward in space with my arms spread. I felt the sensation of hovering above the battlefield like a dark angel, viewing the world through two naked eyes as well as through a mystical third eye, the NOD. And, throughout it all, I was exposed to the powers of nature as well as to the powers of the enemy. The position was dominatingly precarious. I was like a solitary tightrope walker intent on thrilling his most devoted fan—his sole spectator—himself.

Fire from enemy weapons heightened the NOD experience, made it enthralling. The trajectories of antiaircraft artillery rounds were fascinating. Watching the hypnotic orange glow of a tracer shell as it rose toward the gunship was like looking death straight in the eye. Normal society provided no parallel sensation.

I quickly learned that tracer rounds started as barely visible orange dots, no more than sparks on the mantled, distant landscape. Over long seconds in the suspended reality of combat, the sparks gradually increased in size, transformed themselves into growing suns that strained to escape their dense blackness of origin. Although traveling at enormous velocities, the growing suns appeared to float up toward the airplane, seemed to slowly cut a wake through the thickness of night. The suns that left the longest wakes were least dangerous because they were racing along patterns more parallel to the flight path of the gunship. Their glows appeared elongated because their trajectories were viewed in profile. Tracer glows that remained most nearly constant in size were the rounds that came closest to the gunship and were called "accurate" by Spectre crewmen. Those rounds emerged from an antiaircraft gun barrel with a lead that kept them pointed head-on at the gunship throughout their flight.

Normally the sunlike rounds flared upward in groups of three to five. They fanned out along the way. When they reached near the aircraft's altitude, their timer fuses detonated and the rounds exploded in showering reddish-orange novas which instantly disappeared amid gray smoke puffs. Inside the drone of the gunship's engines, a NOD operator heard accurate rounds as popping and puffing noises. I developed the habit of snorting at them in reply. The odor left by accurate bursting triple-A was as pungent as the breath of a Twenty.

One night a several-star general from Seventh Air Force Headquarters in Saigon went along for a ride with our pickup crew. The general, who looked younger than any of us, said, "I've heard so much about Spectre that I want to see for myself." Then he laughed, glanced away, and sheepishly added, "Besides, I haven't been shot at since Korea."

The general was squeezed in next to me on the NOD when the sparks of four tracers appeared directly below. The gunship was in orbit, but neither the pilot nor the rear scanner saw the rounds. In fatalistic fascination I watched the glowing dots as they seemingly crept upward, barely changing size, heading directly at me. I remembered the adage: "You never see the bullet that hits you." *Wrong,* I thought. From the corner of my mouth I told the general, "We've had it."

"What?" the general shouted.

The tracers slowly enlarged into four fuzzy orange balls stacked vertically, practically touching. They climbed upward with such deliberate certainty that I could not move my eyes from them. I didn't doubt that they would hit me, destroy me, perhaps send the gunship crashing in flames. Yet the languid pace of the approaching devastation lulled me into hypnotic silence, kept me from calling a warning to the pilot, who could have maneuvered out of harm's way. The event was filled with a certitude that could not be denied. This was death, I knew.

Then, in the same instant and with an invisible rush of speed, the rounds that loomed in the distance simultaneously appeared right before me. My trance shattered and time accelerated along with my pulse. The orange tracer glows bloomed in my face, flooded my vision, filled my mind with a silent light that shone with a white hot inner core. I marveled at the idea that the eye of death had opened on me. Death was never more beautiful, more welcome, I thought. The moments just past ceased to be. How had I arrived in this place? I wondered.

"What?" the general shouted again. He was calling to a dead man.

In that fraction of a second, the tracer rounds shifted dimension, regained individuality, and barely elongated before fanning out ever so slightly. Like incandescent meteorites, two shells flashed above the banked gunship and two below, scant feet away, so close that I heard their sizzle and hiss. I felt as if death had courted me, won me, and then spurned me. I wondered why.

Surprised by the sudden appearance of accurate fire, the pilot, Dave Wine, cried, "What? . . ."

"What did you say?" the general repeated. Or was it an echo in my memory? His head was next to mine; our flak helmets brushed each other.

Had the man seen what had taken place? "Ahhhhh—" There wasn't time to explain. "Nothing important, sir." The general smiled, slapped my back, roughly squeezed my shoulder.

Back on the ground, the general told Wine, "I've never seen such accurate ground fire over supposedly neutral territory." When Wine extended an invitation for the following night, the general shook his head and smiled. "Once was enough," he said. Catching my eye, he winked boyishly. "Once was nearly too much. I got enough to last me for another twenty years."

The NOD had one major advantage over the other sensors: the operator could ignore his equipment and directly view the battlefield. That made it easy to pinpoint antiaircraft guns. My meat. Dueling with AAA sites was a challenge that equalized and personalized air-to-ground combat.

Using peripheral vision I watched for muzzle flashes outside the viewing field of the scope. Upon spying a flash, I slued the scope to the general area of the flash. The next time the gun came up, I owned it.

In the NOD a silent gunpit appeared as an easily overlooked black dot, a tiny, distant speck that seemed nothing more than a pore on the earth's skin. I thrilled when I saw a gunpit erupt into an evil sore, squirting streams of tracer fire that glowed greenly in the cyclopic eye of the NOD. The growing, glowing tracer rounds wafted upward while I centered the NOD crosshairs on their source and called, "NOD tracking that gun." By then, Ed and Dick had convinced other pilots not to take back talk from any gun. Within seconds the pilot realigned the gunship's orbit and banged back with a Forty.

Then came the moment when streams of shells pulsated and passed in both directions, and my heart pounded in tempo with them. My imagination transported me to a level of fantasy outside the scope of that war. I was locked in the middle of an old-fashioned shoot-out . . . Dodge City . . . the OK Corral . . . High Noon, at midnight, in an alien town. My excitement mounted when the gunship's 40-mm rounds finally sparkled around the gunpit. I was unflinchingly trading shot for shot. And that point was merely the beginning of many exchanges. Often, equally fearless North Vietnamese gunners continued blasting out gunfire despite their obvious vulnerability, the disadvantage of having ceded the high ground.

And then I tightened my grip on the NOD, and the pilot refined his aim and tightened the pattern of the gunship's firepower so that our counterattack climaxed with rounds raining on and inside the gunpit and, inevitably, silencing the enemy. After calling, "That's enough," while rounds that had been in flight continued to pound mechanically into the silenced position, I felt a subtle afterglow of success, no more than the slightest tingle of victory. During the exchanges I lived the wild, impossible childhood daydreams in which the bad guys lost forever and, at most, the good guys were singed by the heat of battle. But it all was too fleeting.

Every time the gunship was muzzle to muzzle with a gun on the ground and shells were flying in both directions, I wanted time suspended. I desired to stretch those moments into a perpetual orgasm of firepower. In those frantic seconds, life had a fleeting intensity that I longed to enjoy at length and to examine in minute detail. I wished to live forever while risking my life every moment I was alive.

The NOD provided me with emotions far deeper than any I felt in the cozy confines of the booth. Even dressing for battle while on the NOD differed from suiting up in the booth. Seemingly distanced from external threats, most men grew complacent in the womblike booth and, in time, ignored at least some of the personnel equipment provided for protection. The gear didn't seem as vital. With Spectre untouched and riding the crest of its luck early in the dry season, many men soon ignored the trappings of combat. In the booth, Schmidt and I were totally carefree on occasion, didn't bother to don even a parachute, the absolute minimum in self-protection. Some nights a man just *knew* he was untouchable, indestructible. On such nights, we were the absolute antithesis of Jim Ballard, who donned every piece of gear on every mission, including those pullman flights into Cambodia.

On the NOD, however, that secure feeling vanished. A

man could see the threat, recognize his vulnerability. Dressing for battle became a ritual.

When assigned to the NOD on missions with Dick Kaulbach as navigator, I spent the leg to the Mekong River seated behind him on the floor of the flight deck. Dim red lights illuminated the cockpit. It was pleasantly warm and quiet. Periodically, Dick and I exchanged smiles, were happy to be headed to war together. In the dim redness, Dick's heavily shadowed round face and round head, bald at the crown, made me picture him as a miscreant and cunning friar turned mercenary for the thrill of the hunt. Farther up front, the lighting confused outlines and shapes. With heads encased in flak helmets, the pilots and flight engineer were shadowy forms, took on the hooded appearance of executioners. Were they truly spectres?

Five minutes before crossing the Mekong River, the navigator alerted the crew to dress for battle. That was my signal to leave the flight deck and climb down the short ladder to the NOD station.

Alone at the NOD, in the darkness of the gunship, I girded for battle. Elsewhere on the airplane, other crew members went through similar rituals. Over my heat-resistant NOMEX flying suit (which reputedly withstood flames up to one thousand degrees) I put on a government-issue quilted underwear jacket. It provided warmth and served as padding for my fitted survival vest, which went on next and contained radios, flares, a holstered .38-caliber revolver, a built-in bandoleer, and a long knife. I loved the feel of the survival vest: the authoritative weight of the handgun, the orderly ridge lines of bullets, the scabbard hugging my hip. The same as most NOD operators, I scorned the cumbersome flak jacket because it slowed movement. A few operators draped a flak jacket from the bottom of the NOD to serve as a shield between ground fire and the family jewels. Standing spread-legged in the NOD opening, a man who worried about that sort of thing could easily feel he had them hung out for the world to shoot at. Instead of a flak jacket, I next buckled on a weblike harness for use with a chest-pack parachute. Then I made certain a chest-pack parachute was within easy reach next to me on the floor. I donned each layer slowly and carefully smoothed wrinkles, avoiding overlaps. When I moved I expected the equipment to follow as easily as my skin.

As I adjusted each item I felt a growing expectation. The equipment infused my body with tense purpose and yet nameless intention—an aimless, consuming desire. We were on our way to close with the enemy, to strike without restraint. But to me it didn't matter who we encountered. I willingly would do battle with anyone we found. I felt chosen. My destiny was simply to destroy. Killing was all that mattered. I felt an immodest lust, wanted to kill, to run amok, to fight in the street, perhaps to be killed. From which century was I bred?

I replaced my earphones with a dark brown flak helmet that resembled a football helmet, but without ventilation holes. After snapping and pulling the chin strap taut, I rotated my head in a circle and jerked it violently in several directions. The helmet stayed in place as tightly as an extra layer of skull bone. While on the NOD, a jagged piece of shrapnel had once sliced through Lieutenant Jack Dubinsky's helmet. The kid hadn't noticed until, on the way home, a gunner pointed it out. The shrapnel had come to rest against the skin of Dubinsky's head. The Spectre joke was that the Polack's head stopped what the flak helmet couldn't.

Last of all I stretched on silk glove liners and NOMEX gloves. I alternately punched one fist into the opposite palm to feel the tightness of the gloves. By then I usually was bouncing on the balls of my feet like a boxer who had just entered the ring. I was ready—ready for a fight.

Dressing for battle was the transformation from Jekyll to Hyde. During the process my adrenaline hit flood stage. By the time I finished I felt immortal, invincible, about two-and-a-half steps above God. I was beyond recognition of danger.

To blow off excess energy I braced my feet against the lower corners of the NOD opening, gripped the sides of the opening with each hand, and leaned out of the airplane as far as I could. Fuck the safety line. The muscles in my arms were steel cables. My hands were vises. The spinning propeller of the droning left inboard engine was a few feet to my left. I saw the faint disk described by the whirling blades, the circle traced by the yellow prop tips. I spit into the propeller, then turned my head to the right until I stared into the slipstream. The wind made my eyes smart and water until stars in the sky blurred and the earth became a gray, unlighted void.

I felt suspended alone in space, in a coffin of sky. A low growl in my throat swelled into a roar. I was flying. I was on my way to destroy those who opposed me. Bring on trucks. Bring on guns and gunners. Bring on anything. I wasn't afraid of man or machine. If it fucked with me, it died. *I* was the Spectre of Death, a ghost returning to the same place, which was always different.

Chapter 8

Why Don't We Do It in the Road

AS PART OF in-theater indoctrination, our crew was sent on a one-day tour of Task Force Alpha (TFA) at Nakhon Phanom Air Base (nicknamed Naked Fanny), located in northeastern Thailand. We were slowly scrutinized by the TFA sentries before we were permitted inside the tall wire fence that surrounded the sprawling, air-conditioned, one-story building that housed TFA. "What the fuck's the delay?" I asked of nobody in particular. I couldn't pass up a chance to bitch.

Lee Schmidt said, "They're not sure about Juan. They think he's a Dink spy."

"Show it to him anyway. He won't remember it tomorrow," Dick Kaulbach said.

"He can't be a spy," I said. "The Dinks're too busy fighting the war to waste their time on shit like this."

"Relax, Hal," Ed said. "They're only doing their job."

"Well, tell them to stop doing it on our time. We could be out flying a mission."

"Or getting laid," Lee said.

A captain without wings appeared and escorted us into the building. He looked at his watch and said enthusiastically, "Good morning, gentlemen. I'm Captain Rogers and I'll be your guide for today's tour."

Lee laughed loudly. "They call you 'Buck,' right?" he said.
"No."

"Roy?"

"No." Rogers smiled.

I took a guess: "Ginger?"

Ed loudly cleared his throat, but Captain Rogers didn't need help. Unflustered, he said, "My name is Gary Rogers, gentlemen. I work here. I think our job is interesting, very interesting. I'll show you whatever you want to see. When you're ready to call it a day . . . sawadee." He showed us thousands of tons of electronic equipment. TFA personnel monitored activity on the Ho Chi Minh Trail with strings of microphones and seismic sensors implanted by F-4s at strategic locations along the trail. The sensors were designed to simulate indigenous trees, plants, and foliage. Thousands upon thousands of the sensors were used because their life expectancy and usefulness were limited by the transmitter power pack, detection by the enemy, and changes in traffic routing. "TFA was born from Igloo White," Captain Rogers said at one point in the tour. Igloo White was an earlier, less complex version of TFA.

"Who was the father?" Dick asked.

Captain Rogers said uncertainly, "I'm not sure . . ."

"Suspicions confirmed," Dick stated, but smiled when he said it.

Captain Rogers delighted in playing tape recordings of sounds and voices from the trail. His favorite tapes were of a North Vietnamese soldier inadvertently crawling out on a tree limb to which a sensor hung and proceeding to saw off the limb behind him, and of a Vietnamese man and woman engaged in sex. The conversations were in Vietnamese and we had to believe Rogers' translations except for sawing noises, a scream, and a thud on the first tape, and heavy breathing, sighs, and moans on the other favorite tape. There was a third tape that he claimed was played less frequently. It reproduced the splashes created by an enemy soldier emptying his bladder onto a sensor while commenting in very poor English on the parentage of President Lyndon B. Johnson.

"That's one kid should be killed today," Lee said.

We watched TFA assessment officers work from television screens upon which the NVA road system was electronically projected over a map of the sections of Laos under their control. When the acoustic or seismic sensors picked up truck movement, the truck's location appeared as an illuminated line of light, called "the worm," that crawled across the screen at a rate representative of the truck's progress. Assessment officers tracked targets as far as two hundred miles away. A computer predicted a truck's probable arrival time at preselected geographical coordinates. The senior duty officer then assigned F-4s to bomb the coordinates at the predicted time of arrival. I thought that the technique was as effective as two blind men hunting quail: the first blind man listened and pointed; the second aimed the gun and fired.

As a result of the tour, Dick innovated a procedure whereby, before reaching a target sector, he radioed the TFA assessment officers for the latest traffic information. By navigating to where traffic was heaviest, we avoided time-consuming periods of roadway reconnaissance. Dick then convinced Ed to follow lone vehicles headed toward where TFA personnel estimated that storage depots or rest-and-repair areas were located. The first time we tried the tactic, we followed an extremely slow-moving truck by flying wide orbits around it. "Think the driver died?" said Lee, who was tracking on IR. "He drives like one of our GIs. Oops, sorry, gunners."

"It all counts toward twenty, sir," a gunner said.

"Think the drivers have a retirement plan?" Juan Sueno asked.

"Of course," Lee said. "After sixteen hours of work, they get to go to bed for eight hours." He paused. "Get it? Retire?"

I said, "Groan."

Silence followed.

Minutes passed like hours. Jim Ballard circulated a large plastic container filled with homemade popcorn. Juan offered assorted cookies from a round tin. I propped up my feet and

75

tried to nap. After two minutes, I said, "Let's shoot the fucker and find something else."

Ed was adamant that we continue to track the quarry. At TFA he had learned that tactical needs dictated whether the NVA employed trucks singly or in convoy. In either case, trucks journeyed the length of the trail. Drivers, however, were used in relays. Drivers learned only a segment of the trail, perhaps no more than twenty miles when difficult terrain was involved. Therefore, drivers were changed frequently. Changeover and rest areas were set deep in the jungle, away from the main arteries. Ed told us about the system.

After another five minutes of shadowing, five minutes that seemed like five weeks, the truck left the main road and followed a single-lane trail into the jungle. Then the truck stopped, backed up a short distance, and turned down what looked to be a footpath. A gunner who was watching from the booth said, "Maybe he knows we're up here."

"The son of a bitch is lost," I said.

"That's all right," Dick joked. "So are we."

What seemed like five months later, the Judas goat pulled into a rest area where eighteen vehicles were parked. Grinning, Lee looked back at me and said, "Ed, I think you should know you can have your pick of make, model, and year."

"TV tracking," I said loudly. "Put TV in the computer."

"Bullshit," Lee said. "They're mine. Go back to sleep."

Dick harrumphed after Lee described the scene, then said quietly, "May we attack *now*, Major Zorn?" The booth had a laugh at my expense.

"Let's not rush," Ed told everyone. "First, give that driver time for a cup of tea or a bowl of rice. He earned it."

"And it may be his last," Lee said.

Ed flew two wide orbits before he narrowed into firing geometry and, taking guidance from IR, flattened the trucks. There was no antiaircraft fire. The lack of defense indicated that the area was assumed to be safe because it was far from the beaten path.

F-4 Phantom jets sometimes escorted gunships into Steel Tiger and, with two-thousand-pound high explosive gravity bombs, cluster bombs, and napalm cannisters, provided heavier firepower for flak suppression. Because there had been no gunsites for the two F-4s that happened to be along with us, after Ed finished with the trucks he permitted the escorts to work over the area. The two Phantoms laid down four Thermit bombs in a tight, overlapping pattern. The Thermit burned at eighteen hundred degrees.

When we departed, the rest stop and encompassing countryside were engulfed in flames. Jim Ballard said, "I guess we showed that jungle."

I again had propped up my feet and had tried to nap, but the show was too good to miss.

It was another night on the trail.

"TV has a single northbound mover," I said.

"Ten wheeler," Juan added. "Empty."

"Let's do him," Ed said. "TV in?"

"In. Clear."

"Forty?"

"Got it, sir."

I estimated the truck was traveling twenty miles per hour and led it accordingly. The 40-mm barked and the vehicle stopped. Four rounds impacted well in front of the truck. A moment later the truck accelerated rapidly.

"Look at that," Lee said. "Savvy driver."

"He's moving, Ed," I said and slued the crosshairs ahead of the truck. Before Ed lined up the airplane for a shot, the driver passed my aim point. I estimated the truck was doing fifty, the fastest I had seen a vehicle move on the trail. I picked a spot far down the road and said, "I have an extra long lead, Ed. When I say so, start firing. We'll let him drive into it." Ed orbited the spot where I aimed. When the truck reached a predetermined point short of the crosshairs, I hollered, "Fire, Ed."

The idea was for the rounds and the truck to arrive at the same place at the same time. Ed hosed out a long burst. As soon as the gun fired, the driver braked and put the vehicle into a skid that ended in a one-hundred-eighty-degree turn, then sped off in the direction from which he had come. Juan and I looked at each other in surprise.

"Thunder Road," Lee shouted and applauded.

Ed was firing and rounds were impacting on the empty road. "Knock it off, Ed. Cease fire and all that shit," I told him. The speeding truck was nearing the viewing limits of the TV.

"What're you doing with the crosshairs, Hal? Where you looking? What're you looking at?" Ed said.

"The truck—he's going the other way," I said. "Forget it. Hurry up. Get back in orbit."

"You keep moving the crosshairs," Ed complained.

"Ed, he's driving like . . . " Juan said.

I finished the sentence for him: ". . . a real fuckin' asshole."

Jim Ballard laughed at the chain of events.

"Go, Slope-eyes Mitchum! Haul ass!" Lee shouted over interphone.

"Knock it off," Ed commanded.

"You have to see it to believe it," Lee continued. "Slope Mitchum is doing . . . fifty . . . at least fifty. Maybe sixty."

I couldn't estimate the correct lead distance because the driver unpredictably varied his speed. Shots impacted far behind or far forward of the vehicle. In anger Ed laid down a blanket of 20-mm rounds. The driver slammed on his brakes, whipped into reverse, and backed down the road at a speed near thirty. Shells sparkled and tore up the road where the truck should have been. "He's the best," I admitted.

Jim Ballard said, "Shows what on-the-job training can do, coupled with a strong will to live."

"Maybe he'll blow a tire or overheat or something," said Ed, "and then we'll nail him."

Lee softly said, "That wouldn't be fair." He was beginning to get on my nerves.

We made another unsuccessful attempt to stop the vehicle with a 40-mm. "Ed," Juan explained, "it doesn't matter how fast he drives. If only he held a steady speed and a straight course, we'd lead him and hammer him. But this guy . . ." We made another unsuccessful try.

Ballard said, "The tape'll show you, Ed, *he* really knows what *we* are doing."

"Let's let him go," Lee suggested. "He probably has pussy waiting. All in favor?" Lee raised both hands.

Ballard laughed and said, "Why not? After all, he's empty." He too raised both hands.

Without looking at me, Juan slowly put up one hand.

Over his shoulder, Lee smiled at me and said, "Five to three."

I stretched back in my seat, then said, "Forget it, Ed," and released the tracking handle.

The last we saw, the truck was headed out of sight, speeding off the edge of the wide-angle television picture.

Lee Schmidt announced, "Thunder Road wins again." The Gomer lover!

Before and after missions, the commissioned officers on our crew ate together at the O-Club. We were like brothers, with Ed the big brother and Juan the baby of the family, the youngest. I enjoyed the company and the roaming conversations. Breakfast after a good mission was best. Still on the edge of shared excitement, we were closest then.

"I'd work for the NVA for six months, for nothing," I once said, "if I could travel through Laos and North Vietnam and see how the trucks are honchoed."

Jim Ballard said, "Only if it counts toward my year here."

"I know one thing," Lee said. "If I was with the NVA, I'd have a gunship to my credit by now. Maybe two." At that time, the squadron was on a run of luck: no airplane had been hit since the previous dry season.

The Thai waitress brought breakfast. Juan and I had arranged for her to serve a plate of garbage to Ed. Only after we tipped her and convinced her that she need not fear for her job did she agree to be part of the practical joke. The waitress served Ed last. When she placed the plate in front of him, Ed caught her wrist. He studied the fruit rinds, coffee grounds, egg shells, bones, and other unrecognizable bits that we had artistically arranged to form an H. He pointed at the plate and said, "There's been a mistake. I ordered this well-done."

Our crew exploded with laughter. Another waitress immediately served Ed with steak, eggs, and biscuits.

"I'll bet if I went with the NVA right now, I'd get a gunship within a month," Lee said.

"That's a bet," I told him. "Five thousand dollars. Start packing."

"Hal and I talked about that," Dick said. "We decided the NVA's satisfied with harassing us. If they were interested in shooting down airplanes in Laos, they'd bring in radar-controlled guns, or missiles. Maybe MIGs. Their main concern is getting supplies to troops in the south."

Ed said, "That sounds right. Colonel Godolphin told me that a Pentagon war game of gunship operations in Laos predicted forty percent losses this season. That figure is strictly between us, by the way." Spectre had lost one airplane in each of its first two seasons, a seventeen percent loss rate per season.

"Forty percent would be five airplanes," Juan said.

"We're going to have to take a lot of losses in a hurry to make the computer look good," Dick said.

Ballard reminded us: "You're being morbid." Jim always tried to make us look at the positive side of events. What a troublemaker. But even the Thais instinctively recognized his gentleness and treated him with great respect.

"OK. On the bright side," Juan said, "it's sixty percent in our favor."

"I'll go with the NVA if that's what I have to look forward to here," Jim said.

Lee told him, "They don't need scopedopes. They'd probably make you a driver."

"And chain you to the steering wheel," Juan added.

"We lose forty percent, somebody's going to have to chain me to the gunship," Jim stated.

"Hal and I talked about that the other day," Dick began.

Lee interrupted: "Don't you two ever talk about anything interesting, like pussy or getting drunk?"

Dick waved him to be quiet. "You know how we get an Air Medal for every fifteen missions? Well, we decided the drivers probably get an extra ten feet of chain for every fifteen trips down the trail."

"Right," Juan said. "With the first ten feet, they can make

it to the ditch. Next ten, behind a rock. Another ten, to a bunker."

"No, no," Jim said. "The way I see it, after fifteen trips their commander needs to wrap an extra ten feet of chain around them to keep them in the truck."

We ate in silence for several minutes. Nobody bothered to repeat the Spectre joke that the safest location for a driver to hide when attacked by F-4s was under the truck. There he was least likely to be hit.

Lee looked up from his food and said, "I still don't believe that one truck tonight."

"Captain Schmidt, don't talk with your mouth full," I said with my mouth full.

Lee spit what he was chewing into his hand, said, "I still don't believe that one truck tonight," then put what he was chewing back into his mouth. Ed was the only person who laughed.

Earlier we had found a moving convoy of six and, right off the bat, got a hit on the leader. Flames blossomed from the truck's ass. Instead of stopping, the driver speeded up and the fire went out. We kept shooting and got another hit when the truck slowed for a curve. Again big flames came out the back of the truck. The driver made the turn and floored it. Everything happened in less than a minute. I was tracking the leader; Lee was watching the other five, which had lagged behind. I had shouted across the booth, "Fuck him, he's burning—let's get the others, OK?" when, for no reason, the lead truck stopped in the middle of the road and the fire went out. It looked strange. The fire suddenly grew small, flickered for an instant, then snuffed out. It reminded me of a gas jet being turned off.

"That sort of looked like a new angle on what we fell for," I said to Lee.

Lee glanced at Ed, then frowned at me and shook his head.

Ed caught him in the act. "No what? What's going on?"

"Nothing," Lee said. "Never mind."

"Tell him," I said. "What difference does it make now?"

Lee looked unhappy. "Then you tell him."

"All right," I said. "When we first started, we'd find a

convoy and, as soon as we fired, the lead truck would race off. We'd chase him, bang away, and eventually stop him and blow him."

Lee took a deep breath, then exhaled loudly.

I spoke directly to Ed. "When we went back to where we originally spotted the convoy, we could never find the other trucks. We fell for that . . . "—I looked at Juan for confirmation—". . . three times?"

"Three," Juan said. "The leader was being used to draw us away from the others so they had time to drive into the jungle and hide."

Lee said, "I'll bet that driver tonight somehow controlled that fire. It was one helluvan IR signature."

"I wouldn't be surprised if that truck was armored too," I said.

Ed Holcomb narrowed his eyes and looked around the table: "You let them cheat us out of fifteen trucks. And you never told me."

Juan quickly explained: "You should have seen after we figured it out. There were five. You shot; the lead floored it. Hal moved to number two and we hammered him. The last four were already turning into the jungle. Everything stopped. Lee was tracking the lead, who drove a half-mile before he realized we didn't bite. He left the truck in the middle of the road."

Ed nodded. Before he could speak, Lee said, "What gets me is that we can blow a line of trucks one night, every one a burner, and we go back to the exact spot the next night and it's clean. There's not a sign of a truck."

"They probably have a million people working the trail," Juan said.

Ed told us, "I read that the population of the trail provinces was a quarter million. The NVA supposedly has seventy-five thousand troops supervising them."

I said, "Remember the empty we damaged the other night?"

"I remember the one that got away," Ed said and looked at Lee. "Thunder Road!" Ed was acting more like a father than like a big brother. "That makes sixteen . . ." He shook his head.

"But do you," I said, "remember the big boat you partially damaged? Remember that, Ed? You damaged the shit out of it. But you couldn't make it burn. And did we say anything to you?" The others shook their heads and Father Ed smiled faintly. "Now, remember that truck we damaged the other night and later went back to?" I said. "There were a dozen people around it. You didn't—"

"I got the impression we definitely surprised them," Lee said. "That's a neat tactic. We should use it more."

"Dick's idea," I reminded everyone.

Juan said, "I wonder if they sent another repair truck to repair that repair truck after we disrepaired it."

"You spend a season here," I said, "and about the time you learn the angles . . ." I snorted. "What a waste. There should be a better system. Like two- or three-year tours."

"No, thanks," Jim Ballard said. "One year's enough."

Ed said, "I agree. In one year you get all you're going to get out of flying here."

Lee looked off across the room. "Ed's right. Sometimes I wonder why I came back."

"To fly with Hal," Dick said and grinned.

"Right," Lee said. "My hero."

On that cheery note breakfast ended. Jim said, "I'm going to bed." Ed and Juan left with him.

After they were out of sight, Lee said to me, "For a minute I thought you were going to tell Ed about the ark. I nearly shit. It was bad enough you told him how the drivers faked us out."

"Fuck him," I said. "Don't worry. He knows we're good."

Dick laughed. "Ed really looked angry when he thought about the trucks he missed. He didn't mind being served garbage half as much."

Dick made it a habit to loop back randomly and check out damaged trucks. We also gave them a final look if they were on our route out of Steel Tiger. Then Dick extended the practice. Inbound on late sorties, he contacted the Spectre leaving our sector and obtained the positions of trucks it had damaged. If time permitted, we checked them out.

At first, we several times found repair crews hard at work.

Then nothing. The NVA somehow came up with a perfect counterploy. We not only failed to find repair crews, we also often failed to find the damaged vehicles. At times it seemed as if the NVA pulled damaged trucks out of sight the instant they were hit. We eventually gave up the practice of trying to trap repair crews.

We witnessed three classic examples of the NVA art of camouflage. In the first case, we found two convoys of five separated by a quarter mile. We stopped the leaders, then stretched our orbit to look over the back five. In less than a minute, those trucks nestled into the roadside tree line, under overhanging branches. On TV they were visible during only a quarter of the orbit. If we hadn't watched the trucks take cover, I doubted that we would have found them with normal recce. Their IR signatures practically disappeared. We guessed that, as soon as they stopped, the drivers wrapped the engines with insulation to cut down emissivity.

Another time we saw four trucks slip into a tree line and, right before our eyes, lost them on both TV and IR. For a couple of orbits we fired through the foliage, assuming the trucks were beneath the overhang. Then Lee happened to notice a faint IR shape about a hundred yards into the jungle. We hit it and it burned. There had been no BC signal. We guessed the NVA troops had *pushed* the vehicles after they were out of our sight. We couldn't find the other three trucks.

We also destroyed a pontoon bridge. It was forty-five degrees to the bank, being retracted, when I saw it. Thirty seconds later, it would have been out of sight. When we opened fire, the bridge crew must have released the controls because the bridge drifted back to span the stream. Ed blew the structure to pieces, which floated away. We returned to that spot on several later missions but never located a new bridge. I believed one was there but couldn't see it with TV. IR read only trees.

Garbage for breakfast wasn't the only joke we pulled on Ed. In the airplane we infrequently played a favorite game at his and at a gunner's expense. When there was no triple-A and a gunner entered the booth to get warm, I offered that gunner a chance to track the vehicle under attack. The man usually leaped at the once-in-a-lifetime opportunity. It was an experience he never expected. Without another word, I shoved him into my seat and Juan and I provided a rapid flow of information and advice. "Your chinstrap is unfastened," I shouted, a fact that had nothing to do with the task at hand.

"The crosshairs are drifting. Correct them," Juan ordered. "Hurry." With one hand the gunner fumbled with his chinstrap; with his other hand he reached for the tracking control.

"The reticles are at five mil intervals," I said as if it were a pronouncement from God.

"Hurry. Center the crosshairs on the truck," Juan said. "Hurry, hurry." The crosshairs had drifted well off target by then.

With a sensitivity knob, the TV tracking control could be adjusted from moving the crosshairs sluggishly to making them jump at the slightest touch. Before leaving the seat, I had twisted the knob to maximum sensitivity.

As soon as he landed in my seat, the gunner was excited. Our prodding stimulated him more. He clamped a death grip on the tracking handle and the crosshairs slued down the road and out into nowhere.

"Left," Juan ordered; the gunner pulled the handle to the left.

"Right," I said. The gunner started the handle in the opposite direction. "No," I shouted. "He's right, go left." The gunner paused, shot me a quick look, then pulled left.

"What's happening back there?" Ed asked. The electronic sensor circle had to have jumped off and then back onto the fire-control display.

"TV glitched, Ed. Stand by."

I helped the gunner put the crosshairs near the target and ran the sensitivity to minimum. Now, moving the crosshairs would be like stirring mud. I activated an electronic dot on the TV that indicated where the pilot had the gun aimed. I seldom used the dot. It was distracting and had been designed to aid the FCO. I pointed at the dot and told the gunner, "Six zero eight seven two alpha": my serial number before the air force converted to social security numbers.

Juan pointed at the TV console's eight-inch monitor and double-talked: "Sham the frail up, quibbly."

"Hunh?" the gunner said to me.

I told him, "He said, 'Sham it . . .'"

Ed caught up with the sluggish crosshairs and fired. The rounds impacted under the crosshairs, but the crosshairs weren't on the target.

"You missed!" I shouted.

Juan again ordered: "Sham the frail up—three, up three."

I told the gunner, "You have one more minute. Now take your time."

"Hurry," Juan urged.

Occasionally, ignoring the truck in the background, a gunner happily kept the electronic crosshairs on the electronic dot while, in his fire-control display, Ed kept the equivalent of the dot on the crosshairs. That arrangement made it easy to line up and shoot; however, rounds hit nowhere near the target. Usually a gunner manhandled the tracking control, and the crosshairs slid back and forth across the target or circled around it while Ed rocked and rolled the gunship and chased them. Ed was such a terrific pilot that he often hit a truck while the crosshairs were gliding over it.

To add to the confusion, Lee screeched out bird calls and heaped friendly ridicule upon the gunners.

I doubted that I could have tracked satisfactorily under identical conditions. Nevertheless, the gunners loved every second in the seat. They would have accepted any abuse for a chance to kill something.

While the circus went on, Juan told Ed that a malfunctioning fire-control computer was responsible for the glitches. Ed never was able to express enough gratitude when Juan finally corrected the problem.

To our surprise, Technical Sergeant Rusty Brown was deadly with the tracking control. He instantly picked up the touch and I stretched out on the floor while he destroyed an entire convoy. Of course, he ignored Juan and me. He was a cool, experienced veteran. The other gunners were barely out of high school. Brown claimed that wasting the convoy made his entire year. He was ready to pledge himself to my eternal servitude for another chance. I never gave it to him. Noblesse oblige had limits. Anyhow, a second go wouldn't have been as sweet to him. Besides, he was no fun. I could do what he did. If he wanted to run the game, he should have done what I did: gone to college and had his father buy him a commission.

Chapter 9

Sympathy for the Devil

BECAUSE GUNSHIPS WERE the last air force combat aircraft to carry enlisted men, the hard-core veteran flyers from among those ranks gravitated to Spectre. Spectre was on its third season of combat and several noncommissioned officers (NCOs) were in their third year with Spectre. They wanted no other life: a man flew a mission and put his ass on the line; then he was free to drink and whore until it was time to fly again. Unlike those commissioned officers who had the same philosophy but wouldn't admit it, the NCOs did not pretend to be any more than what they were. For them, there was little beyond today.

Rusty Brown, in his second year with Spectre, told a story that said all there was to say about the philosophy of enlisted flyers. "At Lockbourne, Staley—this gunner, Larry Staley—he broke his ankle in a freak accident just after he crossed the finish line in a dirt-bike race. He wins the heat and some local civilian asshole sideswipes him! Staley kept saying, 'I know it's broke. I broke it before. Feels exactly the same; the ends of the bones rub together.' He put some ice on it for a couple minutes, then said, fuck it, he's going to ride in the finals. He cinched his boot over the break and wrapped his ankle in black electrician's tape. He said black tape wasn't noticeable and there was less chance he'd be disqualified. He rode and won top money, seventy-five dollars. On the way to the hospital, he kept saying, 'Sure glad I'm in the air force. Otherwise, it'd take all my winnings to pay the doctor bills.' First night out of the hospital, he spent the whole seventy-five on a party for the other gunners."

Sergeant Larry Staley was killed on the gunship lost in combat during Spectre's second season, 1969–1970.

The first gunship lost by Spectre, in the 1968–1969 season, was destroyed when it crash-landed at Ubon. The events leading to the crash probably influenced the behavior of the men on the second airplane lost. Over Steel Tiger, the first plane took hits amidships and in the empennage. The pilots were able to maintain flight control, however, and the crew members opted to remain with the airplane rather than bail out into Laos. Upon reaching Ubon, they learned that the main landing gear was battle damaged and could not be lowered. The pilot decided to land the gunship on its belly and save the airframe. He told the crew to bail out. Eight did so successfully (the older gunships carried no fire-control officer and had a NOD rather than a TV; only the IR and BC rode in the booth). The copilot, flight engineer, and rear scanner chose to remain with the pilot for the belly landing. Touchdown was perfect. However, because of battle damage, the airframe collapsed on impact and the engineer and scanner were killed. The two pilots walked away from the wreck.

Eleven months later, events repeated themselves, up to a point. In the end, poetic justice prevailed: only the flight engineer and rear scanner survived. Stan Briscoe and Otis Birdwhistle were those survivors. They told me their story.

From sixty-five hundred feet, their gunship was working a convoy with 20-mms when all the shit in the world came up at it. A lot of the rounds were tracerless 37-mm and went off before Otis saw them. "Accurate, accurate," the right scanner shouted far too late, and unnecessarily. An antiaircraft round slammed into the left outboard engine and black smoke streamed from the engine's tailpipe. "We're hit," somebody shouted.

On the flight deck's overhead control panel, the two red

bulbs in the number one fire-control handle flashed, then came on brightly. The master fire-warning light on the pilot's instrument panel glowed redly. The pilot pulled the fire-control handle. Briscoe shouted, "Shut it down. Feather it," and leaned forward and pulled the engine-condition lever and discharged the fire-extinguisher agent. The engine smoke changed from black to gray to white while the pilot completed the shutdown checklist.

Over his shoulder the pilot said, "I had it, Sergeant."

"Sorry," Briscoe said. He knew he should have kept his hands off the controls until asked. But the pilot had been slow . . . "Sorry, sir."

"Some of this looks bigger than thirty-seven," Otis Birdwhistle reported. It had to be 57-mm, he thought. Many of the flak bursts were at least double the size he was used to seeing. A six-pound 57-mm shell weighed nearly four times as much as a 37-mm. "Hold this heading, sir," Otis said. "Let's get out of here" was what he meant. Antiaircraft fire ringed the gunship. Evasive action was impossible.

"Accurate," the right scanner screamed. "Accurate," he screamed again, an instant before another round gashed through the fuselage and ruptured the right center wing tank. Fuel rained down inside the forward section of the cargo compartment. "We're hit again," the same somebody shouted.

Stretched on the ramp, Otis Birdwhistle twisted around and looked forward in time to see another round detonate up through the floor. In the dim red glow of the cargo compartment, the round exploded with a white flash and the crack of thunder. Its shrapnel slashed away the front half of Airman Bruce White's body from the top of his knees to his sternum. The force of the blast lifted White off his feet and slapped him against the rear of the booth. He slid to the deck, then immediately pulled himself upright. Swaying, he looked down and ran a finger up the length of his exposed thigh bone and along his protruding hip bone. Then he collapsed. Two other gunners who had been knocked down by the blast staggered to their feet. The chief gunner took one look at White and reported to the pilot: "Got a gunner down. White's hit. I think he's dead." Otis hardly believed what he saw and turned his eyes back toward the antiaircraft fire.

By then the pilot had banked the stricken gunship out of orbit. After the way the airplane bucked from the impacts of the shells, Briscoe breathed a sigh of relief when it responded smoothly to the controls.

"Accurate, accurate," the right scanner sobbed, "accurate, accurate . . ." He sounded as if he was in shock.

Otis Birdwhistle said, "Hold this heading, sir. Most of the stuff is behind us now." Seconds later, he stated, "They stopped shooting. You're clear."

The navigator provided a heading to Ubon.

For an instant, Briscoe wondered where so many guns had come from, but just as quickly decided that the NVA had got lucky. Then he wondered if, instead, his luck had run out. Senselessly, "under the cover of darkness" repeated itself in his mind.

"We got an inch of raw fuel on the floor back here," the chief gunner said. "I think White's had it." Then he gagged before he gasped, "Oh, my God. The scanner. Milburn's hit too."

As soon as he had smelled the JP4 fumes earlier, Briscoe had watched the fuel quantity gauges and determined which tank was leaking. Without asking permission he transferred fuel to other tanks as well as dumped fuel overboard from the ruptured thousand-gallon right center wing tank. Starting the pumps was a wild risk: one stray spark . . . boom! However, so much electrical equipment was already operating that a few more pieces hardly mattered, he thought. His gamble was successful, and soon the flow of fuel into the aircraft's interior would stop. Still, he'd catch more hell for not requesting permission.

"Fuel's over my shoe tops," the chief gunner called. "White's dead. So's Milburn, I think."

In the cargo compartment, the kerosene odor of JP4 was suffocating. On the ramp, Otis Birdwhistle was nauseated by the thick fumes that washed over him. He turned his head and looked forward but couldn't see much beyond the booth because of the mist created by the spraying, raining fuel. *One spark,* Otis thought. He clipped on his parachute chest pack, then tightened the leg straps on his parachute harness. As an afterthought, he unhooked his safety line.

From the booth the IR and BC reported that they had turned off their electrical equipment.

Coughing, somebody said, "Don't give up."

The booth door flew open and, in the bright white light of the booth's interior, Otis saw the BC standing, adjusting the size of his parachute harness. *Dammit, he should have done at least that much before we took off,* Otis thought.

The IR said, "I'm getting dizzy. We ought to get out of here." The booth door slammed shut.

"Shit!" a voice shouted.

"On the ground in thirty minutes," the navigator said.

The IR protested: "That's too long."

Briscoe agreed: "I think we ought to get out." He didn't want to land with a damaged airplane, especially one leaking fuel. Saving an airplane didn't mean shit to him.

"Everybody, listen to me, this is the aircraft commander. It is your choice. If you want to bail out, you can go. Go now. Immediately. The rear scanner is jumpmaster."

"Let's get out of here," said the IR.

Otis stood and felt an excited expectancy mixed with hesitancy. He lowered the cargo ramp and faced forward. He saw the booth door swing open.

The pilot said, "Jumpmaster, count heads; tell me who's gone, who's staying." *He means me,* Otis thought: *jumpmaster!*

The IR and BC tried to walk out of the booth at the same instant and bumped into each other. Both stepped back.

Briscoe said, "I'm bailing out."

The IR and BC rapidly went through an Alphonse and Gaston routine before the IR threw a salute and stepped into the doorway.

The pilot said, "I'm taking the airplane to Ubon."

Otis Birdwhistle saw two fuel-soaked gunners step lively around the side of the booth.

The pilot said, "Somebody double-check White and Milburn."

The IR and BC moved in front of the gunners and blocked

their path. The four men were about twenty feet from Otis, who was standing on the end of the lowered ramp when the inside of the gunship erupted.

After much thinking about it, Otis eventually decided that the ignition came from something up front, probably the radar, which, according to the flight manual, was the most hazardous equipment in that situation. Otis saw a fireball blossom near the front of the cargo compartment and watched it bloom and swell as it rushed aft. Like an invisible piston, a blast wave of hot air hit him and pushed him off the ramp. As he left the airplane he saw the fireball roll over the booth and swallow up the gunners, the IR, and the BC. It happened in the tick of a clock, and one picture was engraved in Otis's memory: the four men stretched their arms toward him before they disappeared in the flames. Then the fireball reached off the ramp as if also making a last grab for Otis. Its heat touched his face.

Clear of the gunship, Otis fell, on his back, upside down, tumbling out of control. He thanked God for unclipping his safety line. He clawed for his parachute D-ring, found it, and jerked it so hard that his right elbow popped and he wondered if he had dislocated it. The parachute spilled in front of his face and he again thanked God. He didn't see, but he heard the explosion. Flaming pieces of airplane plummeted earthward. About the time he wished that none of the fiery debris landed on his parachute, the canopy deployed and he was floating. He thanked God a third time.

Hanging nearly motionless in the cool air, Otis wondered why he hadn't registered the parachute's opening shock. He saw large hunks of flaming wreckage fall into the jungle. He searched around, upward and downward. His was the only parachute in the sky, he thought, but he was wrong.

As soon as he said, "I'm bailing out," Stan Briscoe spun from his seat and headed aft. Like the others who sat while in flight, he wore a parachute harness with a full-length back pack permanently attached; he didn't have to worry about finding and hooking up a chest pack. Leaving the flight deck, he leaped over the NOD operator, who was crouched at his station. When he landed in the ankle-deep fuel in the cargo compartment, Briscoe panicked. He thought, *It's gonna blow any moment.* He wanted out. The ramp seemed miles away. He took three strides aft. At that point his actions became reflexive. Only the fringe of his mind was involved as a spectator; he seemed to have no conscious control over his actions. He veered left before reaching the booth and dived headlong through the right scanner's open window. It was a desperate act performed by a desperate person. The window was the last recommended bailout exit. Fear drove Briscoe to use it. Fear saved his life.

Briscoe said, "I guess I knew I'd never make it to the ramp. Then I remembered the window. I saw the right scanner too. He was hanging by his seat belt. I think part of his upper body was gone. We must have taken another hit that nobody registered, like two hits at the same time. At one point, I thought that happened, but I can't remember when. I guess that was probably what killed the right scanner. I'm sure he was dead. All the same, I stepped on him as gently as possible when I went out his window."

The slipstream caught Briscoe and he bounced and rolled along the side of the fuselage before he cleared the tail. He didn't remember pulling his parachute D-ring or anything else until he was on the ground. "Then I was thirstier than I'd ever been in my life. I'd've given a month's pay for a beer, a year's for a six-pack."

When I asked Briscoe and Birdwhistle why they decided to spend another year in Spec, they looked at each other. Eventually Otis said, "We figured we used up our bad luck."

Briscoe smiled: "Here we're celebrities. Back in the States we're just more enlisted swine."

Rusty Brown reveled in Briscoe's off-duty escapades. During ramp time he shared them with the crew. Ramp time was the period when aircrew members stood, sat, or sprawled on the hard surface around an airplane prior to flight. Normally a crew spent only a few minutes on the ramp before climbing aboard the airplane and starting engines to meet a scheduled takeoff time. Ramp time could stretch into hours when maintenance personnel failed to ready an airplane because of unpredictable last-minute problems. Before boredom set in, ramp time conversations were lively. Talkers attempted to amuse or gross out the listeners. Rusty Brown held center stage with Briscoe's latest adventures. Briscoe, who was occupied with monitoring the ground crew's progress in making the airplane ready, was unable to defend himself.

"Let me tell you what . . ."—Rusty Brown paused and looked around to make certain Briscoe was not in the group—". . . that crazy Briscoe started now." He saw that he had the listeners' attention. "Well, Briscoe took a bunch of gunners downtown to the slaughterhouse, and they took turns poleaxing water buffaloes. Eight-pound sledgehammers. Bigger'n a fifty-seven." He waited and gave the listeners' imaginations a chance to elaborate. "At first the Thai workmen didn't want to let the gunners do it. But, you know Briscoe, he had a couple bottles of Scotch and everybody got semishitfaced. It got to be sort of a contest. Stan says it ain't how hard you swing but where you hit. Fuckin' Cody missed completely. I mean, missed! Fuckin' Thai workmen were rolling around on the ground, they were laughing so hard." Brown's smile turned to a leer. "Briscoe's been back a couple times, alone. He says it beats shooting trucks."

"Master Sergeant Stanley Briscoe is a sadist," a young gunner said. Rusty Brown was the only permanent gunner on our crew. The lower-ranking gunners came from a rotating scheduling pool; in that way, the workload was equalized: each man risked his ass the same number of times. "But don't nobody quote me," the young gunner said. "I'll say it ain't so. Briscoe's one tough mother . . ."

"Toughest guy in Spec," a third gunner, another airman, said.

". . . and I don't want him whomping hell out of me. He's mean for nothing. One night we were sitting on the ramp, stone sober, and a frog hopped up to Sergeant Briscoe. That frog sure fucked up, 'cause Briscoe caught its ass, whipped out his issue switchblade, and for fun cut slits in both its eyeballs. Then he let it go . . . a blind frog."

"So why you call him a sadist?" Lee Schmidt asked.

"Some people do things like that for shock effect," Dick Kaulbach said.

"Then it worked," the airman said. "It shocked the shit out of the frog."

Another night: "That crazy Briscoe, now he's screwing his way through the alphabet. He'll do a woman only if her first initial matches a certain letter of the alphabet. See, he's doing it in order. His teelock knows what's going on and she's about ready to cut off his pecker," Rusty Brown reported. He grinned: "Briscoe's hung up on O and he hasn't had any pussy for three days."

"I can see him downtown," Lee said. " 'What's your name, sugar? Forget it. Name please, honey. Good, stick around. Name? Perfect, let's dance.' Only Briscoe!"

"Isn't it delightful," Otis Birdwhistle said, "that while we sit on our cans, Stan is busy helping the crew chief. Otherwise, we wouldn't have a damn thing to talk about."

"Stan is one of a kind, Otis," Rusty Brown explained.

"A fucking press agent's dream," I said and laughed.

Another night: Rusty Brown said, "Did you hear what Briscoe did to the new nav, Captain Wexford?"

"I didn't," Lee said before Otis had a chance to speak.

Brown smiled and told us: "After Captain Wexford's first mission, Briscoe and the gunners told him that since the officers always pay for everything, the enlisted swine were going to treat new officers one time after their cherry ride. Captain Wexford got the honor of being first. Briscoe and a pack of gunners took him to Jimmy's for dinner. They drank Scotch before they ate and champagne with dinner, and Wexford got royally shitfaced. Naturally they took him for a scrub but fixed it so he didn't get his gun."

"Where'd they take him?" one of the younger gunners demanded to know.

"Tokyo, I think."

"Scum City, man. That place recycles the Brylcreem they jack you off with."

"A little dab'll do you," Lee sang, then added, "Nobody ever said how many times."

Rusty Brown continued: "By then Wexford was so horny he honked."

"Could have used him for a hat rack," Lee and Juan Sueno said in unison.

Rusty Brown said, "They took Wexford to Briscoe's hootch and let him throw his lily white body against the yellow

Asiatic hordes. Of course, Wexford didn't know everybody was watching through a hole in the wall. Briscoe had two broads set up and they royally fucked his brains out. They didn't let him sleep a wink all night. The next couple days Wexford went bragging to everybody about how the enlisted troops came through with everything and it didn't cost him a cent. A couple days after that, he came down with the clap. That Briscoe made sure he got everything, all right."

"That's the fuckin' truth," one airman said. "You go out with Sergeant Briscoe, you get screwed, chewed, barbecued, and tattooed."

"Laid for sure," the other airman agreed, "plus waylaid, parleyed, relayed, delayed, and inlaid."

"How come Briscoe runs 'em with the gunners so much?" Ed Holcomb asked.

Without being seen, Briscoe had walked over to report that the aircraft was ready for flight. He overheard and answered Ed's question: "Because, sir, most of the flight engineers are serious old farts, and the gunners are young and wild and half-crazy and will do anything I suggest." He smiled evilly at Brown, who lowered his eyes. "Telling stories, Rusty?" He looked back to Ed. "And you see, sir, I'm smarter than all the gunners put together."

I said, "Smarter than Captain Wexford too," and led the laughter.

In private I once decided to jerk Briscoe's chain: "What's this shit I hear about you and the water buffalo?"

Briscoe reddened, then said, "I'm going to break that fuckin' Brown's head." With his meaty forearms and hands, he looked as if he could do it easily. Briscoe was barrel chested, with a small paunch that looked still firm but ripe to turn to fat. When it did, it was going to be a true beer drinker's gut starting right at the solar plexus. After several false starts, he explained: "The enlisted guys got tired of going along just to hump ammo and get shot at. We needed an outlet. Somebody was going to do it anyway."

"You don't have to apologize to me for your tasteless behavior," I said.

Briscoe looked at me from the corner of his eye. I guessed

that we were near the same age. But he was balding; the hair that remained was dull blond and wavy. He had a big face, chapped and windburned. It reminded me of a large newborn baby who had gone through a difficult delivery. His nose was the worst I had ever seen, except for Fritzie Zivic's. It was wide and flattened, shaped like a potato chip. I wondered if he knew how many times it had been broken.

When he didn't respond to my first barb, I stuck in another: "If you want to go around beating defenseless animals . . ."

Briscoe smiled thinly. "You got a lot of nerve, the way you guys in the booth act." Then, all of a sudden, he said, "Look, don't give me shit. I went through Aviation Cadets."

I hadn't expected a statement like that and asked, "Why aren't you commissioned?"

"I washed out. But not because I couldn't fly. For disciplinary reasons." He smirked. "Mostly, I didn't want to be an officer. I didn't want that responsibility, didn't want to play that game. But I'll tell you, I could fly. I was shit hot." He looked hard at me. "Flying ain't some fucking kind of magic. You wanna go right, you turn the wheel right; wanna go left, turn the wheel left. Anybody can do it. I could've had my wings, if I wanted. Hell, I have a commercial multi-engine license now." He took on a hurt expression. "After being a flight engineer for so many years and sitting behind so many numb-nuts and watching them fuck up by the numbers, I could fly even if nobody taught me. Believe it or not, I deliberately washed out of AvCads. I didn't want to be an officer."

"Ever sorry you did that?"

"Like right now. Maybe then I'd be an LC and I'd be giving you shit—Major."

We eyed each other for long seconds.

Briscoe didn't break his stare when he added, "Let me explain one thing. I don't include Major Holcomb with the numb-nuts. He's an ace, the best I've seen. Otis and I volunteered to fly with him. And we had our choice of everybody."

Chapter 10

Everybody Got Something to Hide Except for Me and My Monkey

HERKY THE TURKEY reigned as Spectre's lone mascot until Sergeant Whale bought a gibbon. "Being a rear scanner is lonesome work," the Gargantuan black sergeant explained. "I need company back there on the ramp." Like a child, the three-foot-tall gibbon held onto Whale's hand and followed him everywhere—stores, restaurants, bars, nightclubs, bathhouses. The few times a proprietor questioned their entry, Whale smiled and said, "He's my son." Objections disappeared in bursts of laughter.

At Raja's Tailor Shop near the base's main gate, Whale had the ape fitted for half a dozen closely cut, short-sleeved, black flying suits identical to those worn by all Spectre crewmen. On a suit's right sleeve was the Thai flag; on the left, the American; on the right breast, the Spectre emblem. Only the left breast differed. Where others wore name and wings, the ape's suit was embroidered with a banana and the letters "GG."

Whale denied that the initials had any relation to our beloved squadron commander, Colonel Godfrey Godolphin, alias Grumpy Grizzly. "I named him after that tough bitch who dances at the Jaguar Club," Whale insisted, "the one who's perpetual motion, if you know what I mean."

Seeing the gibbon being measured by a tailor, Dynamite

Dixon, who was in the shop cadging beers, declared, "The apes're going people."

Initially Go-Go reacted to the AC-130 as if it was a playscape. He leaped from gun to gun, climbed the flak curtains, swung from the overhead lines in the cargo compartment, and danced on the roof of the booth. When it came time for takeoff, Whale strapped GG into a seat next to him. During takeoff, the four gunners and the rear scanner sat on the cargo ramp in makeshift seats that faced aft out the open cargo door. When the plane broke ground GG hooted and clapped with delight. The gunners hooted and clapped along with him.

In flight, Whale put GG on a cable long enough to permit him to roam without bothering the gunners at their loading stations and without falling out the open cargo door. Over the Ho Chi Minh Trail, Whale stretched his pro-football-size body on the ramp and GG stretched out beside him. It was time to work.

When the first 37-mm AAA tracers came up, the ape hooted and reached into the darkness as if to touch or to catch them. When the orange streaks exploded in white flashes the ape clapped, then threw an arm around Whale's neck and hugged him protectively. Whale swelled with pride at the animal's courage.

Everything was perfect until the gunship pilot answered with a 40-mm cannon that was bolted to the deck about fifteen feet from where man and ape were stretched on the ramp. The pilot triggered a long burst—*Ka-pung, ka-pung, ka-pung, ka-pung, ka-pung!*—and Go-Go lost his composure. Screeching wildly, he tried to leap off the ramp to escape the noise. Held by the cable and unable to flee, he attacked the nearest object, Whale. "Now I know what it's like to have a monkey on your back," Whale said. "The ape went ape. He scratched me, near to tore me apart. Then he bit me. Then he bit himself. I thought about chucking him overboard but decided maybe he was right and I was the crazy one. I mean, I volunteered for gunships. He never had a choice."

Between bursts from the Forty, Whale subdued the creature and shortened his lead. For the remainder of the mission the ape squatted in the aft left corner of the gunship, behind the toilet, and screeched and hooted with every burst of fire. His hideout was appropriate because, as Whale discovered, Go-Go filled his flying suit again and again. Whale wailed, "Tell me, somebody, how can a fifty-pound animal shit sixty pounds?"

By his fifth mission Go-Go got with the program. He stretched on the ramp and watched the antiaircraft artillery tracers like a veteran or, especially when a 40-mm was busy, cuddled against one of Whale's huge thighs. "He's Mr. Cool," Whale bragged to anyone who would listen. "We ever get shot down and captured, Go will drive the NVA interrogators nuts. He won't give even name, rank, and serial number."

Every time they flew, Whale entered the ape in the crew forms as "G. G. Gibbon." The administrative airman who tabulated the missions flown by each man added G. G. Gibbon to his list of rear scanners. After he had recorded fifteen combat missions opposite his name, the clerk submitted G. G. Gibbon for an Air Medal. It was the normal procedure.

The decoration, routinely approved by headquarters, was intercepted by Colonel Godolphin when it came back to the squadron. He asked the airman who had submitted the paperwork, "Do you know who G. G. Gibbon is?"

"A scanner, sir. Rear scanner."

"Are you pulling my leg?"

"No, sir. He's a scanner. I can check my records, if you want, to make sure."

Godolphin was waiting for Whale at the preflight briefing that evening. Whale stepped into the briefing room, saw Godolphin, grabbed Go-Go, and was backing out the door when Godolphin called, "Hold it, Sergeant. Bring your friend here." It was the first time the commander confronted the ape. They stared at each other until Go-Go blew a kiss. "I don't believe I'm doing this," Godolphin muttered. "All right," he ordered, "everybody, on your feet." The men in the room came to attention. Godolphin cleared his throat several times, then smiled weakly. "I unofficially presented an Air Medal to a turkey. I guess I can *officially* present one to a monkey." He looked at Whale, who showed ivory from ear to ear. Godolphin scowled. "Jesus Christ, GG!"

"Go-Go, sir," Whale said. "Named after a dancer downtown, sir."

"In a pig's ass," Godolphin said. "Get her up here on the table."

"Him, sir," Whale said and lifted Go-Go.

Godolphin pinned the medal to the ape's flying suit and Go-Go leaned over and kissed his cheek.

"He ain't queer, sir," Whale hurriedly explained. "That's his way of saying thanks."

Godolphin laughed until his eyes watered, managed to say, "That's it. No more medals for pets." Wiping his eyes, he walked to the door. "Carry on," he snapped, then added, "The monkey looks brighter than most of you guys."

Being in a strange land and suddenly confronting the opportunity to own an exotic animal somehow distorted judgment. Shortly after Go-Go got his medal, I found a pet that took my fancy. I couldn't resist buying it. I rushed back to base and burst into the room: "Dick, come on, come on, see what I bought." I ran outside.

Dick lit a cigarette, opened a fresh beer, then walked to the door. I pointed to a cage made of heavy wire; inside the cage was a coiled, slumbering, enormously thick python. "You bought that?" Dick said.

"Stole it, really. Twenty-five dollars. The cage is worth that much." Back in the States I once owned a crummy little three-foot boa constrictor that cost almost as much.

Dick drank deeply before asking, "How long is the snake?"

"Sixteen and a half feet," I proudly announced.

"And a half, huh? Take it out and measure it?" He was muttering more to himself than talking to me. "And a half." Dick looked into my eyes and spoke as if addressing a mental deficient: "Hal—please tell me—exactly where—do you—intend—to keep—the snake?"

"In the room."

"*Our* room?"

I nodded: "Under my bed?"

"In the cage."

I nodded vigorously.

"It won't fit," Dick said.

"I was afraid of that." I opened a door in the cage and stroked the snake. "Feel him, Dick."

"Hal, listen carefully. I will not sleep in the same room with any animal larger than me, let alone three times as long as me."

"After I bought it, on the way here, I wondered about something like that." I looked back and forth between Dick and the snake. "Son of a bitch is *big*," I said admiringly. I had needed the help of three Thais to carry the monster from the taxi to in front of our room. "What a bargain." I folded my arms and watched Dick: "What do we do now?" I hoped he would change his mind.

"We?" Dick said. "We?" He went back into the room and opened another beer. "We," he called, "meaning you and the snake."

Nobody on base wanted the bargain. After a week, I sold the snake back to the taxi driver who had sold it to me. When Stan Briscoe heard about the transaction, he laughed long and loud. "Maj, you're about the two dozenth guy who bought that snake. Fucking Boon's Rent-a-Snake. Nobody can resist the price and nobody wants to keep it. How much did he rip you off for?"

"The whole deal cost me twenty bucks."

"Plus double taxi fare when he brought it out and when he took it back. Am I right?"

"Yeah." I laughed at myself.

"Boon's a sharp motherfucker. He knew you were an officer. He usually takes enlisted guys for ten." Briscoe poked me in the ribs. "Welcome to the East, sir."

Crew members took mascots other than live animals on missions. There were several Snoopy dolls and a few Charlie Browns. A copilot who was an Air Force Academy graduate perched a stuffed falcon above his instrument panel until two sensor operators kidnapped the bird for a ransom of twenty-five cases of beer. Each day that the copilot refused to answer the ransom demands (notes were assembled with words clipped from the *Stars and Stripes)*, the sensor operators sent him a piece of the bird, starting with the left claw. He never paid. The kidnappers kept the head.

One flight engineer hauled a life-size wooden statue of Buddha aboard the gunship for each mission. With straps he stowed it upright behind his seat. He claimed it had no religious significance. He also wore a Saint Christopher medal and a Star of David.

The rubber ducks that gunner Chuck Wallace received as a joke from his wife in the United States became fought-over talismans. Wallace decided to combat qualify the first duck by carrying it through fifteen missions. Unbeknownst to him, gunner Jerry Mitchell, who was twice his size, emphatically vowed to "destroy all ducks in Laos."

Rubber Ducky I died on its fourteenth mission. Wallace had the toy on his lap, where he normally carried it while he was right scanner. Mitchell snatched the duck, ran with it to the ramp, and blew off the duck's rubber head with his .38-caliber revolver. Rubber Ducky II died almost as soon as it arrived from the States. On its second mission, while the gunship was being buffeted by heavy and accurate antiaircraft fire, Mitchell crawled up to Wallace, who was preoccupied with duties, slashed open the leg pocket of Wallace's flying suit, where the duck was hidden, and yanked out RD II. Wallace made a near-saving, last-second grab, but Mitchell hacked off the duck's head with his survival knife while the animal was stretched between them. In the same manner, Mitchell got hold of Rubber Ducky III during its first flight. Wallace leaped on him before he damaged it; Mitchell broke free, however, and ran aft through the gunship. At the moment Wallace brought him down with a flying tackle, Mitchell threw the duck off the ramp. "Another fucking KIA duck," he triumphantly roared and the other gunners cheered.

After the arrival of Rubber Ducky IV, Wallace refused to

fly with Mitchell. Furthermore, he carried the duck taped to his body, beneath his underwear. On RD IV's fourteenth mission, Mitchell stowed away. Everyone knew he was aboard, except the intended victims. Once the plane was over the trail, the only permissible duck killing ground, Mitchell crept down from the flight deck and rendezvoused with another gunner. "We make the grab when the trip-A opens up," he said.

"He has the thing under his underwear," the other gunner said. "Like it's under his flying suit, survival vest, flak vest, parachute, all that shit."

"Hmmmmm? That changes things," Mitchell said. "Let's go." He walked over to Wallace, who as right scanner was concentrating out the open window, and tapped his knee.

Wallace looked around, was surprised, and cried, "Get away from me."

"Save yourself pain," Mitchell said, "and give us the fuckin' duck."

"Get away from me," Wallace said. He was cornered between the front of the booth and the right side of the fuselage.

"That duck is not going to see fifteen missions," Mitchell said.

Wallace smiled. "You miscounted, asshole. This is his fifteenth."

Mitchell squinted. "That's a lie."

"It's fifteen, asshole, and I can prove it."

Mitchell fumed. "Give me that fuckin' duck." He was angry. "Give me that fuckin' duck or—or—or *you* go overboard with it." Mitchell and his cohort grabbed Wallace. The struggle was brief. Wallace wouldn't have won if he hadn't grabbed the wide coal shovel normally used to clear away the heaps of machine-gun brass. Fortunately, his opponents had on flak helmets (although Mitchell's was split open) and flak vests, which probably saved their lives. Mitchell explained to Colonel Godolphin: "We weren't really going to throw Wally overboard. It was like a figure of speech that backfired."

Wallace made one statement: "Self-defense, sir. Attempted murder. I'm not saying another word until I talk to my cousin, who's an ACLU lawyer. I do know that he'll want depositions from everyone on the crew."

"For Christ's sake," Godolphin moaned, "that's all we need. We're supposed to be fighting the North Vietnamese, not each other." He paced. "Whale's monkey has better sense than you three." He paced some more. Then he stopped and said softly, "You'll get together and you'll work it out among yourselves, if you know what's good for you. And, Wally, that includes your cousin. Keep him out of it."

On their way to the Spectre Hootch, a bar kept open twenty-four hours every day for only gunship crewmen, Mitchell asked, "You knew we wouldn't really throw you overboard, didn't you?"

"Bullshit! I don't trust you big assholes."

"You gonna call your cousin?"

Wallace didn't answer.

"Come on, we were only joking."

"Prove it," Wallace said. "Buy me all the booze I can drink."

"On one condition. Tell the truth. Was that really RD IV's fifteenth mission?"

"Yep. Exactly."

"You sneaky fucker, how did you do that?"

"I had him with me the night you killed RD III. Then, later, I faked his arrival in the mail."

Herky the Turkey had his problems too. He had been retired from combat duty after fifteen missions because he was unable to adapt to the noise and confusion. He grew more excitable with each mission and eventually his flapping and leaping about caused him to injure himself.

Even on his own Herky was a miserable flyer. Normally he was penned outside the turkey control officer's room. The TCO was the lowest-ranking lieutenant in the squadron and, as such, was responsible for the feeding, grooming, health, security, and welfare of Herky. Whenever the bird escaped or, to harass the TCO, was let loose from his pen (it was never confirmed, but rumor had it that the Swine Brothers delighted in clandestinely freeing Herky), the bird craned his neck, fixed his eyes on the roof of the gymnasium—the tallest building on base—and trotted off in high gear. He had one objective: elevation, the highest perch.

About a block from his goal, Herky started beating his wings. The closer he got to the building, the faster he flapped. Usually, the faster he flapped, the more his wing beats became unsynchronized. The left wing always seemed to trail slightly behind the right. That unbalanced his body. Often, before reaching takeoff speed, Herky careened wildly off course. At those times he never got off the ground. After one such failure, Dynamite Dixon walked into the NCO Club and told the bartender, "Maybe I should cut back. I swear I just saw our giant chicken try to commit suicide, try to screw himself right into the road."

When Herky reached takeoff speed and remained coordinated, nine times out of ten he miscalculated his takeoff point. He either left the ground early, reached the apex of his flight trajectory before he reached the roof of the gym, then, despite wildly flapping wings, lost lift and sank; or he overshot his takeoff point and, while still climbing under full power, reached the wall of the gym several feet below roof level. In either case his flight terminated with an impact against cinder block. He fell to earth in a heap of ruffled feathers.

Undismayed by failure, the dazed Herky wobbled off around the quarter-mile track next to the gym. On rounding the far turn he flapped his wings and raced down the backstretch, again aimed for the gym's roof. By then, however, all traces of coordination were eradicated. Herky soared and crashed and crazily tried again and again until restrained by the TCO or by some humane passer-by. The bird's behavior was a guaranteed traffic-stopping exhibition.

On the rare occasions that Herky attained the height he sought, he refused to come down. Food was useless as a lure. He gobbled loudly and strutted about the rooftop until after a day or three, with the aid of the fire department ladder team, the TCO scaled the gymnasium, chased Herky around the roof, eventually cornered him and wrapped him in a blanket, then descended amid the cheers of onlookers.

The rest of the time Herky was simply another pretty face.

GUNSHIP

He was the guest of honor at squadron social functions and generally was pampered and admired. Herky was loved by every Spectre, except the incumbent TCO.

Herky suffered his greatest indignity, however, when men from flying units outside of Spectre established turkey feathers as signs of counting coup on the gunship squadron. Before the TCO recognized what was happening, Herky was trucking around bare-ass.

It was about then, about halfway through the dry season, that Spectre's ass also began taking a beating from antiaircraft artillery.

Chapter 11

Play with Fire

THE VOLUME OF antiaircraft fire in Steel Tiger increased tremendously around the midpoint in the dry season. The NVA had to be upset with the heavy toll that Spectre's 40-mm cannons were taking from traffic. After stopping 632 trucks in December, Spectre halted 1,742 in January. February came on with a roar. On the fourth, our crew destroyed 25 and damaged 5 trucks; the next night, we destroyed 22 and damaged 11. Spectre wasn't the only team getting hits, however.

Not only the volume of NVA fire increased but also the accuracy. In one week, four gunships limped home to Ubon with battle damage. The first victim was Major Billy Killeen. A 57-mm shell blew a three-foot hole, outboard of number one engine, through the wing of his airplane and, with fuel streaming out the hole, he made a straight-in approach and landing from 120 miles away.

I never understood why a pilot would risk his life for an airplane, let alone risk the lives of others. I agreed with Briscoe: saving an airplane didn't mean shit. Gunships were government property designed for war. They were built to be destroyed. Hearing about a pilot replaying "The High and the Mighty" was impossible to comprehend when leaking fuel was involved. Loose raw fuel was nothing to fuck with unless a person was a Buddhist monk.

As far as I could guess, a man stayed with his airplane because it was familiar; bailing out was an unknown. From experience a pilot believed he could accurately estimate the dangers involved in the airplane and, with flying skill, influence events in his favor; his background did not provide enough knowledge to anticipate a successful outcome to parachuting. We crewmen were lectured on how to parachute and we practiced certain techniques on the ground, such as executing the landing fall and roll. We never jumped from an airplane as part of training. The instructors told us that it was useless to practice something we had to do perfectly on our first, and very likely only, try. To crewmen, bailing out was an irrevocable, last-resort action.

Another reason a pilot remained with his plane seemed stupid to me but was probably perfectly sound: like a naval captain who went down with his ship, an aircraft commander felt responsible for the fate of his plane, which he considered an extension of himself. To such commanders, a motorized juggernaut was as one with the man who controlled it. In that vein, a good pilot never owned a ratty automobile. Old maybe, but not dilapidated. An automobile was a saintly object; an airplane, godly. Pilots did not understand that both were merely metallic shapes whose karma was to emerge in the next life as junk.

A case in point—1968 Tet Offensive, Tan Son Nhut: The first incoming mortar round (of one of many bombardments) smacked a C-130 dead center atop the wings. The wings drooped, the fuel tanks ruptured, and flaming JP4 spread across the parking ramp to threaten nearby airplanes.

Major Jerry Prager, Sergeant Stu Upton, and I had walked out of Ops a moment before the 130 took the direct hit. The explosion and fire were eye-catching. We watched for maybe ten seconds while mortars whumphed and rockets cracked up and down the flight line. When a rocket hit two buildings away, I decided I had seen enough. Prager, a pilot, held me by the elbow, however, and said, "That plane—that fire's going to spread to the planes on both sides. It could spread down the whole line."

"It sure could," I said while looking for a low spot on the concrete. Two fundamental rules for survival in Southeast

Asia were, one, don't walk under the coconut trees and, two, don't stand up during a rocket attack.

I was trying to pry Prager's fingers off my elbow when another fuel cell erupted on the burning C-130 and fire boiled upward, roared outward, reaching toward the plane downwind in line. We knew the fire department wouldn't arrive until the attack ended. Prager said, "We ought to do something."

We were, I thought. Like three rubes, we were watching the son of a bitch burn.

"We ought to save them," Prager said, "the ones in danger."

Mortar rounds impacted on the taxiway.

"Jer," I said, "they're airplanes—government property—they were made to be destroyed."

Prager never heard me. He said to Upton, who was a flight engineer, "Let's crank 'em and taxi 'em out of there. You take the one on the right," and he sprinted toward the more seriously threatened airplane downwind from the fire.

Upton looked at me. I shrugged. Starting engines and taxiing airplanes wasn't *my* job. Upton ran off and did as he was ordered.

They started the inboard engines and moved the airplanes beyond range of the fire. The entire time incoming mortar rounds were dropping and rockets were whizzing around them.

Prager then ran from his airplane, located three man-size portable fire extinguishers, and waved Upton and me to him. We wheeled the twenty-gallon extinguishers upwind from the fire and sprayed CB at the burning C-130, a raging inferno. I never felt more stupid. Pissing would have done as much. I wanted to shout, "You could have at least brought marshmallows," but knew Prager wouldn't think it was funny in front of an enlisted man.

Around then the attack ended. Bombardments usually lasted four or five minutes at most. Designed to harass as well as to destroy, many attacks consisted of only a few rounds. The VC concentrated its available firepower and delivered it as rapidly as possible; then the gunners faded into the countryside before the U.S. or RVN forces could counterattack. (The best combination of shooting skill and luck that I saw came right after Tet, when the VC destroyed a revetted RF-4 with only four mortar rounds—all fired within half a minute and two scored direct hits—and then the following night destroyed another RF parked in the same revetment with another four rounds. The VC gunners probably never moved the mortar tube from one day to the next. Cost effective out the ass!)

By the time the fire trucks arrived, our burning C-130 was reduced to an outline on the ramp, except for a wing tip and one scorched outboard engine which we had managed to protect, thanks to Jerry Prager.

The man was typical of all pilots. Any man who felt that strongly about an airplane on the ground was bound to be beyond reason concerning one in flight. A few months later, in May, I had the last laugh, albeit a grim one, when the C-130 which Prager had taxied to safety was shot down immediately after takeoff while trying to evacuate two hundred fifty Vietnamese civilians out of Kham Duc: total loss of crew, passengers, and plane.

Kham Duc was a perfect lesson in how the other half lived. When the fighting was most intense, a C-130 that landed there with resupplies was swarmed by U.S. infantrymen who broke into crates before the plane was parked. The crew navigator, who was a friend, told me that soldiers ran aboard his airplane, broke open crates before unloading, and scooped up armfuls of ammunition. They raced to the edge of the runway and fired into the hillside nearest the airplane. My friend grabbed up an M16 and joined them. Standing tall, he plinked one round at a time into the trees, picking shots carefully, firing only at locations where he detected movement. He was still on his first clip when a grimy infantryman hit him on the back and shouted, "No! Like this!" Crouched, with his M16 set on full automatic, the soldier emptied a clip in three seconds, changed, and emptied the next clip as quickly. The soldier went through a clip of thirty rounds in the same time my friend spent on a single shot. "Like that," the soldier cried. My friend said he nodded and, when the soldier turned to blow out another clip, returned to the airplane.

Major Rabbit Ripple was Spectre's second victim of Steel Tiger antiaircraft artillery. Two shells tore holes in his aircraft's empennage, one in the vertical and one in the horizontal stabilizer. Rabbit returned safely to Ubon. The holes caused no control problems, although both were large enough to throw a bushel basket through.

The third hit was a 57-mm round that ripped up through the floor and out the top of Lieutenant Colonel Pete Angelino's airplane but didn't detonate. The round cleared the right scanner's seat by six inches. The right scanner happened to be on his fiftieth mission, which was significant only because it marked the first time he had been aboard an airplane that was hit. There was no limit to the number of missions that a Spectre crewman could fly.

To men on an airplane struck by gunfire, the squadron presented shoulder patches that read "Battle Damage Qualified, AC-130 Spectre" and listed the year of the event. The patch was worn on the black flying suit. A few men also wore patches that read "100" or "200" or "300," which denoted their total combat missions with Spectre. More coups, more feathers.

Rabbit Ripple took the fourth hit. Lucky Rabbit! Dick Kaulbach, Juan Sueno, and I were flying with him as part of a pickup crew. On target less than an hour, we had destroyed two vehicles and were working a third. Triple-A had been moderate. Suddenly, the rear scanner reported accurate fire from nine o'clock and called for a right break; simultaneously, the right scanner warned, "Three o'clock, accurate, three rounds. Stop!" The gunship was bracketed. There was no safe direction.

Afterward, Dick and I laughed about the right scanner's call: "Stop!" It was like shouting, "Don't shoot!" when facing a firing squad.

A 57-mm shell blasted through the floor of the booth underneath the BC. The explosion lifted the booth out of alignment. While in Hercs, I had experienced having the airplane struck by small-arms fire *(thuck, thuck, thuck . . .)* without flinching. The 57-mm shell produced a splintering report that made me recoil. With the explosion echoing in my mind and ringing in my ears, I leaped to my feet. Fight or flight? I was prepared to abandon the booth and the airplane.

Rabbit made a sharp maneuver and, thrown off-balance, I landed draped over the FCO's console. I saw that the BC's seat had tipped forward and pinned him against his console. Wind rushing through the shell hole created a vortex filled with debris. I worked my jaws and valsalvaed, which popped my ears but didn't rid the ringing. Thick fumes from exploded gunpowder made my eyes sting. "The BC's hit," the IR shouted. "Franklin's hit." I partially regained my balance and took an awkward step aft. I felt as if I were in one of those crazy rooms in an amusement park funhouse where everything looked straight but was really misproportioned and misaligned. I pushed the booth door open and the cyclone effect abated. My balance seemed to return, but I felt light-headed until we were back on the ground.

Dick Kaulbach announced the heading to Ubon.

Rabbit Ripple asked, "Anyone else hurt? Booth?"

"IR's OK. The BC's seat's wedged against . . . Hell, wait a minute."

"TV, FCO, you all right?" Rabbit asked.

"They look OK. They're trying to . . . Stand by." It took the three of us to pull the BC's seat away from the console. The hole in the floor was larger than I expected. "Hold him. Hold him. Don't let him fall out of the airplane," the IR shouted.

Rabbit continued his survey: "Gunners?"

"Negative. We're all in one piece."

"Scanners?"

"Negative, sir."

"Negative, sir. Sir, I'm sorry, sir. There was no way to go."

"It's not your fault," Rabbit said. "Don't worry."

In the booth we tilted the BC's seat backward and leaned it against the TV console. The BC had his lap belt fastened. I thought that he was repeating "My fuck" and expected to find he had been hit in the groin. Then I understood that his words were "My foot." The six-pound shell had shredded his left foot and lower leg. Without the armor plating that had been added to the floor since the previous dry season he'd be dead, I thought.

"We should be on the ground in twenty-seven minutes," Dick informed the crew.

Juan kicked out the booth's side escape panel and covered the shellhole with it.

"Cut off his boot," the IR said and pulled at the laces.

"Leave it alone," Juan Sueno said. He was as calm as if we were on a training mission.

"Cut off his boot," the IR said.

"That won't help." Juan gently pulled away the IR's hands. "Relax," he quietly ordered. "I'll take care of it." The bleeding was oozing. There was not a great amount of blood. We lifted and dragged the BC to the rear of the aisle. "Raise his feet, keep him warm," Juan said. We placed a flight jacket beneath the BC and covered him with two others, then propped his feet on the BDA recorder carrying case. Juan found pressure bandages in the medical kit and wrapped them around the wounds. He put them over the boot, which I thought was clever. "I don't believe we need a tourniquet," he said.

I reported the actions to Rabbit Ripple. I felt thankful that the BC took the hit instead of me, or Juan.

Juan felt along the BC's groin with his thumb. We took turns applying arterial pressure. "I don't know if this is doing any good or not," Juan said.

"We got nothing else to do," I said. The BC was the first wounded person I had ministered. In Vietnam, we had hauled dozens of wounded marines out of Hue Phu Bai during Tet. I was surprised by their cleanliness when they walked or were carried aboard the airplane. Before reaching us, they had passed through only a field hospital. The walking wounded wore pajamas, robes, and slippers. Their bandages were bloodless and white. Inflatable splints covered arm and leg wounds. Litter cases were tucked in army blankets. Each litter case was escorted by a navy medic. The seriously wounded were heavily sedated (in retrospect, a few of the medics probably were also). The lack of blood and visible suffering made the situation appear unreal to me, more theatrical, staged. I felt little compassion for the wounded. In the same way, I felt little sympathy for Franklin, the wounded BC. He was a stranger. He'd had a tough break, but he was going to live. I wondered if I would have felt differently if Jimmy Ballard had been in his place.

The IR consoled Franklin, who repeated, "My foot."

By the time we landed, Franklin's face was a translucent alabaster white. I ran my fingers across his cheeks and they felt clammy. I sniffed my fingers. They had the metallic odor of nervous sweat. I wondered if the smell came from Franklin or me.

Franklin's color improved when the doctor and stretcher bearers arrived.

Ed Holcomb was outside the airplane. "You three all right?" he asked with a look of genuine concern.

"Yeah," I said. I felt tired yet bursting with energy, happy but nervous. I told Ed about Juan's actions, his coolness and professionalism. I was talking twice as fast as normal, caught myself, then clammed up.

"Close, hunh?" Ed said and gripped Juan's shoulder.

I responded to the rhetorical question without filtering my words: "Another foot in any direction . . ."

Dick grinned and said, "Sick."

I ended the night downtown with four little brown maidens ministering to my needs. To prove I was alive, my mind drove my body to exhaustion.

One night in Vietnam I had auditioned for God. Our Hercules crew had been diverted to Phu Bai to pick up two passengers: an American marine who had been wounded less than an hour earlier in downtown Hue, and a navy medic. A small-caliber bullet had entered the marine's head slightly left of the center of his forehead and touching the edge of his eyebrow. The bullet had not exited and the marine had been unconscious from the moment he was hit. He had been evacuated to the Phu Bai Airport by helicopter. I walked back to the cargo compartment during the short flight to Da Nang. The medic was resting in a sling seat with his feet propped on the edge of the stretcher that held the marine. I shouted above the drone of the engines: "How's he doing?"

"He's gonna die," the medic shouted back.

"What? Can't you do anything?"

The medic shrugged, then shook his head uncertainly.

"You can do something, can't you? Come on, do something!"

"I can give him a shot to stimulate him. But it'd be a waste."

"Do it," I said. The medic looked away. "Do it." I tugged at the medic's shirt. "Give him the shot, right now." The medic performed the act with a speed that left me in doubt. "Is that it?" I asked. "Nothing else?"

"That's it." The medic spent several minutes examining the man. As soon as the airplane turned off the runway at Da Nang, a helicopter touched down behind it. Four stretcher bearers double-timed onto the transport and transferred the casualty to the helicopter, which immediately took off for a hospital ship anchored offshore. "That ship is supposed to have the finest equipment in the world for brain surgery," the medic said to no one in particular. He turned to me: "If it makes you feel better, his life signs improved. But I'll bet he dies. If he lives, he'll be a vegetable." He gave me a peace sign. "Keep 'em flyin', commander."

Quite a few Spectre aircraft commanders grew reluctant to orbit targets more than a few times after triple-A opened fire. They struck as many vehicles as possible in four or five orbits, approximately ten minutes, then flew a short distance away and loitered briefly before returning to resume the attack. Dick once slipped us across the line into an adjoining target sector when another gunship moved off in that manner, and we poached what remained of its convoy. When the rightful crew returned, the air war over Laos nearly reached a new dimension: gunship versus gunship from opposite sides of the orbit. We were a thousand feet above them, however, and they were unwilling to risk entering our line of fire. Dick engaged their nav in a prolonged discussion about the aircrafts' positions until Ed finished the last truck. Dick was slick. When things were slow in the sector assigned to us, he got on the horn to TFA and arranged for us to go where the action was. One night we busted a line of trucks in North

Vietnam, a mile or three above the DMZ, outside Spectre's approved operating area. TFA logged the kills exactly on the Laotian border.

When a gunship temporarily moved off, trucks sneaked away. Aircraft commanders who used that defensive tactic didn't care. Their concern was to prevent antiaircraft gunners from predicting the gunship's exact flight path and thereby increasing chances for a hit. "I don't agree with your thinking," Dick told the first aircraft commander whom he heard voice belief in the tactic. "There's no rhyme or reason for taking a hit."

"We're having a run of bad luck," I said. In public Dick and I stood together. We disagreed in private.

"Surely you'll agree that the gunners have established our pattern of attack," the aircraft commander said. "It's only a circle! By now they must have timed our orbit. They have to know that we fly standard three-degrees-per-second turns, two-minute orbits."

"If they didn't know, they know now," I said. "You just told them." We were seated in the Officers' Club and I cast suspicious glances at the waitresses. The ones who saw me giggled at my beady-eyed expression.

The aircraft commander, a lieutenant colonel ready for retirement, ignored me and continued his argument. "All they have to do is barrage a point on our orbit as we approach it. They can't miss."

"But all the hits haven't been in orbit. Billy Killeen got clobbered *entering* geometry on his first target of the night," I said.

"And Pizza Pete was doing road recce. He wasn't going around and around," Dick said. "No rhyme or reason. Only bad luck."

"The gunners are shooting into the dark . . ." I said.

The lieutenant colonel said, "Not when the moon is full." Spectre crewmen superstitiously feared the full moon. They claimed it silhouetted the gunship, made it an easy target. No evidence supported the theory. Nevertheless, when the moon was brightest, on the videotape crewmen could be heard cursing and shouting obscenities at the moon. Major Chief Bender, the only full-blooded American Indian to fly as a

Spectre pilot, rolled the gunship into a *right* bank and fired a clip of 40-mm rounds upward at the full moon prior to attacking a target. He called his act "a tiny insurance sacrifice." Old customs died hard.

"The gunners are shooting into the dark," I said, "at a black airplane with no lights."

"Have you watched a gunship climb out after takeoff when the moon is full?" the aircraft commander said. "You can see it plain as day."

"But that's here," Dick said, "where everything on the ground is lit up too."

"Yeah," I agreed. I loved the goddamn full moon. It made the television picture perfect. Nothing escaped detection. Full moon was the best time of month for hunting. Ed insisted that we fly as a crew every night of the week surrounding a full moon. Our crew didn't really give a shit if the NVA troops could see us. We could see them and that was what counted.

The aircraft commander said, "It doesn't matter where you are, when you pass in front of the moon you're a sitting duck."

"Don't you mean a sitting turkey?" Dick said.

"Hey, listen," I said, "have you considered how difficult it is . . ."—I pulled back my eyelids at the corners and made my eyes slanted—". . . how difficult it is to see when your eyes are like this? Like the NVA gunners. Try it." I stretched the corners back more.

The lieutenant colonel looked at me as if I had two heads, or maybe none at all.

Dick pulled back the corners of his eyes. "You're right! My eyes are watering already," he said. "I can hardly see."

"Come on, try it. See how the gunners see," I urged the older officer.

He gave a weak smile, said, "I'm taking my leg back now," and walked away, muttering to himself. The following day, Colonel Godolphin made a command decision that had every crewman in the squadron talking to himself.

Chapter 12

Let's Spend the Night Together

"AS OF THIS moment, once you find a truck you *will* stay with it until it is destroyed or damaged. You will *not* be driven off by antiaircraft fire," Colonel Godfrey "Grumpy Grizzly" Godolphin announced at a special meeting for only the officers of the Spectre gunship squadron. "You will hang in there and live with antiaircraft artillery fire. Nobody promised you it would be easy. Now, let's kill trucks. And no excuses." Scanning the hundred or so warm bodies in the briefing room, he asked, "Do I make myself clear? Are there any questions?"

Nobody in the audience spoke. From experience the crewmen knew that Godolphin's idea of a group discussion was "You are the group and I will do the discussing." Like my dear departed mother often said, "The boss is always a son of a bitch."

As squadron commander, Godolphin was within his rights. He set the pace. In his mind, his attitude was justified. For a week he had read After Battle Reports and had grown angry at aircraft commanders who explained that they had searched out but then failed to destroy certain trucks because of intense ground fire. All that wasted time and energy. Such reports drove him wild.

In typical military fashion, Godolphin's blanket declaration insinuated that every man was guilty, whereas a small minority of aircraft commanders actually broke off attacks. His announcement created unanimous resentment. The guilty felt misunderstood and the innocent stood unjustly accused, even convicted.

We crewmen felt Godolphin had talked down to us. We knew that even the guilty pilots risked their asses often enough to be considered professionals and deserved better treatment. Godolphin's speech would have been understandable if crews had been completely fucking off and not attacking, period. As it was, we were killing trucks faster than anyone had thought possible. Along with killing trucks, we already had eaten so much flak that we could have existed on an iron-free diet for the rest of our lives.

Naturally, Grumpy Grizzly knew all that. He'd never been one to win medals for tact, however. His nickname proved it. But he asked no more of his troops than he produced. For a semi-old guy, he flew the AC-130 and shot better than the average bear.

I liked Godolphin. He was congruent. When he was pleased he showed it with big, honest smiles. And he left no doubt in anyone's mind as to when he was pissed off. He'd look daggers. To me, he and Ed Holcomb had similar personalities: hard-nosed, single-minded, goal-oriented, and loyal beyond belief to men who were loyal to them. Godolphin and Holcomb also were physically alike: tall, husky, lumbering types. The Bear and the Elephant. With a little imagination they could have passed for father and son. Godolphin, who was about ten years older, had developed deep lines in his face and neck that, when added to his thick black hair and heavy features, gave him a rugged handsomeness that Holcomb was only beginning to acquire. And they both loved gunships.

Following Godolphin's special meeting, Ed Holcomb didn't comment on the edict. He had no need for concern. He never had backed off from a target. Strangely enough, however, in the brain of even the bravest warrior a single cell of self-doubt lurked somewhere. That night when Colonel Godolphin showed up unannounced to fly with our crew, Ed's single cell erupted into a tumor. He whispered to me, "Did you know he was coming?"

I shook my head, said, "I didn't even hear him breathing hard."

Ed was in no mood for humor. "Why do you think he's here? What's up? You have any idea? He say anything to you?"

Godolphin said he desired to fly as copilot and Ed's tumor turned to cancer: The Man was going to sit and watch and take notes, he thought, and in some way make an example of him, perhaps of the entire crew. Everything that had gone before—endless rows of trucks damaged and destroyed—had no validity now, Ed concluded. He decided that he must once again, beyond a shadow of a doubt, prove his crew's skill and courage under fire. But mostly courage.

With Godolphin's attention diverted, Ed quietly told Dick Kaulbach, "I want to go to Tchepone straight off. Downtown."

Jim Ballard exhaled loudly.

Lee Schmidt stared at me.

I shrugged. I outranked Holcomb, but he was the pilot, and the pilot was the aircraft commander. If he wanted to fly us to Hell, it was all right with me. On second thought, maybe along the way I might bail out at Purgatory.

Actually, I could have said something about his present plan. A former Spec commander had declared the area within three miles of the center of Tchepone off-limits to gunships simply because the triple-A there was too heavily concentrated. Our crew had poached along the edge of the area before and had sucked up a lot of flak, but it had been worth it because the trucks were there.

After Ed finished with Dick, he turned to Lee, Jim, and me. "When we get there, find something right away." We nodded. It would be impossible not to find something, I thought. Or something would find us. There was no way to discuss things with Ed once he locked into his charge mode. Gunners used to complain that *they* had no say in what the crew did. If only they had known . . .

Godolphin's appearance gave Tex Tyler the night off. It was

too bad there wasn't a malt shop on base so he had someplace to go.

As he had been ordered, Dick navigated us straight to Tchepone. The BC was picking up blips from ten miles out. Lee grabbed a convoy of eight loaded trucks about a mile from the center of town. Ninety-five hundred feet above the terrain and at an airspeed of one hundred fifty knots, Ed rolled into a thirty-degree left bank and went to work with a Forty. One. One-two-three. Mr. Rhythm.

We were on our third orbit when the antiaircraft gunners joined in the beat. One moment we were sailing along undisturbed, and the following moment we were barraged by continuous streams of fire. The scanners sounded like two auctioneers simultaneously trying to sell different items to the same audience.

"Two o'clock, five rounds," said the right scanner, "no problem. One o'clock, three rounds, hold what ya—"

"Nine o'clock, four rounds, accurate, break right," rear scanner Otis Birdwhistle shouted.

"Got it. Thanks," Ed said and rolled out level until rounds passed on both sides of the gunship, then rolled back into a left bank and resumed firing.

"Six o'clock, three, six, nine rounds, hold what you have," Otis said.

"Two o'clock, four rounds. Three o'clock, three rounds. No sweat," the right scanner called.

"Eight o'clock, four rounds, accurate, break right," Otis shouted. The rounds detonated below and behind the turning aircraft. "Damn. That watered my eyes," he said. "I won—"

"Three o'clock, three rounds, accurate. Oh, shit!" The right scanner's call was late and the rounds went off directly in front of the gunship.

"Close," said Godolphin from the copilot's seat. "Damn close."

Too much, I thought. Never before had I heard so many triple-A calls made so rapidly. The flow of words from the two scanners was continuous. Of course, never before had I been to downtown Tchepone.

Apart from following the scanners' directions, Ed added

evasive maneuvers of his own. I pictured him hunched over the wheel, hell-bent for glory, steering a course that only he saw, pumping the rudder pedals with the fury of the Phantom of the Opera before an antiquated aerospace pipe organ. Ed's maneuvers were beyond cha-cha-cha tempo. The gunship's movements would have better accompanied a symphony by a madman.

Things got worse. It seemed as if all of Otis's calls were breaks.

The gunners were flung helplessly to and fro across the cargo compartment, Rusty Brown later told me. One gunner passed clips of 40-mm shells from on his knees in order to lower his center of gravity, to keep his balance. "I'm going to be black and blue for a month," Brown moaned. On one break, he bounced off the side of the booth and was thrown against the number one Forty just as it commenced firing. "Goddammit to hell," he shouted and leaped back in surprise only to be thrown into the firing, rapidly cycling gun again. "How the hell can he shoot in the middle of this? Let's go, hurry up, pass the ammo."

Undaunted, Ed found segments along his flight path where he blasted off long strings of 40-mm rounds. But his rhythm was gone. He was shooting as if trying to keep time to an album titled *Jimi Hendrix Goes Completely Fucking Nuts*.

In twenty minutes, Ed set fire to four trucks. "Look at them burn," he said to no one in particular. Or was he talking to Grizzly?

The booth was bedlam. It took every bit of our skill to hold the crosshairs on target throughout Ed's erratic movements. The sensor platforms were being slammed from one extreme to the other, taking stresses beyond design limits. As usual, we were communicating without using interphone. Ballard, who as Black Crow was required to record the number of rounds called by the scanners, shouted, "That's a thousand."

"In twenty minutes?" I said. Mental math told me that was fifty rounds a minute. On an average sortie we logged three, maybe four hundred rounds. But that was in three or four hours. I couldn't recall taking more than eight hundred plus on an entire mission. "You sure?" I asked. "A thou in twenty min—"

The gunship lurched left and then right. It shuddered briefly, then lurched right again and then left before Ed fired off another dozen rounds.

FCO Juan Sueno flung his pencil on his desk. "Screw the BDA log." He threw up his hands.

"One thousand," Jim shouted. The scanners still were calling a steady stream of advice while Ed manhandled the gunship through the sky.

When I lined up the TV crosshairs on one gunpit, a pit next to it opened fire. I'd swing onto the new pit and still another would open up. The whole world was a gunpit, I thought. Tracers blurred across the television screen from every direction. Their flashes overdrove the camera beam current and left long, dark streaks on the monitor picture.

The gunship lurched, shuddered in a partial stall, yawed.

"Where're the escorts?" Juan said.

I looked at him. "Escorts?" *If they were smart, they went home,* I thought and then remembered that we hadn't been assigned escorts. "We need a squadron of B-52s."

"What the fuck's Ed doing?" Lee shouted. He had both hands wrapped around the IR tracking control and was out of his seat, swaying, throwing his body weight against the handle in order to gain greater leverage. He was attempting to overpower electrical impulses with sheer physical force. I watched him strangle the tracking control handle and laughed without restraint. "Fuck," Lee screamed.

"Unreal, hunh, John?" I said. With unexpected suddenness Ed violently pushed down the plane's nose, a maneuver that (like going over the top of a roller coaster ride) negated gravity inside the airplane. We were weightless. Juan's eyes grew enormous. Floating two inches above my seat, I answered myself, "Yes, unreal," and laughed again.

Ed recovered from his dive by hauling back on the control wheel, and (like hitting the bottom of a roller coaster dip after a steep drop) we were jammed into our seats with the force of several gravities. By hanging onto the tracking control, Lee stayed on his feet. As soon as the lost altitude was regained, Ed resumed firing.

The thought flashed through my mind that such a maneuver was unsafe in a high-wing aircraft such as ours. I didn't need those kinds of thoughts. I was aimlessly stirring the TV crosshairs from one gunsite to another. The situation had lost meaning. It was like a dream that made no sense. All I could do was wait for it to end. A low, rumbling laugh that I couldn't control bubbled out of me.

Then Ed spoke. "Listen up, everybody. That's it. Those gunners have zeroed in on us. We've got to move."

In the booth we slumped in relief. Juan threw back his head. Lee dropped limply into his seat. Jim stuck up a thumb. I realized that for some time I had been contracting the muscles of my upper body as if performing a prolonged isometric exercise. It had been an unconscious gesture. I felt as tired as if I had just finished twenty minutes of push-ups.

"That's it for up here," Ed said. "We're going down to seventy-five hundred feet, and all that stuff will be above us."

Juan's chin nearly hit the floor.

Lee slapped himself on the helmet.

Jim's thumb turned down.

Why was I again laughing?

Ed dived the aircraft two thousand feet. For moments we again were weightless. Ed maneuvered back into orbit, confirmed that corrected ballistics were in the gunfire computer and that Lee was tracking, and resumed firing. After a few minutes, he chortled over interphone: "It worked. That stuff is going off above us. The gunners have the fuses set for the wrong altitude."

The intensity of the ground fire had diminished only slightly, probably because the antiaircraft gun loaders were tiring. The scanners were calling out a steady flow of warnings and advice, exactly as before. "Doesn't he know," Jim shouted, "that shit has to go through this altitude to get up there?" Jim seemed to have misplaced his usual, graceful self-assurance.

Juan had drawn up his feet until he was hunkered in his chair. "I wish we'd take a nice clean hit so we could go home," he said.

We destroyed the remaining trucks. We were in orbit forty-five minutes, and Jim recorded sixteen hundred and eighty-four rounds shot at us. Later he admitted missing several calls.

Dick Kaulbach then directed the gunship away from Tchepone. Over the next two hours we searched out and destroyed two trucks and damaged four before the ammunition was gone. Ed had been prodigal at Tchepone. We were reserved and methodical in our work. There was little opposition from the ground. Dick knew Steel Tiger. One of his credos was "If you want to find trucks, you have to go to where the guns are. The NVA doesn't position guns to protect trees and karst. Find guns, you find trucks. If you don't want to get shot at, you won't find batches of trucks." We didn't find many trucks and nobody complained. Tomorrow was another day, once we got Ed through this one.

Back at Ubon we deplaned and boarded the waiting bus. Everyone was dragging. Colonel Godolphin took Ed's arm and led him behind a revetment wall, out of sight of the rest of us. Stan Briscoe grinned broadly when he saw them walk away. "I'll bet I know what he's saying," Briscoe said. "Poor old Grizzly was white-knuckled 'til I thought his skin was gonna pop. He sweat clean through his backpack. I know he ate at least a quarter pound of lower lip. Shit was lighting up the sky like Fourth-a-July. You could read a newspaper from the flashes. Major Holcomb was jukin' around it and old Grizzly was shaking his head and looking at me. Hell, I wasn't going to say anything. You know how Major Holcomb is. He wouldn't look at Colonel Godolphin. He'd just watch the flak and fly through it and be back in the gunsight and blaze away. I admit, there were a few times when I didn't think he'd make it." Briscoe laughed at his memories. "Better check my drawers for skid marks. That Major Holcomb, he's a flying fool. Definitely, the best."

Somber-faced, Godolphin and Holcomb eventually reappeared and boarded the bus. Briscoe grinned at them throughout the ride to the squadron building.

The following afternoon Colonel Godolphin met with the aircraft commanders. He explained that his previous day's decision had been hasty. After reconsidering it, he recognized that in certain situations discretion was better than valor. He flatly stated that he did not expect anyone to commit suicide in order to destroy trucks. Despite his humaneness, Godolphin had the final word. He removed the restriction from operating over Tchepone.

Several nights later our crew was assigned a sick bird and we ended up making a very late takeoff. While we were waiting on the ramp, Dick Kaulbach told us: "Last night, Big George—Dave Wine's navigator—had the runs but flew anyway. They found a bunch and George was busy plotting shots when he had to go. He didn't want to leave his position—they had a new FCO and George didn't trust him—so he told a gunner to pass up an empty ammo can. He decided it was easier to strip out of all his gear. He ended up sitting on the ammo can in nothing but his flak helmet, T-shirt, and flying boots. He did his business and never missed a shot. Then he remembered he didn't bring paper to wipe. Being a true navigator, he refused to use his forms or charts. Somehow, he took off a sock and used it. After Dave polished off the trucks, Big George directed him to fly over them, and George went back to the ramp and threw the ammo can down at them. George was still wearing only his helmet, undershirt, and boots. He said that when the rear scanner saw him, the guy almost leaped off the ramp. He thought that maybe Big George had gone berserk and intended to rape him or something. George wrote on his report: 'We not only hunted for them, found them, attacked them, and destroyed them, but we even shat upon them.' Colonel Godolphin called George in today and made him redo the form. George doesn't know it, but Godolphin is having the original report framed. He's also having an ammo can enameled white and fitted with a toilet seat. He plans to give them to George as going-home presents."

After a couple hours of ramp time, our airplane was replaced with a NOD-equipped gunship that had returned in good shape from an early sortie. As a result of the change and a very late takeoff, we were over Steel Tiger with an hour of on-target fuel remaining when the sun came up. "I've never been out here before in daylight," Ed Holcomb said. "It's beautiful."

Narrow mesas of gray-and-black karst rose from the deep jungle canopy. The trees appeared so densely overgrown that it was a wonder how roadways had been cut through them. Ed made a right turn and then banked back to the left. "Chcck that out, Hal." A watcrfall about a thousand feet high bounced spray and mist into the morning sunlight. Apart from wisps of smoke in the distance, there was no sign of activity on the ground. "Like Eden," said Ed.

The terrain was perfect for antiaircraft gunsites, I thought. The necessities were present: fresh water from the stream formed by the waterfall, numerous side trails for service and resupply, and paralleling the main road a dense tree line with open areas at regular intervals for clear fields of fire.

"I hate to ruin this travelogue but, if anyone is interested," Jim Ballard said, "BC has movers."

A gunner said, "Give BC a cookie."

Ed followed BC guidance and rolled into orbit over four trucks which were idling along a two-lane road. One truck passed another, then stopped and permitted the other truck to overtake it. Two trucks halted side by side as if the drivers were talking. Each truck advanced several hundred feet, stopped for a number of seconds, then again advanced. "I'll bet they don't realize we're up here," Lee Schmidt said.

"Probably think we're unarmed," I said. "Probably never saw Spec in daylight."

Lee said, "That's right. To them, this period of the day must be like—no man's land."

"Fucking beautiful simile," I said from the NOD. "Goddamn . . . time like dirt!"

"You know what I mean," Lee said hotly. "There's never any activity out here at this hour. It's a time of tranquility. The gunships have departed and the fast movers haven't yet arrived. Is that better, Hal?"

"Don't forget the sands of time," Jim said.

"Is anybody tracking?" Ed asked.

"NOD."

"IR."

"Dick, put somebody in the computer."

"NOD in. Ed, it's daylight. You don't need either of them."

"Thanks, roomie," I said to Dick and didn't hesitate to add, "Too bad, IR."

Ed muttered some things about force of habit and about being awake all night and then fired a 40-mm at the trucks at play. They stopped in the middle of the road.

"You got their attention," Lee said.

"This is pretty good," Ed said. "I can see trucks for once and nobody's shooting back." He fired another burst, and another. He scored hits and smoke rose from one of the vehicles.

A moment later the sky was polka-dotted with the dark gray puffs of exploding shells. It appeared as if a dozen antiaircraft guns had commenced firing upon the same command. Flak surrounded the gunship. "I think you took the gun crews away from breakfast," Tyler said, "and made them angry." Ed turned toward Thailand. Puffs of flak chased us part of the way to the border. "Maybe it's good that we fly at night and don't see all of this stuff hanging in the sky," Tyler added. That from the hero who wanted to drive his own blowtorch. I was sorry he had missed the night with Godolphin.

"Definitely a nighttime operation," Ed said.

"I'll bet this is the first time the gunners have had a chance to shoot at one of these turkeys in broad daylight," Lee said.

"If I have any say," Jim said, "it's also the last."

"Damn. Damn!" I said. "I wish Colonel Godolphin was with us. We'd've probably stayed."

Chapter 13

Now I've Got a Witness

THE FEATURE THAT set the AC-130 gunship apart from other combat aircraft in Southeast Asia was a bomb damage assessment recorder that videotaped what appeared on the sensors. The tape included a sound track of interphone conversations. As soon as a gunship landed, an instant replay of its combat action was available in dying black and white.

The BDA recorder provided the most interesting combat photography from SEA because no special skill was needed to interpret the pictures. The viewer simply watched television reruns. Real-time action was vivid. The tapes showed much of the antiaircraft fire directed at the gunship as well as the destruction wrought by the gunship. The sound track provided a colorful background.

After the sensor operators reviewed a videotape and reconfirmed the night's kills in the presence of an Intelligence officer, the tape was flown to Seventh Air Force Headquarters in Saigon, where it again was reviewed and, from there, the most interesting tapes were sent to Air Force Headquarters in Washington, D.C. Because of the volume of tapes, Seventh AF Photographic Intelligence personnel eventually converted the most interesting footage from the tapes to sixteen-millimeter film and forwarded only the film, which was titled "AC-130 SEA Gunship Activity—The Best of the

Week." Running time of the summary was twenty to thirty minutes. By then, the president and the Joint Chiefs of Staff were reviewing the pictures.

Within the air force Intelligence community a state of mind existed that probably harked back to the days when the messenger who bore bad tidings was executed on the spot. Intelligence briefers tended to emphasize only good combat news, particularly when reporting up the chain of command. Furthermore, many briefers acted as if they deserved credit for achievements they reported. Perhaps in deference to the poor souls who had been slain by less humanitarian leaders, commanders often punctuated particularly glowing Intelligence reports with statements such as, "Good show, Blank," or "Nice work, Blank—keep it up." Then Captain or Major or Lieutenant Colonel Blank, who in many cases had never flown on a combat mission, actually took a little bow while he basked in approval. Higher-ranking briefers frequently risked a reply, such as, "We give it our max effort, sir."

"AC-130 SEA Gunship Activity—The Best of the Week" provided Intelligence briefers with a foolproof opportunity to ham it up. The motion pictures were every briefer's dream come true. They showed the enemy's world being blown to shit with no ifs, ands, or buts. Briefers became instant experts on gunship operations and tactics. A few boldly projected the films with the sound track turned off and narrated the action in a manner that made the viewers feel as if the briefer had been there. All the films were victories. They left the audience in an appreciative, positive frame of mind. They were perfect endings for otherwise gloomy days. Symbolically, they allowed the messenger to live another day. In fact, they made the messenger appear to be a hero.

To improve crew coordination, Juan Sueno, Lee Schmidt, and I mandatorily reviewed the tapes from our missions and also voluntarily studied successful or unusual missions flown by other crews. As a result, we developed a cynical attitude toward "The Best of the Week."

"They pass up a lot of good stuff," Lee said.

"Those assholes at Seventh don't know what they're looking at," I told him.

"I'll bet they don't review all the tapes," Lee said.

Juan said, "They probably take a random sample."

"Then," I said, "they should title the goddamn flick 'The Best of What We Bothered to Look At.'"

"The crime is," said Juan, "what doesn't go into 'The Best' is erased." After finishing with the tapes, Seventh returned them to Ubon, where they were demagnetized, then reused. Otherwise, a separate building would have been needed to store thousands of rolls of studio-style, two-inch-wide videotape.

Down at Seventh, somebody must have had his stool together, however. One week we received a motion picture titled "AC-130 SEA Gunship Activity—Special Edition." It was like a Keystone comedy. It led off with the results of impacting 40-mm rounds that caused frightening near-misses: NVA drivers swerved their trucks off roads and tumbled down ravines, crashed into trees, and attempted to drive up steep hillsides before stalling or turning over. In one sequence, a pair of drivers abandoned their truck on an uphill grade and forgot to set the brake; with both doors wide open, the truck merrily rolled backward down the road for minutes while other trucks wildly swerved to avoid it. Another sequence showed two trucks destroyed by a single 40-mm round which impacted at exactly the moment the drivers passed abreast, headed in opposite directions. The shell exploded on the hood of the truck nearest the gunship and the major portion of its shrapnel continued into the other truck's cabin. The two transports with their obviously injured drivers veered out of control along the highway before crashing. In the reel's finale, the lead truck in a speeding, tailgating convoy of five took a pair of 40-mm shells head on and stopped with an abruptness that caused the trailing four trucks to tailend each other in a chain reaction, freeway-type pileup. The flick was a laugh a minute.

"The Best" also showed the 40-mm stopping tanks, and *trying* to stop tanks. One big-ass tank reacted like the plastic bear in an electronic-eye shooting gallery. Each time a 40-mm round bounced off the tank's armor, the tank driver reversed course. The only thing needed to complete the farce was "The Anvil Chorus" on sound track. The tank driver zigzagged back and forth across a field with shells sparkling harmlessly off his vehicle until the Spectre crew lost interest. On the sound track, somebody said, "We probably at least gave him Excedrin Headache Number Forty."

Tanks were uncommon targets. The squadron claimed around a dozen during the season. Our crew never saw one. In the Eighth Tac Fighter Wing Intelligence debriefing room, targets destroyed or damaged by wing aircraft (ninety-five percent of the total was attributable to Spectre) were listed on a large chart: gun positions, tanks, trucks, bulldozers, boats, barges, buildings . . . The single item that, after months, still listed a zero was "grader" (short for roadgrader).

The BDA procedure was that upon landing, a crew was verbally debriefed by an NCO and made its initial claims; a short time later, an Intell officer, the FCO, IR, and TV reviewed the videotape and adjusted the claims, up or down.

Following one mission, I sucked on a tooth, innocently looked off into a corner, and initially reported, "We got a grader." The sergeant who was debriefing asked me to repeat the claim. When he was positive he had heard correctly, he rushed away and minutes later was replaced by a beaming Intelligence lieutenant colonel who said, "You got a grader. Terrific! The old man will love it. Describe it."

I scratched my head, then tugged at an earlobe. "I'd guess . . ."—I squinted and bit my lip—". . . it looked like about . . ." The lieutenant colonel was leaning forward, hanging on my words. ". . . about . . ."—I widened my eyes— ". . . a third grader! We put a Forty dead through the little fuck's lunch box that he was hugging against his chest."

Of course, an occasional truck escaped destruction and Seventh Air Force Photo Intell eventually developed enough confidence to include an escape in "The Best." In the sequence, for several minutes the gunship crew fired 40-mm rounds at a slow-moving truck without hitting it. The truck stopped of its own accord, and the Spectre pilot told the F-4 escort leader, "Lay a CBU on my sparkles." The Phantom screamed in low and released a Cluster Bomb Unit at the stationary vehicle. Normally a CBU cannister burst open and its 192 fragmentation bomblets spread evenly in an oval pattern, sixty by thirty yards; the bomblets then exploded randomly for a quarter of a minute. In this instance, the Phantom pilot either released the CBU at the incorrect altitude or the cannister malfunctioned. Whichever, the bomblets did not disperse properly and landed in a large ring perfectly encircling the vehicle. For long seconds the bomblets exploded and flashed like a glittering wreath. A voice on the sound track said, "That looks like a halo. If he drives away, I think we ought to leave *him* alone." Several seconds after the last bomblet detonated, the truck moved off slowly down the trail. Nobody chased it.

Lee, Juan, and I frequently reviewed the videotapes of pilots whom we knew to be shitty shooters and sighed with frustration at what we saw. That captain with whom Juan and I had rolled on the floor found ninety-seven trucks, the greatest concentration of vehicles in Spectre history, massed somewhere out in the jungle. Lee saw the trucks on videotape and gasped: "It's like—Detroit."

Juan said, "Must have caught them with the camouflage net down. Whoever's responsible is probably back planting rice."

The captain's crew displayed a mass case of buck fever. The sensor operators described what was below and the captain opened fire. No sensor was tracking tightly. An electronic beep on the sound track told when the guns fired. The first five or ten rounds impacted outside the sensors' fields of view. The sensor operators aided and abetted the confusion. They established no pattern of attack and aimlessly stirred the crosshairs through the parked trucks while the gunship circled and 40-mm round after 40-mm round hit in the dirt. The FCO either had the reciprocal wind or the wrong ballistics set into the fire-control computer, Juan guessed. When the pilot finally hit a truck, the sensor operators and FCO sounded like a junior high school pep squad:

TV: A direct hit, direct hit. A direct hit.

IR: A direct hit. Yes, a direct hit. He's burning.

FCO: He's burning, he's burning.

TV: He's burning. He's destroyed.

FCO: Destroyed. He's destroyed. Definitely destroyed.

IR: Chalk up another destroyed.

"Another?" Juan Sueno said. "That was the first one they

hit." On videotape, the sensor operators held the crosshairs on the burning vehicle while rounds impacted nearby. Juan nodded: "Tracking there isn't a bad idea. They'll never hit that one again; bound to hit something else." After several more orbits, Juan said, "You noticed, no ground fire? NVA never expected anyone to find these."

"They didn't find them," Lee said, "they tripped over them."

The crew sat at ten thousand feet, used up five hundred rounds of 40-mm ammunition, and departed. I was grief-stricken: "I don't fucking believe it. He walked away . . ."

"And they claimed every one destroyed," Juan said.

"Has Grizzly seen this?"

Juan shook his head. "He's down Seventh." He sighed. "He's gonna shit. Photo Intell agreed that they got 'em all."

We spent three hours reviewing the tape and, giving full benefit of the doubt, calculated that our favorite captain destroyed fourteen trucks. I turned off the television monitor and said, "He didn't put in the escorts."

"Not only that, he didn't tell Moonbeam, or TFA, or any other Spec about what he had. He came straight home. Said he was low on fuel," Juan told us.

Lee said, "Then that's why he didn't go down and use the Twenties or minis. He couldn't have missed."

"Wanna bet?" I said.

Juan told us, "Seventh sent out a recce bird around sunup, but it couldn't find a thing."

"No wonder," I said. "Fuckers all drove away."

When Colonel Godolphin returned and saw the film, he called Seventh and told the scorekeepers to subtract eighty-five trucks from Spectre's total, which was nearing five thousand for the season.

The most outlandish videotape we saw was cut by an old crew. The IR found numerous, densely packed hot spots under thin foliage. At first, the spots appeared as one huge, ghostly blob. The crew attacked with a 40-mm, and the hot spots scattered. "They're not trucks, they're elephants," the TV said when several beasts broke into the clear. Without discussing it, the crew gunned down five or six of the animals.

Then somebody said, "I don't think this is right," and the crew flew off in search of other targets. The footage didn't make "The Best." It never left Ubon.

The sound track on the BDA videotape caused trouble for Spectre crews. In the heat of combat the crewmen's language often became blasphemous and obscene. It came to pass, because Seventh Photo Intell was unable to bleep out unwanted words and because the film "AC-130 SEA Gunship Activity—The Best of the Week" was distributed up the chain of command as far as the president, commanders at different echelons requested that crew members communicate in a more refined vocabulary. Commanders at each level feared that the sensibilities of their superiors would be offended. No directions were put into writing, however. The issue would have been laughable had the chain of command possessed knowledge of the coarse language revealed years later in the presidential tapes of Richard Nixon, the man whose ears ultimately were to be protected.

Much of the crews' bad language was used in good humor. For example, the FCO was responsible for recording reference data at the start of the tape but, because it was a chance to be on stage, the other men in the booth insisted on taking turns doing the introductions. A typical opening to the tape came from Rory Hansen's TV operator, one of the notorious Swine Brothers: "Hello, Mr. Tape. This is your guest announcer for the twentieth of February, nineteen hundred and seventy-one, Major Shoat Jackson, all the way from that thriving, driving, striving metropolis of Deeeee-Witt, located in Arkansas County, Arkansas!" He, the pilot, and the IR bellowed out a longwinded, ear-shriveling hog call that was next poorly imitated by the ten others on the crew. "We're flying old five-zero-niner into Steel Tiger, VR sector . . ." After several seconds of blank time, he said, "Hey, nav, what the fuck sector we going to?"

"Beats," the navigator answered. "You obviously have me mistaken for somebody who gives a shit."

"Come on, nav," Shoat Jackson said, "you're supposed to know that stuff. That's why you got twelve fingers."

"Sector six," the navigator said.

"All right, then!" Shoat Jackson said brightly. "Old five-zero-niner into—"

"You shithead, you already said that," Major Hog Morris, the IR, shouted. "You already gave the aircraft number."

A chorus of "Yeah" followed from the other crewmen.

"Quiet, everybody," Shoat Jackson ordered and, with great seriousness, announced, "Spectre five-zero-niner inbound to Steel Tiger, sector six, twenty February, nineteen hundred seventy-one, to attack and destroy them dirty, stinky, pinky Commie ratfuckers. Let's hear a hymn for Ho Chi Minh. And-a-one, and-a-two . . ." The crew of thirteen sang a perfectly modulated one-note repetition that went "Hymnnnnn. Hymnnnnn. Hymnnnnn. Fuuuuuck. Himmmmm."

On target, profanity was impersonally directed at the antiaircraft fire, or at the moon, or at the airplane itself. I didn't think the language was any worse than what was heard elsewhere. But who was I to judge? I was a garbage mouth from way back. Some men, like Ed Holcomb, never swore; others, like Rabbit Ripple, seldom said a sentence without swearing. That was their nature, their style.

Our sensor team delighted in working with Rabbit. His eagerness to get the job done, coupled with his quick frustration, was a constant source of entertainment. On a mission when a gunship had an intermittently malfunctioning fire-control computer that stymied even Juan Sueno, Rabbit Ripple was unable to hit several trucks stopped neatly in line. He fired a four-round burst from a Forty. Earlier three-round bursts had missed badly.

"That was fifteen mils forward and ten low," I said. "Maybe you're holding your mouth wrong, Rabbit."

"That wouldn't fit the graph," Juan Sueno said, as if he used one.

Rabbit Ripple fired a burst of five.

"Twenty-two and a half aft," I said. "Almost off the screen."

"But a tight pattern," Juan said laughingly.

Lee suggested, "Maybe we can land and slash their tires."

Rabbit Ripple fired a burst of fifteen rounds and above the

noise of the gunfire shouted, "This shit—this shit—this shit isn't worth rat shit, pig shit . . ."

Juan laughed over interphone: "The tape's on."

Rabbit's words came out like 20-mm rounds, a staccato stream: "Yeah? Yeah? Well, fuck you, F-C-O. And fuck I-R. Fuck T-V. Fuck the computer. Fuck this airplane. Fuck this fuckin' war. And fuck *you,* video-fuckin'-tape."

In the booth we laughed until we were panting for breath. What difference did such an outburst make? That tape certainly wasn't going anywhere.

As with most debatable matters, the issue of bad language became a battle of wills. Crewmen figured it didn't matter what they said as long as they killed trucks. After they failed to clean up their vocabulary voluntarily, despite repeated warnings, Colonel Godolphin took matters into his hands.

When he wanted to be, Godolphin was eloquent. In his welcoming speech to our crew, he had dramatically tied together mission accomplishment, self-sacrifice, camaraderie, and esprit de corps in a manner which inspired every one of us despite the conviction, as we confessed afterward, that we were too experienced to be influenced by rhetoric.

Now, Godolphin called his crews together to establish interphone discipline. He translated the requests of his superiors into terms he thought his audience would understand: "Look, dammit, several times you've been *asked* to cut down the swearing and cursing on the tapes. Now I'm *telling* you. I don't care what you say at other times, but, from now on, knock off the shit completely when the tape is running. You aircraft commanders *will* enforce this policy. If you don't, or can't, I'll consider it lack of discipline and unprofessional airmanship. I'll lower the efficiency rating of you and anybody you can't control."

I was the TV operator on Major Rabbit Ripple's crew the night following Colonel Godolphin's pronouncement. On the way to Steel Tiger, I decided that if the commanders wanted it sweet I would make it sweet until it was cloying. Upon locating the first vehicle of the night, I called out, "Forsooth, TV doesth spy a truck from hither glen."

The IR operator turned, gave me a look, then smiled and

nodded twice. "Aye, 'tis so," he said. "Thou art keen of eye, TVeth. This 'umble servant beseeches thee, my liege navigator, pray puteth TVeth into thine computer—eth!"

The nav picked it up: "Alas, 'tis done. Thou art clear to fire, liege pilot."

Mutely, Rabbit Ripple commenced fire. He scored a direct hit with the first long burst and the truck exploded so violently that it virtually disintegrated. There was no fire and little smoke. A most unusual sight. I had been tracking the target and paused, astonished for the moment. "Woweth," said the IR.

"Verily," said I. "I perceive yon truck to be interdicted to an irreparable degree. Vis-à-vis the existing criteria: annihilated."

Rabbit Ripple said, "Knock off the cocksucker talk and tell me, did I hit the fucker or didn't I?"

Rabbit Ripple was his own man. At the crew's pretakeoff briefing following Colonel Godolphin's warning, Rabbit had said, "If thinking about what you say cramps your style, forget it. Say whatever you want. I'll take the blame. We're not afraid of trip-A. Why be afraid of a shitty mark on a piece of paper?" Then he had laughingly added: "Before you know it, we won't be allowed to say 'Eat it' in the dining room."

Foul talk was rampant among flight crews, and especially among combat crews overseas. Because there was so much repetition, during one phase of the war several officers developed the "TFA Code," whereby numbers replaced standard phrases of discontent. "One-oh-five," for example, meant "It's so fucking bad, I can't believe it." "One-oh-six" was the classic "I hate this fucking place." "One-oh-seven" expressed the feeling that "This place sucks." And "one-ten" goddamned the Officers' Club.

Codes also expressed sentiments of an interpersonal nature:

101 You gotta be shitting me.
102 Get off my fucking back.
108 Fuck you very much. (Selected as "Sentiment of
     the Year" in 1969 and 1970)

113 Balls!
123 Get hosed.

There were numbers for expediting inflight conversations:

103 Beats the shit out of me.
104 What the fuck? Over.
112 Let *me* talk to that son of a bitch.
146 It's hot.
199 Can do.
299 Will do.
300 No can do.
501 Stand by, the AC just went to piss.

Of course, "one-oh-nine" stood alone: "Beautiful. Fucking beautiful!"

The use of the code came and went from month to month and year to year. It was assured of one annual reappearance, however: "One-fourteen" said "Merry Fucking Christmas," and "one-fifteen" replied "Happy Fucking New Year."

The Spectre crews refused to accept the code as a solution to their problem. Their outbursts were too spontaneous.

Major Tim FitzHugh, an IR operator, also openly ignored Colonel Godolphin's edict. The two men despised each other. Their differences started over cocktails at a Spectre dining-in when General Slade Hunchworth, who was on an inspection tour from Seventh, said, "When it comes to truck killing or close support, I believe Spec is doing the best job in Southeast Asia."

FitzHugh said, "If that's true, sir, then how come the guys who are doing that job aren't getting the best efficiency ratings in Southeast Asia?" FitzHugh and several other navigators recently had received ratings of eight and nine out of a possible ten.

Godolphin leaped into the pause that followed. "This is a social function, Major. General Hunchworth doesn't want to discuss business."

"Truck killing and close support are business," FitzHugh said, "and the general brought them up."

The general turned red. "Look, Major," he snapped, "watch it."

"See me first thing tomorrow morning," Godolphin told FitzHugh.

"Why, so you can lower my ER more?"

"When I finish with you," Godolphin shouted, "you'll be happy if you're still in the air force."

"Now who's discussing business?" FitzHugh said quietly.

"You insubordinate—" Godolphin clenched his fists. "I'll have—"

General Hunchworth had recovered his composure by then and said, "Hold it a minute, Go. Major, what did you receive on your last ER?"

"An eight," FitzHugh said. He stared at the general, who looked away. Both men knew that, with the inflated system, the rating placed him in the lowest twenty-five percent of his peers and thereby greatly reduced his chance for promotion.

The upshot of the confrontation was that General Hunchworth had the Spectre ratings compared to the air force average and, when he learned the Spectre average was low, especially among navigators, ordered Godolphin to be more liberal in the future. The decision didn't help FitzHugh's ER, however, and it reflected unfavorably on Godolphin's judgment.

Although he knew he was engaged in a battle that he couldn't win, FitzHugh continually confronted Godolphin. FitzHugh refused to perform the unwritten tasks that other officers took for granted. He believed that servile tasks belonged to the enlisted men assigned to the section involved. For example, he stopped inspecting and cleaning his personal flight equipment. When Colonel Godolphin pointed out the shortcoming, FitzHugh said, "Show me in writing where that is *my* duty."

"That's just the way it's done," Godolphin told him, "and you know it."

"That doesn't make it right," FitzHugh said.

Godolphin reminded him that it was traditional for each man to oil his personal handgun weekly. "*I* clean *my* gun," he stated.

"Then that's wrong too. You of all people should have more important things to be concerned with," FitzHugh said. "I suppose you think the gladiators swept out the Colosseum."

Godolphin let him win that one, and FitzHugh bought two cases of beer for the enlisted men who worked in the personal flight equipment section and now inspected and cleaned his gear.

FitzHugh next refused to wear the standard metal identification tags on flights, despite air force regulations. When challenged by an aircraft commander, he said, "Those are for people who expect to die. I'm not in that category. But if you screw up and we get killed, I'll be the body without them." The aircraft commander reported the infraction to Godolphin. When again confronted, FitzHugh said, "Why should I wear identification tags, Colonel? I know who I am." Godolphin told him to wear them and not to press the issue. FitzHugh said bitingly, "And if I don't? What are you going to do, send me to Southeast Asia and make me fly combat missions?"

Godolphin bided his time.

Colonel Godolphin's edict concerning interphone discipline made FitzHugh more recalcitrant. When his crew set fire to a truck, he sang passages in Latin from a Roman Catholic high mass. When one truck was burning while another truck was under attack he continued singing the mass in low tones. It was dramatic background music on the videotape. During pauses in the aircrew conversation, he increased his volume. The singing amused FitzHugh's crewmates; however, it enraged Colonel Godolphin, who after viewing one of the tapes told FitzHugh, "This is a direct order. You will not ever again sing inside a gunship."

"You're singling me out," FitzHugh said. "I've seen the Swine Brothers' tapes and they give that hog call whenever they get a burner. What about that?"

"They do that in fun," Colonel Godolphin said. "You're malicious."

"What about Rabbit? He still swears in at least every other sentence."

"I've discussed that with Major Ripple," Godolphin said, "and he's making an effort to improve."

"Yeah, and he's also a pilot."

Colonel Godolphin quietly told FitzHugh, "I have no more time for you."

On his following and final mission with Spectre, Tim FitzHugh spoke only Latin. That behavior disturbed his crewmates as much as Godolphin. Within a week, FitzHugh was transferred to the AC-119 Stinger squadron at Da Nang Air Base in South Vietnam. Da Nang was known as "Rocket City" because of the large amount of incoming it took. The Stingers had no videotape recorders. In fact, they had little of anything. For FitzHugh the transfer was comparable to trading a new Silver Cloud for a used Beetle and moving from Beverly Hills to Watts.

FitzHugh's rebellious attitude infected others. I caught a small dose. While Fitz was singing in Latin, I was carrying a copy of the little red book *Quotations from Chairman Mao Tse-tung,* which I had bought in Hong Kong during my first SEA tour. The book, printed in the People's Republic of China, supposedly was a first edition. "While you're sucking your thumbs in solitary," I told other crew members, "I'll have something to talk about with my interrogator." The book was an irritant except to Holcomb's crew, which was entertained when I read from it—and I frequently read from it. Other crews weren't as receptive. Therefore, I forced the scripture upon them and flagrantly quoted out of context. "Officers teach soldiers, soldiers teach officers, and soldiers teach each other" was my favorite passage and I repeatedly interpreted it to mean whatever I wanted it to mean. Juan Sueno pointed out that discrepancy and then asked, "How come in this great classless society they still have officers and soldiers?"

"For that astute question, Johnny, you get an A," I said, "and graduate from the course. That means you no longer have to take notes when I read out loud."

"That doesn't answer my question," Juan said.

I got out my little red book and flipped pages with my thumb. "Mao wrote that quote . . ."—I found the page I sought—". . . in 1948." I closed the book and slid it into my pocket. "In '65, the Chinese abolished personal rank. They did away with all insignias, except for the red star on the cap, and they made everyone wear the same shit-brown uniform, regardless of branch of service. So there. A great classless society, and military!"

Juan raised his eyebrows. "Is that true?"

I nodded. "Read it myself." Juan seemed satisfied. Then I added, "Of course, there are still commanders and command positions. Now you explain that to me."

A few officers complained about the book, and Colonel Godolphin confronted me. "What's going on with you and Mao's book? You're upsetting people."

I took the book from my pocket, leafed through the pages, then read, "In this world, things are complicated and are decided by many factors. We should look at problems from different aspects, not from just one." I turned backward through the book, then continued: "After the enemies with guns have been wiped out, there will still be enemies without guns; they are bound to struggle desperately against us . . ."

Colonel Godolphin laughed. "Confucius say . . ." He rocked back in his chair. "What bullshit!" He laughed again. "Whatever you're trying to do, there's probably a more positive approach to it. Tone it down for the crybabies." Then he thanked me for the job I was doing and for willingly flying day after day. I was surprised by the outcome of the conversation because I was not positive what I had been trying to do with Mao's book, other than stir up a little shit.

About the time FitzHugh arrived in Da Nang, Captain Tommy James hit a truck carrying either special explosives or some exotic chemicals. The truck erupted with a flash as bright as the rising sun. "Holy fuck!" Tommy James spontaneously cried. "What the fuck was *that?*" The explosion boiled into a cloud that swiftly rose to the altitude of the aircraft. "What the fuck *was* that?" James repeated. The cloud formed into a mushroom shape. It was the most awesome explosion recorded by Spectre. The cloud continued to rise and expand and eventually towered over the airplane. "It looks like a fucking atom bomb," Tommy James said. The pictures highlighted "The Best" regardless of the sound track.

In the midst of the concern over interphone vocabulary and discipline, the United States ambassador made an inspection tour of the Spectre squadron. Colonel Godolphin briefed him on the role of the gunship and concluded the briefing with: "Mr. Ambassador, if you desire, we can now go through a gunship. Or, if you prefer, we can first look at recent BDA photography."

The tall, distinguished, white-haired ambassador smiled and said, "I would be goddamn delighted to view more of those 'fucking atom bombs.'"

Chapter 14

Heart of Stone

STRATEGIC AIR COMMAND bomber crews had a saying that I liked: "A hundred million casualties aren't a lot as long as they're on the other side." One North Vietnamese casualty caused me as much mental anguish as I wanted out of war. A professional soldier was a fool if he second-guessed what he did in the heat of the moment. He was twice the fool if he permitted another person to act as his conscience. And he was an absolute idiot if he answered to that conscience.

In the middle of the dry season I was involved in an event that opened my eyes to an idea I never had suspected: I saw a limit to fury. Until then, nothing, with the exception of killing friendly troops, had appeared criminal. Schmidt and I had been judge, jury, and executioners regarding whatever we encountered.

The midseason event showed me that regardless of how powerful a being was, for every action there was a reaction, if not immediately, then in hours, days, or years. Later I extended the reaction time beyond that. It became "If not in this world, perhaps in other worlds."

I understood the action-reaction principle as it applied to physics. It was Newton's third law: *For every action there is an equal and opposite reaction.* But I hadn't considered relating the principle to warfare, at least not at the conventional level where we were fighting. And I certainly hadn't related it to my psycho-social being. I suppose, in the end, it was my psyche that was damaged most.

The lesson came about in the most innocent manner.

During mission debriefing, the videotape replay was clearer than the actual event had been while in the air. Within the same instant, the truck stopped, the cab door swung open, the driver jumped out. With churning arms and knee-high pumping, long-striding legs, the driver ran back down the road away from his vehicle, sprinted for his life. Electronic crosshairs slid off the truck, slued along the road until they passed the running man and were aimed ahead of him, then held the lead. A moment later four cannon rounds blew the man apart. The crosshairs glided back to the truck.

The action didn't fully register until after Schmidt and I saw the replay. Schmidt then asked to see it again, and again. We had been chasing the truck for minutes. The driver had been speeding, swerving wildly to avoid our gunfire. Finally we had hit on the road directly in front of the vehicle, had forced the driver to slam on his brakes.

Then Schmidt had yelled, "There goes the driver."

I hadn't seen the man at first, had been focused on the stationary truck. Already in firing geometry, the gunship had had a 40-mm cannon on the line. Prodded by Schmidt's cry, I had slid the crosshairs ahead of the driver and had called to Ed Holcomb, "Hurry up and shoot." My actions had been pure hand-eye reflex, no brain involved: There goes something, kill it!

Holcomb had been holding the computer display in coincidence and, in the blink of an eye, had pressed off four rounds. I'd had a perfect lead on the fleeing driver. Four two-pound shells had hit directly on the running man, obliterating him.

It was a perfect example of "driving nails." A single direct hit with a Forty on that small a target would have been phenomenal shooting from a gunship orbiting at sixty-five hundred feet. Four hits seemed impossible. "Unreal," I said when the footage played a second time. "We couldn't do it again if we had to." The event had taken so few moments in the air that I had forgotten about it until it came up at debriefing.

On the third viewing the action took place very slowly. The

door drifted open, the driver floated down and took off running, seemingly in slow motion. The crosshairs glided after him, brushed over him, led him, hovered and waited. On the sound track I said, "Hurry up and shoot." Every step appeared premeditated. Of course, by then we knew what to look for. It always was that way. Events that flashed by in a blur during combat slowed to a step-by-step pace in the calm of debriefing. The more a person studied a tape the slower events unraveled.

On the third viewing I felt with intolerable vividness the rounds noiselessly impact on the straining muscles of the running driver, felt soul smashed out of flesh. That a single fleeting act should brim such cloying empathy measured within me a new oppressive despair.

Watching the tape along with Schmidt and me was Lieutenant Bernard Marconi, a photo interpreter whose duty was to review tapes with sensor operators and confirm kills. After the third viewing Marconi stopped the playback and said, "It's bad enough you blow up the trucks, but do you have to kill the drivers too?"

In a flash I was overwhelmed by anger. My face burned. Yet I said nothing, stared at Marconi, couldn't believe what I'd heard.

Schmidt glowered. "What the fuck you think they're trying to do to us out there?" No smile lurked in his look.

I surprised myself by quietly asking, "What's the difference between killing a driver in the truck or one on foot?"

"He surrendered when he gave you the truck," Marconi said. Getting no response, he added, "There are limits, even in war."

The killing had been so unconscious that I had trouble believing an issue was being made of it. Yet I felt an intensifying guilt. In self-defense I asked myself, "What right does Marconi have to question me?" I caught myself pressing clenched fists against the edge of the debriefing table. Muscles in my shoulders and thighs bunched. Was I preparing to spring to the attack?

"Whose side you on?" Schmidt asked Marconi.

"That's not the point," said Marconi. "The point is that it wasn't fair to kill that driver."

Fair! The word screamed out at me. I considered myself to be scrupulously fair. Hard but fair—the air force way. Yet, within my silence I saw the situation from Marconi's perspective: at Ubon, night after night, videotape after videotape, Spectre crew after Spectre crew pounding truck after truck. The war had to appear terrifically one-sided. Obviously Marconi had no idea of the dangers crews faced, of the thousands of antiaircraft rounds shot at them. From Marconi's viewpoint, I saw myself as a bloodthirsty, heartless killer. And that wasn't right, I thought. Or was it?

From the depth of memory I recalled a time during the Second World War when I was a kid. Admiral Bull Halsey's portrait appeared on the cover of *Time* magazine above the quote "Kill Japs, kill Japs, and kill more Japs." I'd pasted that cover to the door of my room. My father and I had gloated over the caption. "What's the matter with young guys today?" I asked silently. Did I mean me or Marconi?

"Hey, Marc," Schmidt said, "you're not over here to judge us. If the air force wanted us to have a conscience, it would have issued us one. We don't want yours." He laughed alone.

In shooting the driver, I'd responded reflexively. Didn't thoughtlessness diminish the scope of what I'd done? Or did it expand my culpability? Was my disregard for life inhuman? Cowardly? I'd always considered myself to be brave. Not caring to pursue such ideas, I hit the play button and started the videotape rolling forward, beyond the death of the driver.

Morality wasn't an issue among flyers of jets that traveled beyond the speed of sound or that invisibly dropped bombs from the stratosphere. Those men were distanced from the battlefield, at times were gone before their weapons inflicted damage. They struck targets designated by others. Afterward, unarmed reconnaissance crews photographed strike results. Nonflying specialists analyzed the pictures. No one person was inextricably involved with a mission from beginning to end. Detachment was the norm.

But within the slowly orbiting, propeller-driven AC-130 gunship, the videotape machine personalized the sensor operators' war, forced each man to relive the actions of hunting and killing, to view consequences. That infernal apparatus salvaged images, reproduced ghostly shadows, and thereby resurrected men otherwise reduced to ciphers. Eerily, in a perverse reversal of logic, the apparatus tolerated a man's rebirth in order for him sequentially to be destroyed again. Yet, in the final analysis, should retrieved reality exceed introspective bounds, the tape could be ritualistically demagnetized and the flickering spectres consigned to the dead forevermore.

How did something so apparently simple become so complex, I wondered. Fundamentally . . . they shot at us . . . we shot at them . . . eventually, somebody got killed. What could be fairer?

And then Marconi performed a most remarkable act.

He quickly rewound the tape, jerked the reel from the viewing machine, then crossed the room and dropped the reel onto a spindle inside a foot-square metal box, spinning the reel with his fingers.

"What're you doing?" Schmidt said.

"Demagnetizing it. Erasing it."

Nobody spoke for almost a minute. In the background Marconi's stereo tape player was grinding out a number by Joan Baez. Joan and Buffy and Dylan topped our crew shit list. We disliked them for their scruffiness and nasal whines as much as for their anti-America sentiments. Janie Fonda we accepted. After seeing *Barbarella* we decided a great-looking piece like that could believe anything it wanted to believe.

Now, on top of everything else, Joan was clucking and wailing and rubbing me wrong. She probably was some sacred earth-mother figure to Marconi, I thought. Joan must have got to Schmidt too because he suddenly shouted, "Marconi, you shouldn't have done that. That wasn't right."

"Let's not talk about what's right," Marconi said. He was acting very calm. "Please."

Marconi had made a gross error and he knew it, I thought. I let a dozen beats pass before I quietly said, "But you were wrong for doing that, Lieutenant." I decided to shove his nose in it. What choice did I have? I couldn't allow the low-ranking son of a bitch to get away with having played God at my expense. "What you did doesn't change a thing," I said. "That fuckin' driver is still dead."

"I know," Marconi said.

"And we're not," I told him. "So that makes us right, Lieutenant." I said it off-handedly but, nevertheless, Marconi's face filled with unfiltered, two-hundred-proof contempt. I switched to a businesslike tone. "By the way, we forgot to claim him." I pointed to a pile of papers in front of Marconi. "So write it down. Credit us with one killed by air."

Marconi hesitated. Did he fear that a pencil stroke would scar him?

I gave him a hard-eyed, tight-lipped stare, then ordered, "Mark it."

He looked down and scratched a thin line on a sheet of paper.

I nodded. Our business was finished. "We'll see you another night, Lieutenant." I stared at him. His eyes ran away from mine. The curly haired little shit still had acne. "Good night, Lieutenant."

"Night . . ."—he croaked it out—". . . sir."

On the walk to the O-Club for breakfast, Schmidt said, "I guess you were right. My dad always told me, when you have a problem ask yourself two questions. First, can you do anything about it? Second, do you really care? If you can't honestly answer yes to both questions, screw it."

There was an old army saying that endured in the air force: "What a man does overseas doesn't count." That saying included everything from cheating on the old lady to killing without cause. The saying had to be believed in order to get the job done. Any believer found it very easy to live with himself.

Had Lieutenant Marconi seen the special performance Ed Holcomb's crew put on the following week, he might have defected to the NVA. Colonel Godolphin selected our crew to combat test new 40-mm rounds made from heavy metal, shaped flint, and zinc. General Slade Hunchworth flew from Saigon to Ubon to talk to the crew prior to the mission.

The general's image would have put Steve Canyon to shame. He looked terrific: thick gray hair, tanned craggy features, clear blue eyes, and an easy smile. His physique belonged on a man half his years: thick neck, broad shoulders, heavy hands, slim waist, and long legs. I'd heard he played tennis daily. I would have paid money to meet him on a handball court. He appeared masterful, had an aura of command. Without his rows of four stars on each collar, men still would have looked to him for leadership. Yet his low-keyed manner made me feel that he was working for our crew as much as our crew was working for him. How could anyone not want to please such a man? Some commanders were figureheads, but Hunchworth brought ease and strength, however deceptive, into the spectre of authority.

He had a word of greeting for each officer before he got down to business. "We have great hopes for this new ammunition," he said. "It should make it easier to get burners. The warhead is rare earth, called misch metal, and its shrapnel is pyrophoric, ignites spontaneously. Like the old magnesium incendiary, it won't go out until it burns itself out. It should set fire to just about anything. The round was tested at Eglin against static targets. You'll be using it for the first time against live targets." He smiled. "Get good pictures."

He displayed a chart that compared a misch metal round to a standard 40-mm round. Both projectiles weighed 1.97 pounds. The misch metal warhead broke into 150 pieces of shrapnel, with the largest pieces around one hundred grains (slightly heavier than the weight of a U.S. twenty-five cent piece). The standard round broke into 250 pieces, with none larger than sixty grains. Misch metal shrapnel traveled slower (nineteen hundred feet per second, or thirteen hundred miles per hour) than shrapnel from the standard round (twenty-five hundred fps). Both projectiles had a lethal radius of ten feet against vehicles and thirty to forty feet against personnel.

"I want you to test the misch against as many different targets as you can find," Hunchworth ordered. "As long as you're on the other side of the river, you're free to hit *anything*. You have my personal clearance."

To the majority of professional soldiers, one was a fool if one questioned what was preordained. For example, Strategic Air Command bomber crews waited on alert with weapons a thousand times more powerful than the Hiroshima bomb. If launched, those crews were expected to commit murder that seemed fated, if not premeditated, by excessive, or overriding, limits of fury in technology. There were options under which the crews counterattacked, under which they struck preemptively, and under which within the reflexes of the aircraft they sought revenge in the very ashes of defeat. Whatever the case, however thin or deep the ashes, millions upon millions of Soviet citizens would die as the phoenix of retaliation flared.

The instructions from General Slade Hunchworth to fly to Laos and to test new munitions by destroying anything in sight fell into the realm of reflexes of war transcending the immediate target. Within each truck or Vietnamese truck driver, within each target of machine or man, a million shadowy enemies clustered speaking with accents of Ho Chi Minh or Mao or Lenin.

We flew to Laos and almost immediately the BC found a forty-foot boat motoring up the Se Kong River. The electronic hum it made was the voice of the enemy. The craft appeared to be carrying supplies. Holcomb called for the misch metal.

The first of the special rounds detonated on the surface of the water in front of the boat, and shrapnel danced and skipped across the river in silvery streaks. From the air the explosions were the sparkling language of the stars. From eye level the explosions were more startling: mute faces raised their voices as dozens of passengers on the boat appeared from under tarpaulins and leaped overboard before the helmsman turned hard and aimed for the riverbank to run the vessel aground.

Swimmers were left thrashing in the river, in the wake of the boat's propeller. As if following a script written by the wake's foam, I suggested switching to a Twenty. After the flip of a switch, we hosed down the swimmers. "Saved them the agony of drowning," Schmidt said. Then with a Forty back on the line we went after the boat, which had run into the bank, had its prow buried beneath jungle. Holcomb fired misch rounds. Shrapnel flashed into glowing pinwheels. "What is that stuff?" Holcomb asked. There was no reply, but in two orbits of the pinwheel the boat and the jungle were aflame.

"Ed likes it 'cause he can see it at night," Jim Ballard said more to himself than to his boothmates.

A short time later, when the crew intercepted a convoy of six southbound trucks, Ed Holcomb fired without pause. Trucks exploded. The misch rounds reacted unpredictably, seemed to possess lives of their own, seemed capable of any feat. One round hit short, arced a fiery streak over one truck, and ignited a different truck behind. Another round caught a boulder beyond, detonated, then ricocheted as a fireball back into a truck to set it ablaze. The misch rounds eerily sought objects, discriminated nontarget from target, inflicted double damage, multiple damage to nature and to man. I wondered if shrapnel from normal rounds did as many strange things but without being visible. Even clean misses with the misch created rings of fire on the roadway. In the booth we shook our heads in awe. Almost as soon as the shooting began, six trucks were burning. Then we moved elsewhere.

At that point in the flight, the world as we knew it ceased to exist. From an altitude of five thousand feet we shot up a town. We first hit one-story huts on the edge of the town. The huts were on stilts, and several of the rounds passed through the roofs and floors and exploded on the ground beneath the structures. Schmidt complained about the erratic detonation characteristics of the heavy metal while we burned one row of the huts. We then moved to the heart of town.

I put the TV crosshairs on the tallest building, a four-story structure, probably the town's hotel. Suddenly a fiery flush passed over me. The videotape recorder was running and I knew we had approval, but nevertheless I felt a tug of hesitation, the pull of a humane gravity that tried to drag me back to reality. What we were doing was the same as destroying an open city, I thought. There was no opposition from the ground. No people were in sight. Remorse was raw material for a nervous breakdown, I decided, and said, "TV tracking."

Holcomb commenced fire and together we walked misch rounds up and down the sides of the tallest building. Shells shot through windows and doors. By the third orbit fires were leaping out every window. Along the fringes of my mind, I thought of persons trapped inside the building, trapped in a small piece of hell on earth, a hell of my design.

Was I creating and destroying in the same act?

I had an impulse to stop but in the same instant felt a desire for a larger weapon, one that would level the town with a single shot. Did I wish for greater naked power or for a merciful coup de grace?

My conflicting emotions made the destruction incalculably exciting. What we were doing was forbidden by the normal rules of engagement and, on a loftier level of thought, prohibited by moral decency. Yet our fury had no apparent consequence. Our crew had been unleashed. Raw arrogance and aggression bred the devastation.

Aboard the gunship there was no conversation. We were engrossed in creating havoc. After finishing with the tallest building, we smashed in the facades of the smaller structures surrounding it. At one point I thought that none of it was really happening; it was simply an exciting and realistic television show of my creation, a satire of imagination run amok. I laughed inwardly because I was watching the action on two television monitors. Deep in my psyche the waste was repulsively gratifying.

After what seemed hours, Holcomb said, "While we still have some misch, take us to a suspected storage area, Dick."

Along the way we found two more trucks, which we set on fire. Then Schmidt located a passenger car abandoned alongside the road. He said, "That looks like somebody's Renault. Let's leave it."

"What," Jim Ballard said. Whether he spoke in agreement or disagreement was immaterial because I told Schmidt, "Fuck that noise. TV tracking, Ed." We struck the small vehicle until it rolled into a ditch and burned. "Clear those dinky toys off the road," I said.

"Sorry," said Schmidt. "For a minute I thought—"

I shouted down the length of the booth: "For a minute I thought you were the same IR who shot that poor son of a bitch off his motorcycle." My mouth spoke words meant only for my mind. Why had the event surfaced in my consciousness at that moment? Why had I thrown it up to Schmidt?

"Hey," Schmidt shouted back, "I said I'm sorry."

At the coordinates of the suspected storage site, we decided to hit the thickest stand of trees in the vicinity. The technique of shaking down the landscape with high-volume bursts of gunfire was popular with army troops, who called it "reconnaissance by fire." The technique probably evolved from the philosophy of "Kill them all and let God sort them out." As if God gave a shit!

Anyhow, we attacked the jungle with all our might. Ed destroyed trees. Nothing else happened. Schmidt redirected gunfire to the next thickest stand. It burned easily. The blaze rapidly grew in size and intensity, turned white-hot. Unexpectedly a secondary explosion ripped the jungle. Trees swayed as if trying to escape before being swallowed by the inferno. "A big one for the misch," Ed said. He orbited for ten minutes and Juan videotaped a chain of secondary explosions.

"Chalk up another jungle," Jim Ballard said softly to himself.

Hunchworth and Godolphin thought the tapes were outstanding, judged the test a total success. "All targets on the other side of the river?" the general asked but didn't wait for an answer. "From now on, Go, each crew gets fifty misch rounds on each sortie. When production and delivery pick up, raise the amount accordingly. The misch is to be used at the aircraft commander's discretion." Before he left, he told us, "Thanks, men. Good work, Ed." He took the tapes.

Chapter 15

A Little Help from my Friends

THE HALOED DEVIL and the machine-gun-wielding eagle on the emblems of the 433rd and 435th Tactical Fighter Squadrons were slow to befriend Spectre's shrouded skeleton. The F-4 Phantom jet jockeys in those squadrons believed they could do any job, any time, any place. Slowly they learned that they couldn't bust trucks like Spectre. Nobody busted trucks like Spec. By the end of February, Spectre was credited with slightly more than five thousand vehicles: four thousand destroyed, one thousand damaged.

During that month, the Eighth Tac Fighter Wing conceded that the gunships and their 40-mm cannons were perfectly suited for the role of truck killer. In a bid to share the glory, the 433rd and 435th were tasked to provide escorts for suppressing antiaircraft fire aimed at the gunships.

In the beginning the decision was unpopular. Fighter pilot egos were jolted by having to "baby-sit those turkeys." On the other hand, gunship crews felt capable of protecting themselves. Flyers in the three squadrons had willingly accepted an occasional mission together. But they thought that a plan for full-time protection sucked. However, the commanders decreed that the fighters would complement the gunships and complement the gunships they did, eventually.

Conflicts developed because Laos was pitch-black. AC-130s had the ability to see in the dark, but F-4s didn't. The

Phantoms were equipped for visual bombing, which required well-defined landmarks and aiming points to attain accuracy. In the darkness, the Phantoms depended upon Spectre for eyes to pinpoint gunsites. Spectre crews, however, had eyes primarily for trucks and claimed if they had to waste time directing F-4 traffic, they would be just as happy if the fighters stayed home. The attitude was a defense mechanism: Spectre crews lacked the training to direct fighters onto targets, a skill called forward air controlling (FACing).

It was a distinct art for one man to direct another to strike a target effectively, particularly when both men were airborne. FAC pilots attended a three-month course devoted entirely to learning the skill.

The way things were arranged between Spectre and the Phantom escorts, even if Spectre crews had possessed FAC training, the situation would have remained unmanageable for several reasons. First, Spectre was preoccupied with shooting trucks, which was its primary task. FACing was a single-minded pursuit. Second, the controller (a position foisted upon the gunship copilots so they would at last have something to do) saw practically nothing and guided the escorts with information provided by the sensor operators. That procedure was adopted because air force commanders believed that only pilots had the suavity and vocabulary to communicate with other pilots. As a result, the controller was a blind voice in the communication link. Third, but equally important, the Phantom pilots dive-bombed into darkness. They had no visual references, except when the moon was full. As an F-4 jock described it: "On a really dark night, you sort of *think* where the ground is, then hope you don't hit it before you release."

The FCO was able to record conversations between the gunship and its escorts and the videotape sound track evidenced the resentments, frustrations, and shortcomings inherent in the system. The escorts worked in pairs called a flight of two, and the aircraft were designated "Lead" and "Two." Proof hot from the tape:

SPECTRE COPILOT (bored and more or less making conversation): Eagle Lead, you located that gun again?

EAGLE LEAD (PILOT OF LEAD F-4): Negative. (He already made one pass at the AAA site in question. It is outside the gunship's orbit. Earlier, when the gun fired at Spectre, he focused on its location in the dark, mentally held that spot on the blackness below, then dive-bombed it with a pair of MK83s, one-thousand pounders. His action had temporarily silenced the gunners, but by now they have worked up another batch of courage and have resumed sniping at the gunship.) We'll get it as soon as it comes up again. (He doesn't want to admit that he had been out of position to make a pass when the gun most recently fired. In the tight pattern F-4s are required to fly in order to remain close to the gunship, it is normal to be out of position half the time. He isn't certain the Spectre crew understands his problem.)

SPECTRE COPILOT (after talking with the TV operator): Eagle Lead, you see the trucks we're shooting? (Thus far the gunship has merely damaged two vehicles. Nothing is burning.)

EAGLE LEAD: I see your sparkles. (Which means he can see the flashes from the gunship's rounds when they explode. To him, they are tiny, winking lights.)

SPECTRE TV OPERATOR: Fuck that! Does he see the trucks?

SPECTRE COPILOT: Affirmative, Eagle Lead, but do you see the trucks?

EAGLE LEAD: Negative. (There is an edge to his voice.) It'd help if you got a burner.

SPECTRE IR OPERATOR: Fuck him! We don't need that sarcastic shit.

TV: Ask him if he can see the road.

SPECTRE COPILOT: Eagle Lead, can you see the road?

EAGLE LEAD: Not too well, Spec.

TV: OK, forget that. The gun is—about—about—the gun is six hundred feet, make that two hundred meters, below, make that south, of the fork in the river, make that south-southwest.

SPECTRE COPILOT: TV, can you give me that again.

TV: Just ask him if he can see the river.

SPECTRE COPILOT: Eagle Lead, can you see the river?

EAGLE LEAD: Not too well.

IR: Ask him if he has his eyes open.

SPECTRE COPILOT: Eagle Lead, do you have your eyes open?

SPECTRE PILOT: Dammit, why did you say that?

SPECTRE COPILOT: Sorry. I was—

EAGLE LEAD (angrily): One-oh-eight, Spec.

(The gunship pilot resumes firing at the trucks. He is satisfied. The gunship crew made an effort to assist the escorts, and the square is filled. For the remainder of the tape, in the background, the TV operator and FCO discuss miss distances and assess damages.)

IR (impatiently): Co, ask Eagle if he can see the moon.

SPECTRE COPILOT: The moon isn't—

IR: Ask him, dammit! (Rank prevails: the IR is a major; the copilot, a lieutenant.)

SPECTRE COPILOT (somewhat confused): Eagle Lead, can you see the moon?

EAGLE LEAD (disgustedly): The moon's not up.

SPECTRE COPILOT: Affirmative.

IR: Can he see the ground?

SPECTRE COPILOT (obviously not relishing his role but attempting to remain neutral): Eagle Lead, IR requests to know if you can see the ground.

(There is no reply from Eagle Lead. He knows the gunship crew is attempting to make him sound like a fool.)

IR (threateningly): Ask him again.

SPECTRE COPILOT: Eagle Lead, can you see the ground? (Again there is no reply from the escort.) Repeat, can you see the ground, sir?

EAGLE LEAD: Affirmative.

IR (smugly satisfied): Tell him to hit the ground.

SPECTRE COPILOT: IR says to hit the ground.

SPECTRE PILOT: Dammit, what's wrong with you? Give me that radio; let me talk to him. (Smoothly sincere) Eagle Lead, I apologize for that. Let's try and start over . . .

* * *

The introduction of the misch metal round helped the situation. A gunship sparkled a gunpit and the fighters then bombed the spot where the shrapnel lay burning.

The most dramatic change in tactics took place when a few fighter pairs decided to solve the problem themselves and in so doing won the hearts and minds of the Spectre crews.

Captain Animal Jones developed the tactic of "trolling." To locate a gunsite Animal rolled in from twenty thousand feet and called for all the world to hear (it was commonly believed that the NVA monitored our radio frequencies): "Yo, Gomer. Here, Gomer. Come on, Gomer. HereGomer, hereGomer, hereGomer." (I pictured Animal grabbing and shaking his crotch at the night while he broadcasted his challenge. When I asked him if my image of him was correct, he told me, "Only until I realized that unconsciously I was doing just that." Then he grinned. "Aw, fuck, I *still* do it. It adds a lot to the maneuver.") "HereGomer. Gomer-Gomer-Gomer-Gomer-Gomer!" Once into his dive, Animal switched on every light the Phantom owned: wing lights, rotating beacons, strobes, even the bright white landing lights. From the gunship, it looked as if a Christmas tree was attacking Laos. Animal dived right down to the deck. His wingman trailed five thousand feet behind and remained blacked out. When a gun fired at Animal, the wingman bombed it. The tactic became effective to the point that Animal would fly around at five thousand feet lit up like the North Side of Chicago and nobody would dare fire at him. "Fuckingcowards, fuckingcowards, fuckingcowards," he chanted over fighter freq. The Spectre crews loved Animal. His act was an ultimate show of balls.

Captain Hopalong Toomey was another Spectre favorite. The first antiaircraft gun that fired at Spectre caught Toomey's full load. He salvoed everything on his initial pass and produced a fireworks display that lighted half of Laos. The second gun caught the wingman's load. Then with a mighty, "Ho hi, Spec, see you in a sec," Toomey and wingman Mach-2ed back to Ubon, regassed and rearmed, and returned in a flash. The ground crew knew the act and was waiting. Hopalong Toomey said, "That first time over is to let them know I'll be in the area most of the evening."

On a night when the moon was full, I saw an F-4 attack a 37-mm gunsite and prove the bodyguard's worth beyond a doubt. Juan videotaped the light show. Otherwise, my alien mind might have failed to record it. Aren't all men who have been to combat alien to the real world? Juan's pictures were prime-time quality.

The confrontation was a spontaneous duel that I watched unfold with the jaded curiosity of a demigod immune to death. Was my jaded curiosity the beginning of forgetfulness, a kind of sleep that served one to ignore terror, to forget nightmares?

We were working a road spur lined with a convoy that unwillingly had reached its final destination. We were making chaos from order when the 37-mm gun came to life. Circling at seventy-five hundred feet, we were on the fringe of the weapon's effective range.

I picked up the gun at its first burst, draped ghostly white crosshairs over the distant, tiny, donut-shaped site, and for a few moments considered hosing its black hole with 40-mm rain. The effort seemed a waste. The gunners were harassing rather than hurting, scattering meager bursts of four each time the gunship passed on their side of the orbit, doing little more than fulfilling their nightly quota of rounds expended. After a few orbits I forgot the gun.

Moments later escort Lead came up on interplane and said, "Spec, I'm going in on that site." Was this valor predicated upon boredom, jaded curiosity upon terror? The Phantom driver had a drawl that reminded me of John Wayne, a voice that mocked all the war heroes from all the war movies I had seen. I expected this false John to fail miserably, perhaps to bust his ass.

While we circled, John maneuvered down to our altitude and held somewhere off to the side until the next time the 37-mm fired. At that instant he called, "I'm in," and dived his jet along a shallow, suicidal glide path.

Because the moon was full the gunners saw him coming from the start. Conversely, moonglow helped John to lock on the gunpit visually. His shallow dive angle gave him ample time to pinpoint his aim. Black hole, black deed?

The gunners resolved John's final alignment problem by opening up at him with a stream of pound-and-a-half high-explosive rounds. After that, all he had to do was fly down a pulsing beam of flaming steel.

He did it.

With tracers flashing at a rate of two a second, he headed for the gun, moved against the strobing fire at his own pace, appeared to take his own sweet time. Making slight adjustments as he advanced, he otherwise flew an unswerving course. How could he not be hit?

I waited for him to be shot out of the air, to be turned into another fiery smear across the jungle, reduced to an ember of memory. But John pressed on. His wing tips cut narrow white parallel ribbons of contrails that hung in the clear night air like streamers of gallantry, were as brilliantly unfading as his courage.

John appeared to be below a thousand feet when he released a napalm cannister and zoomed over the gun. By then the gunners had long forgotten about simply filling squares. Their gun was stroking at full bore. They traversed it with such dexterity that the flow of tracers didn't slow as the Phantom streaked overhead.

From my seat, it appeared as if, for an instant, the flaming gun muzzle caressed the belly of the jet, as if the two pieces of weaponry momentarily linked in some ancient rite, like taking coup. Then the airplane separated, miraculously slipped away unharmed.

The gun crew was hammering steel into the wake of the juking, departing Phantom when the tumbling napalm cannister cleanly disappeared, end first, inside the ring of the gunpit. The rapid movement resembled speeded-up motion pictures. The huge cannister appeared to be sucked from the sky by tiny, puckered lips of earth.

Within the same heartbeat, prolonged and distorted by the unreality of the occurrence, nothing seemed to happen forever. My mind sped over the idea that the cannister was a dud—that victory was hollow—that the back of an alien mind was an empty universe. The 37-mm gun still blazed.

Then from the gunpit's earthen mouth a ball of fire shot skyward, like a meteor in reverse. Solar flares danced alongside the hole. Tracer rounds cooked off and pinwheeled into the gray night, producing glowworms of destruction. The gunpit expanded into a volcano of death.

Holcomb radioed words of admiration.

True to form, John dryly answered, "Roger that."

Valor to what avail?

Juan reported that he'd recorded the whole episode and Holcomb invited John to the videotape debriefing. All the crew's officers showed up to see the magnificent drop. When both John and his wingman arrived, dragging along their navigators, a new era in Spectre-Phantom relations began. Suddenly, everyone was on the same team. For a while thereafter, it was SOP for fighter jocks to "catch a few minutes of telly" whenever Spec produced "a really big show."

Around that time, after reviewing hours of other crews' tapes and suffering through unsatisfactory personal experiences, I developed a curiosity to see a demonstration of how a professional directed fighters to a target. I took a day off from the gunship and arranged to fly with a Nail FAC.

I was assigned to a young lieutenant named Cox, who was unduly formal during the mission briefing, which consisted of only the two of us. He went exactly by the book. In the middle of his briefing I raised my hand. It took him a second or two to recognize that I had a question: "Do you mean to tell me it's going to be you and me, *alone*, in broad daylight, over Laos?" I left my mouth hanging open.

He gave me his profile with jutting chin and said, "Most days, sir, I go out there by myself."

"Bet you wish this was another one of those days."

He didn't confirm or deny my words, but from then on he was comfortably loose.

I didn't pay much attention to where he intended to take me. One end of the jungle looked like the other. I was interested only in watching him at work. Self-criticism would be appropriate at this point. Chairman Mao wrote "If we have shortcomings, we are not afraid to have them pointed

165

out and criticized, because we serve the people." To be blunt, most of the time that I was airborne in gunships, I had no idea where we were other than "somewhere over Laos." I held a senior navigator rating, but fixing the gunship's position wasn't my responsibility. I was content to play with my sensor. I paid little attention when Dick announced our position or when I saw a familiar landmark on TV. Sensor operators were required to carry maps, but I seldom unfolded mine. I was along for the shooting. After five thousand hours of navigating, it was a nice change *not* to care where we were.

Nail FACs flew OV-10 Broncos, small twin-engine, prop-driven two-seaters designed to fly low and slow but with enough reserve horsepower to haul ass if the situation got hairy. Cox helped me strap into the rear seat and familiarized me with the ejection seat. I had spent a couple thousand hours in downward ejection seats, and most of the procedures were the same; only the direction of travel varied. Cox jumped in the front seat, revved up the engines, closed the canopy, and away we went. We zipped over to the Mekong at low level. It was a delight to be small and maneuverable, a swift instead of a turkey.

Cox stuck his nose in everywhere. He acted like a policeman walking a beat. Laos was his turf and he wanted to know everything that was going down. He reconnoitered by skimming low along roads and over villages. When we came into sight, the few vehicles we saw stopped. All were small trucks, rattletraps. Drivers and passengers stepped from them and stood by the side of the road. Cox flew tight circles above a couple of them. He waved. The people on the ground stared back. "They never wave," Cox said. "It makes you wonder."

He did a slow roll directly over one group and still got no reaction.

"Once in a while," Cox told me, "the NVA tries to sneak trucks down the trail in the daytime. Well, they're probably always doing that but, I mean, once in a while we catch them at it. I once got a truck with a smoke rocket. It hit sort of behind the cab and, I think, must have got the gas tank. The truck just burst into flames. Somehow the driver got out. I don't think he was hurt. But he sure was pissed. He stood in the road and shook his fist at me. I could see him shouting.

He looked pretty funny. I'd've given a hundred dollars to know what he was saying."

When we approached a village, I saw people. By the time we were overhead, the dirt streets were empty. I made out figures, outlines, shadows in the doorways and windows of huts. The inhabitants watched us closely. "They know we're not armed," Cox said. "Otherwise you wouldn't see them watching."

The people were thoroughly afraid, I thought and asked, "Does it always get this quiet when you show up?"

"Yes." Cox circled no more than fifty feet off the ground. He was peeking in windows, I thought. I suddenly decided the air force was hated beyond belief. I had never really thought about the subject prior to then. I had assumed that the enemy troops who bore the brunt of aerial attacks naturally hated airpower. Now I saw that innocent (if anyone could be considered innocent) civilians who perhaps had no interest in the war, other than to survive it, were also intimidated by airpower. Without warning, it disrupted their existence and threatened their lives. One misunderstood action could be the last: it was safer not to move, not to be seen.

"Don't you worry about taking small arms down this low?" I asked.

"Once in a while somebody takes a potshot. Usually it's when they're trying to hide something and they think I spotted it. Then they want to protect it. I'm usually not this low in that situation, or where that's likely to happen. I've been working this sector for almost five months. Right around here is pretty safe."

I decided the low-level maneuvers were for my benefit and smiled to myself. The poor son of a bitch seldom had an audience. I was getting a little bored. We found nothing on or off the roads that could be classified as hostile. Therefore, Cox climbed the Bronco to four thousand feet and, with four F-5s inbound to him, picked a predesignated target. "How come you asked for fighters when you don't have anything special to hit?" I asked.

"The fighters are running low on fuel and Hillsboro wants them cleaned off before they go home. It's safer to clean them off than to land them with ord hanging. Anyhow, nobody else has anything worthwhile either . . . Stand by!" The leader of the flight of four called and reported fuel and ordnance. With a grease pencil, Cox wrote the information on the inside of his Plexiglas canopy. ". . . and this," he said to me, "is what you came along for. Ready? Down we go."

Without my knowledge, Cox had flown directly over the predesignated target. He rolled the OV onto its back, pulled the nose through, and dived straight down. The airplane effortlessly turned on a dime, smoothly cut ninety-degree corners. It was a pleasantly responsive machine and Cox's finesse with the control stick made the flight one continuous, fluid sweep through the sky. The kid could fly. In a slow, vertical dive, seeming to hang nearly motionless, Cox lined up the nose and fired a rocket which came off rails beneath the wing with a faint *whoosh*. It left a smoke trail, then exploded in a puff of white along the bank of a stream. Like a marker grenade, the rocket belched smoke and served as a reference point.

By then, the F-5s were one minute away, and Cox gave them the whole story. "I have you inbound. I'm five miles, low, your eleven o'clock position. There is white smoke on the target, directly below me." He explained that the F-5s would be destroying a ford across the stream. He crisply and clearly told the fighters where he wanted them to hold, the order and direction of their attacks, and how to pull off. He left no question as to what he expected.

Once the bombs started dropping, Cox was like a mother hen with a brood of chicks. He flitted about as closely as possible to the target but always out of the bombers' paths. All the while he talked to them. He designated an exact spot for each bomb by referencing the smoke, tire tracks on both sides of the stream, or previous drops. He was encouraging, flattering, and, when one bomb missed by several hundred feet, sharply critical. There was no doubt that he was in control and wanted perfection. "Just because it's a shitty target is no reason to be sloppy," he told me. Cox was as professional and competent as any man I had ever watched at work, and he made it appear surprisingly easy.

The F-5 pilots were good too. They pointed the fighters

straight at the ground and, with flaps lowered and dive brakes extended, descended slowly, seemingly floating downward. They dropped one five-hundred-pound bomb at a time with an accuracy that made me say, "You could hire out to dig fence-post holes."

"Yes. They're accurate, all right." The four F-5s walked bombs at ten-foot intervals along both riverbanks. "That's called fucking up a ford," Cox explained. "This evening or tomorrow evening, Charley will come out and fill it in and then in a couple days we'll come back and fuck it up again."

"What do you do at night?" I asked.

"Go to bed, sleep."

"No . . . I mean about FACing."

"FACing at night?" Cox chewed on the idea for only a second or two. "No such animal," he said. "Better to go to bed and sleep."

"No wonder we have so much trouble in Spec." While we awaited more ordnance in the form of a flight of four F-4s that also needed cleaning off, I told about FACing from the gunship in the dark. Cox laughed appreciatively.

Cox put the F-4s in on suspected storage areas. The Phantoms attacked in a sixty-degree dive. They were just as accurate as the F-5s. Their performance was tree killing at its finest. I lost interest after the third or fourth pass. "You see that?" Cox asked me.

"What?"

"Was that a secondary?"

"Where?"

"Following that last explosion. Did you see it?"

"No," I said. "To be absolutely honest, I wasn't watching. I was thinking about being on the beach in Florida."

Cox said, "Oh . . . I didn't mean to screw up your day-dream, sir."

"No sweat."

"You have a lot of time for that in the gunship? Day-dreaming?"

The youngster was putting the needle in, I decided. "Only when it gets really, really boring."

Cox caught on. "Like now?"

Back on the ground, Cox apologized for a dull afternoon.

He had the last laugh, however. When I removed my boots, I found a sixteen-pennyweight nail inside each. The Nail FACs had surreptitiously delivered their calling cards without my suspecting a thing. And Briscoe had warned me!

The perfect solution to the problem of FACing in the dark was the laser-guided bomb (LGB). The two-thousand-pound LGB had an electro-optical sensor mounted in its nose. By commanding aileronlike movements of the bomb's fins, the sensor homed the weapon to the spot illuminated by a laser beam.

The gunship had a laser designator mounted on the bottom of the TV platform and aligned with the cameras. When the TV operator found a gunsite he wanted destroyed, he lased it while an F-4 delivered a bomb which guided onto it. Fifty percent of the LGBs impacted within eight feet of the aiming point. Most of the others hit within twenty-five feet, an acceptable miss distance when employing two-thousand pounders. The rare LGB that landed beyond that distance completely failed to guide and came to earth somewhere outside the viewing ranges of the TV and IR.

Because of their accuracy LGBs were called "smart" bombs, until an air force general decided that if there were smart bombs, then there also had to be dumb bombs. He said, "The press will extend that line of reasoning and eventually draw one conclusion: we also have smart pilots and stupid pilots to operate such weapons." Use of the terms "smart" and "dumb" was forbidden in reference to bombs. Among navigators the terms continued to be applied when classifying pilots.

A smart pilot once asked another smart pilot, "What's a gross error?" When the second pilot didn't know, the first told him, "A hundred and forty-four navigators." The second pilot laughed, said, "That's funny," and laughed some more. "That's sure funny, all right," he said, then asked, "But why a hundred and forty-four?" The first pilot didn't know.

Other than a rare guidance malfunction, the only problem with LGBs was that the electro-optical sensors were very expensive. Any bomb could be converted to an LGB by adding the sensor and a special fin assembly. However, the sensor was used only on the two-thousand-pound MK84, the largest high-explosive bomb available for fighter aircraft. Because of their expense, sensors were not available for all MK84s.

It was a treat to be assigned an escort armed with an LGB. When everything worked correctly, the gunship-escort-LGB performance was a beautiful medley. On videotape it was awesome:

The TV crosshairs are centered on a gunpit which is inside the gunship's orbit. The gun fires several rounds at the circling plane.

SPECTRE TV OPERATOR: I have that gun. Co, let's put an LGB on it.

SPECTRE COPILOT: Devil Lead, we'd like a Sword. (The package of laser designator and LGB is code-named Pave Sword.)

DEVIL LEAD: Affirm. Stand by one.

TV: Tell him it's inside our orbit, and he should be able to line up on the sparkles.

(The gunship pilot continues to attack the convoy with guidance from the IR. The gun being tracked by the TV fires again.)

SPECTRE COPILOT: Devil Lead, target is inside our geometry, near the sparkles. We're ready when you are.

TV: Affirm, TV tracking. (Because the gun position is in proximity to the convoy under attack, the TV and copilot can work the triple-A problem independently while the IR and pilot continue to shoot trucks. The antiaircraft gun fires another burst at the gunship.)

DEVIL LEAD: On the perch. (Which means he is in position and ready to make his bomb run. He flashes his rotating beacon for a second so that the gunship's copilot can locate him visually.)

SPECTRE COPILOT: I have you vis. We're passing under you—ready—ready—now!

(The Spectre pilot puts down a heavy stream of gunfire so that the escort pilot has the visual reference of the exploding rounds for his initial line-up.)

DEVIL LEAD: I have your sparkles. I'm in. (He starts a dive from twenty thousand feet.)

TV (unguards and activates the laser target designator power switch on his console): Laser on. (On the TV console, the lasing light on the laser control panel cycles from bright to dim red. On the ground, a spot of light invisible to the naked eye is projected over the point where the TV crosshairs are aimed.)

SPECTRE COPILOT: Devil Lead, you have music.

DEVIL LEAD: Roger that. My Sword's locked. (The fighter's initial line-up must be within eighteen thousand feet of the aiming point, a parameter known as the "basket," in order to obtain laser acquisition by the LGB's electro-optical sensor. Before the bomb is released, the LGB's sensor feeds information to a computer which guides the pilot toward the target. From twenty down to ten thousand feet the pilot refines the line-up. At ten thousand feet he releases the LGB, then climbs upward.) Bombs away!

(Aboard the gunship, on both TV and IR, a moment before impact the bomb can be seen flashing downward. It is a blur. The two-thousand pounder produces an explosion that fills the narrow-angle TV picture with rolling smoke. The act is conclusive.)

Employing a laser bomb gave a TV operator a feeling very close to being a true god: he pointed a finger and had a bolt of death strike the enemy.

A jock from the 435th put the event into words to accompany the music from "Streets of Laredo":

> As I was escorting my Spectre one evening
> And we were in orbit round Delta One-One,
> Some non-Christian Gomers who didn't speak English
> Were shooting at us with a Communist gun.
>
> The Spectre TV was locked on their location.
> I started my bomb pass from twenty-one grand.
> My Sword heard the music; I dropped in the basket;
> Those slope-headed bastards lie dead in the sand.

Chapter 16

Midnight Rambler

MARCH 1971 WAS a super month, until the second. On the first, the lieutenant colonel promotion list was released and my name was on it, effective immediately. Billy Killeen also was on the list but with an effective date a few months in the future. Our crew had the first off and, at my expense, we celebrated my success, beginning at the Spectre Hootch and ending downtown. Stan Briscoe and Rusty Brown drank as much as everyone else combined, not counting Lee Schmidt, who was the only obvious drunk. It was good therapy for him. He let it all hang out: *"Colonel* Zorn! Oh, shit! I don't believe it. If *you* made lieutenant colonel, there's hope for every one of us." He kept up the friendly abuse most of the evening but never became obnoxious. Some hour after midnight, we left him on the ninth floor of the Ubon Hotel with a fresh bottle of Johnny Walker Red and two tired but smiling Thai ladies. Lee and the women were covered with roses. As a parting gesture I bought the flower vendor's entire stock and decorated the three of them. Ed didn't accompany us downtown. And somewhere along the way, Dick detoured to his bungalow. The rest of us finished the night squeaky clean.

The way events developed on March second, I nearly set an air force record for the shortest period of holding the rank of lieutenant colonel. Our crew had the earliest takeoff, which meant we got to Steel Tiger the same time it turned dark. Up until then it was a fun-filled night.

Lee Schmidt arrived late for the preflight briefing. He had missed supper with the crew, which indicated he had also missed lunch and breakfast. He definitely missed another trick we pulled on Ed, who ordered a filet for supper.

The Thai chefs performed a feat of heavy construction when they put together a filet. They used as many as five or six toothpicks to hold the enormous "buffalo burgers" together. For days we had waited for Ed to order a filet. That afternoon, when he finally did, Jim Ballard, who was least suspect, excused himself to the rest room and slipped into the kitchen. After the usual bribe to the chef, Jim worked another forty or fifty toothpicks into Ed's filet. When Ed cut into the meat, he hit solid wood. Between nibbles he pulled toothpicks until he had a small pyre by his plate. He never mentioned them. The rest of us were in tears from snickering and pretending not to notice. Even Tex Tyler was grinning. After Ed finished the last bite, he raised his head, looked around the table, worked his tongue against a tooth, then said, "Excuse me, does anyone happen to have a spare toothpick?"

Anyhow . . . back to pale-faced Lee, who crept into the briefing room. "Thank you very much for taking time out from your busy schedule to join us, Captain Schmidt," I said. Lee smiled weakly and slumped into a chair.

"The only new item in the reading file," Ed Holcomb said with a set expression, "is a reminder for the IRs. In the future, when operating in an alcohol-threat area, do not let your mouth accept a check that your butt can't cash." He looked up from the briefing book. "Colonel Zorn, please confirm that Captain Schmidt has an audible heartbeat and then make certain he understands that." There was a short round of chatter and laughter in which Lee didn't join.

The navigator's briefing was short. "Steel Tiger, as if you couldn't guess. Everything's the same as always." Dick Kaulbach paused, then asked, "Lee, will you be going with us in the airplane or flying out by yourself?" After another

round of chatter and laughter, Dick asked, "Any questions?"
There was no response, and he made the mistake of voicing
an afterthought. "Sensors, have your maps?"

"No," said Juan Sueno.

I nodded vigorously and said, "Negative."

"Maps?" Jim Ballard said.

Dick asked, "Anyone want a time hack?" Again there was
no response. He said, "OK. In twenty-three seconds, it'll be
fifteen seconds until forty-two minutes before the hour.
Hack! five seconds ago." He hurriedly sat down.

"Hey, I missed that," Juan said.

"Me too," I said. I didn't wear a watch, another bonus for
not having to fix the airplane's position. Anyhow, there was a
clock on the TV console.

"Where was Mickey's little hand?" Juan asked.

"Do it again, please," Jim Ballard said.

Dick ignored us and told Ed, "That's all I have."

"Today's emergency procedure," Ed said. "Forty-
millimeter failure to fire." He studied the gunners who had
been assigned to him for that day. No one made eye contact
with him. "Airman Butkovic?" Ed said.

Looking as if he had been asked to define integral calculus
in fifty words or less, Airman Whitey Butkovic slowly stood,
then said loudly, "Advise pilot. Attempt to fire round
manually, one time. If weapon again fails to fire, move
arm/safe switch to safe; move firing selector lever to stop fire;
remove ammo from loader. Then open breechblock, manually remove round, and heave that worthless fucker off the
ramp, *sir!*"

"Taking great care," Master Sergeant Otis Birdwhistle
added, "to avoid hitting me in the ass, *Airman!*"

Ed nodded approval. The briefing broke up, and we drifted
off to collect our personal equipment.

I spun the combination lock right-left-right and popped it
open with a speed that always brought a smile from Juan
Sueno, who had the locker next to mine. I had owned the lock
since junior high school and undid it partially by feel, a
necessity because many of the numbers were worn away.

I quickly blocked my new black baseball cap with the silver clouds and silver lightning embroidered on the bill. The "farts and darts" were reserved for lieutenant colonels and above. I was proud to have earned the right to wear them. The crew had presented me with the hat the day before and I appreciated that it had taken a pile of baht or some heavy influence to have it made on such short notice, like half a day. The cap was fronted with a silver oak leaf; on the back was a miniature of the Spectre emblem above "Zorn." I carefully placed the hat on the locker's shelf.

Gunners had the custom of freezing any hat left unattended when its owner went off to fly. Lieutenant Colonel Goforth recently had fallen victim to the prank three times in one month, a squadron record. The first time, the gunners merely sprayed the hat and placed it in the freezer of the squadron refrigerator. The hat was neatly blocked, although icy, when Goforth found it and donned it with good humor. "Cool," he had said, "not a bad idea." The second time, the gunners soaked the hat and flattened it like a pancake before freezing it. Goforth's humor was strained to the point that he loudly made vague threats. The third time, urged on by Juan and me because we couldn't believe one man was stupid enough to fall for the same trick three times (and, as much as I hated to admit it, the son of a bitch was a navigator), the gunners tightly wadded the hat and froze it into an iceball. "Gofart" trashed the hat in rage. Weeks later, Juan and I saw the hat on a Thai flight line laborer. It looked good as new.

Nobody wore a hat out to the airplane, except Rory's Razorbacks and that fuckin' Aguilar, who had an oversized, floppy sombrero. That crazy son of a bitch even carried a fresh rose clenched in his teeth. And he could shoot too!

I suddenly regretted not having spent more time with other crews in the squadron. There were some good guys among them. I hadn't made an effort to approach and become close friends with them, and I had been closed to their advances. My allegiance was to Holcomb's crew. We were clannish, snobbish, and, I guess, often acted as if we were the only ones doing the job. At heart, I felt we were the best. That was enough for me. All I needed was a nice little war (preferably against non-Europeans) fought side by side with a few good friends. It wasn't too much to expect considering the number of Third World troublemakers.

I counted the bills on my money clip, $227, then slid the wad under my hat. The only other thing in the clip was my air force ID card: no need for credit cards or driver's license in SEA. From the locker I took my Geneva Conventions identification card and dropped it into a breast pocket, then jammed E-and-E maps with a blood chit into the left-leg pocket of my flying suit. The Geneva Conventions card was a crewman's only identification: name, rank, serial number, branch of service, date of birth. My card said I was a major. If we were shot down and captured, I wondered if I could convince the NVA troops that I was really an LC in order to get a better room at the Hanoi Hilton. The escape-and-evasion maps were *National Geographic* quality on silk, detailed down to the puddles. I opened the package and admired them once but then decided that, because I seldom knew where we were, their value was limited. If we were shot down in Laos, my E-and-E plan was to head west until I ran into a massage parlor, or a handball court. A blood chit was a white silk cloth printed with a large American flag on the top half; below, in every language of the region, was a message that the bearer was an American fighting man and great rewards would be given to whomever helped him. At the bottom was a control number. The blood chit alone was worthless; the control number was the key. Supposedly, it was told to whomever provided aid along the way and that person later contacted the proper authorities and filed a claim. I could hardly wait to explain that bureaucratic procedure to some little brown fuck in a loincloth and with a bone through his nose. As an experiment, Rabbit Ripple showed his blood chit and gave its number to one of the girls at a bathhouse. The crap really hit when she showed up on base and staked her claim.

I lifted my dog tag off a hook in my locker and draped the chain around my neck. I wore only one tag for the same reason Willie and Joe threw away the jokers from their deck of playing cards in World War II: travel light.

By feel, I made certain the seven pockets on my unadorned green flying suit were zipped shut. No reason, just habit. All but two were empty. *Losing weight,* I thought when I put on my survival vest and it felt loose. I decided it fit well enough. It was too much trouble to redo the laces that ran full length down both sides. I promised myself to stoke in a few extra calories when we got back. Looking down the aisle, I saw Dick Kaulbach in profile and noticed that he was putting on the pounds, becoming a living Buddha. Semimarried life was ruining him.

I draped my headset around my neck; lifted my helmet bag, which contained flak helmet, checklists, flying jacket, and gloves out of the locker; then, in what was one movement, slammed the locker door and snapped the lock in place. Vaguely thinking about marriage, I said to Juan, who was closing his locker next to me, "How's your wife?"

Juan's face went blank. "Better than yours," he said. We exchanged smiles and together moved to the personal equipment controlled-items cage. Picking up two radios, I asked the PE duty airman, "Test 'em?" He said, "Of course, sir," and I worked the radios into pockets on the front of my survival vest. Next I loaded and holstered my revolver. For several weeks, Colonel Godolphin had expected his crewmen to carry unloaded guns. "You can load them if you need them once you're on the ground, after you've bailed out," he explained. "I don't want anyone to be shot by accident before then." He rescinded his order when he recognized that nobody was obeying it. First, he gave permission to load the handguns on the other side of the Mekong; then he backed down the rest of the way. I passed up the opportunity to test the microphones on my headset and flak helmet. Like many other flyers, I believed that more equipment was worn out by testing than by actual use. We operated on one principle: "If it was working when I took it off, it should work when I put it back on."

The crew piled into the big blue bus and, after Ed counted heads, the bus took us to the airplane, which had a minor maintenance problem. "No use getting in everyone's way while they're working. We have plenty of time," Ed told us, then turned to Stan Briscoe: "When it's ready, let us know. But, Stan, if you see they're not going to get it fixed, tell me right away. Maybe we can pull a switch, or find a spare, or something." He winked and Briscoe raised a thumb. Ed and Stan should have sold used cars, or real estate, or, better yet, insurance: a pair of fuckin' schemers.

Most of us stretched out on the hard surface of the revetment, beneath the aircraft's tail. A few moved off the paved area in order to smoke. A little more ramp time! "I remember," I said, "Rabbit once said the day would come when we wouldn't be allowed to say 'Eat it' in the dining room. I think that day's here. A couple nights ago I was watching a USO troupe at the club—Ramon and the Ginger Sisters—anyone see them?"

Juan said, "I caught the late show. Nobody was there."

"I saw the early show and it was packed," I said.

"They only did fifteen minutes," Juan said. "They were bad."

"They were fuckin' horrible," I said. "They couldn't sing, they couldn't dance, and the girls were ugly as shit. Zit faces. Even their costumes sucked."

"What didn't you like about them?" said Dick.

"I was standing in back," I said, "and after about five minutes, I booed once. Half the audience turned and gave me dirty looks. I don't think there was a Spec in the crowd. After a few more minutes—it was so bad I can't describe it—I hollered, 'Show us your tits.' Three guys came over and told me I was out of line and I should be quiet or leave. And all three were wearing . . ."—I flicked the front of my flying suit—". . . green bags. Can you fuckin' believe that?"

"Yes," Lee Schmidt said quietly.

"It can talk!" Dick said. "Welcome back to the Land of the Living, Lee."

"Wait a minute," I said and explained that "Show us your tits" was historically valid as a critical comment. "When I was in Nam, most USO shows were one or two songs, a dance, then skin. If a woman couldn't sing or dance, the cheer went up: 'Show us your tits.' It saved everybody a lot of grief."

Lee broke into laughter. "You don't have to convince me. That's the way it was here too. I'll never forget the time a *guy* came out, solo, a USO comedian, a first. Fat, middle-aged guy. He told two or three jokes that were total bombs. People just looked at each other; they didn't even groan. Somebody down front yelled, 'Show us your tits.' The guy said, 'Stop it. Give me a chance.' He got through another two or three jokes and they were worse than the first batch. More troops down front hollered, 'Show us your tits.' Right there, on stage, the guy broke down and cried."

"That's cruel," Jim Ballard said. "Poor guy. I hope that stopped the shouting."

"Are you kidding?" said Lee. *"Everybody* joined in, like it was a football cheer: 'Show-us-your-tits, show-us-your-tits . . .' The guy walked off in tears. He never came back."

Briscoe appeared and, wearing a big smile, he called to Ed, "Airplane's ready, sir."

"Thanks, Stan," Ed replied. "OK, men, let's saddle up and go show 'em our tits."

Juan looked at me and said, "I don't think Ed understood the story."

Still well before sunset, Ed dropped into the pilot's seat of the Spectre gunship: "Good morning, world. The start of another day." Stan Briscoe frowned. Tex Tyler yawned and set off a round of yawning that included me. Lee had cut a fart as he entered the booth ahead of me and I detoured to the flight deck. Ed stretched and said, "That yawn made me tired. We have external power? GTC clear?" From in front of the airplane, a ground crewman wearing a headset looked up toward the cockpit, nodded repeatedly, and raised both thumbs.

"What difference does it make?" Briscoe said. "They'll get out of the way when they hear it turn over. Starting GTC—set, start, run." The gas turbine compressor roared to life. "Bleed air valve switch—open, got pressure. ATM and generator—as required. Inverters—set, AC, DC."

"Bisexual instruments," Tex Tyler said. Nobody smiled with him. "Hydraulics—on, on, on—love that suction boost pump. Have to buy one of those for my girlfriend next Christmas."

"Buy one for yourself and you won't need a girlfriend," Briscoe said. "Ground idle button—normal." The copilot and flight engineer read from and followed on individual copies of the same checklist.

"Ready to crank," Ed said. He adjusted the radios: "Ubon Ground, Spectre four-niner-zero, requesting permission to start engines."

"Spec four-nine-oh, 'firmative, suh," a lazy-voiced controller replied.

"That's probably a recording," Briscoe said.

"Number three clear?" Ed asked, then answered his own question: "I know. What difference does it make?" Nevertheless, he looked outside for approval from the ground crewman. "Turning number three!" He moved the engine condition lever to the run position and depressed the engine starter button. The light in the starter button glowed and the right inboard propeller turned over. The three men scanned the instruments while the engine smoothly accelerated to ground-idle RPM.

Briscoe said, "Hydraulic pressure up, checked. Generator —checked. DC power—battery."

"Clear number four?" Ed asked and, in unison, the three men said, "What difference does it make?" Ed looked at the ground crewman, hit the button, and the right outboard engine turned over.

Briscoe said, "Generators—on. Remove external power." Two ground crewmen unplugged the power cart, disconnected the grounding wires, and removed the wheel chocks before backing away from the gunship, snapping to attention, and popping salutes toward the cockpit. Ed saluted in return. Briscoe said, "ATM and generator—checked, on." They were preparing to start the left inboard and outboard engines when I decided the booth was clear and went back to settle down for takeoff.

In the booth, Lee was moving in a fog. He said, "I couldn't feel worse," and cut a rumbling fart.

"Goddamn you, Schmidt," I shouted. I guessed the son of

a bitch had been saving it for my return. "That is one thing that is absolutely forbidden in the booth. You ill-mannered fuck!"

Lee let out a squealer and said, "Excuse me. Didn't quite finish the first time."

"Shit," I said.

"I hope not," Lee replied. "But at this point, it wouldn't matter. My head is killing me."

"And your ass is killing us," I said.

"Schmidt the Shit," said Juan. "That's your new name, you keep that up."

Jim Ballard fanned the air and laughed. "You know what I always say: 'If you can't laugh about it, you just can't laugh about it.'"

I finished my preflight checklist the same time the aircraft taxied away from its parking spot. I told Juan, "See you later," and walked to the ramp, where, next to Otis Birdwhistle, I strapped into one of the makeshift seats that faced aft, out the open cargo door. Three gunners also rode there for takeoff. Other than the NOD station, the ramp was my favorite spot on the gunship. On hot evenings, the backwash from the propellers produced a breeze that blew alternately warm and cool as the airplane changed directions during taxi. The breeze dried my flying suit, which by then was soaked with sweat from being in the booth without the air conditioner cranking. The breeze made me feel cleansed in body and renewed in spirit. I likened the sensation to baptism until I recognized that I had not one memory from that ceremony.

I craned my head backward, pointed my toes, and stretched my legs. That afternoon I had won three out of three from the only person on base capable of giving me a decent handball game. I squeezed the muscles in my thighs in order to feel my strength. This was what it was all about. This was freedom. Only the next four or five hours mattered. Nothing from yesterday had value. There was no tomorrow. Everything was now. I felt my freedom strongly. I had nothing—no house, no fucking mortgage, no car, no snotty noses, no bitching wife; therefore, I had everything. Before I left the States, I shitcanned my belongings: books, notes, letters, greeting cards, photographs, military and civilian records, the personal accumulation of twenty years, maybe more. I even gave away a couple rooms of furniture (that was easiest), most of it to a girlfriend: living room stuff made of butter-soft leather, heavy chrome, thick Belgium glass; king-size bed; stereo; color TV; the works, really good stuff, about a year old. I didn't care. I had walked away from that clutter three times now, twice by decree and the last by choice. The last time gave me a nice feeling. Someday I'd start over. I knew I could do it. But right now, I was free.

I believed that Lee and Briscoe, maybe Dick and Otis, and probably Billy Killeen felt pretty close to the same way. Free!

Leaning forward, I studied the rows of airplanes facing the taxiway. They were surrounded by activity. Ground crews raced here and there while readying their planes for flight. Aircraft were starting engines, taxiing, taking off, landing. Waves of heated air randomly gave a mirage effect to the reality of preparing for war. Phantoms heavy with bombs dominated the scene. Their hot jet exhausts scrambled the horizon into a wavering confusion of colors. At the start of their takeoff rolls, the thunder from their afterburners thrilled me. The fighter pairs accelerated down the runway, lifted off together, and, while the two fiery, reddish-blue glows of each airplane's tailpipes distortedly appeared to undulate wildly, the airplanes smoothly streaked skyward. Those fighters were reduced to brightly glowing dots when, on the hammerhead of the runway, the next two fighters boomingly cut into afterburner and drew attention to themselves. Air power! Their strength was the strength of thousands.

I felt the same anticipation that I always felt before takeoff: We were headed to battle, we were going to go out and *do it*, one more time!

Ed turned the gunship onto the runway. It was our turn. My skin contracted. I clenched my fists. Ed advanced the throttles to maximum power: the four engines roared. As the gunship started its roll, I broke out in goosebumps. I growled softly as the runway lengthened behind us. Otis Birdwhistle nudged me with a shoulder. We picked up speed, faster and faster. Then the gunship gently lifted off and nosed upward, away from the base and city. The freedom of being airborne . . . I loved it. It was an overpowering ecstacy. "Every time,"

GUNSHIP

I shouted at Otis. The air grew cooler, purer. "Every time is as good as the first time."

"A-firmative," Otis said.

We grinned at each other. We already were over jungle. Civilization was behind us. There was no place else on earth that we would rather have been.

Chapter 17

Run for Your Life

THAT NIGHT WE slaughtered them. We were the first gunship on target and trucks were everywhere. In less than three hours we destroyed twenty-one and damaged fifteen. In the booth we felt as if we had free passes to a shooting gallery. With an hour of on-target fuel and a couple hundred 40-mm rounds remaining, we broke into laughter when Jim Ballard found sixteen more trucks. It appeared certain that we were going to run up our highest score of the season.

Ed Holcomb blew the leader and we were circling the last truck in line when Our Lady of Loreto or Saint Thérèse of Lisieux or Saint Joseph of Cupertino or whichever bony relic supposedly protected the living flesh of flyers snoozed off at the switch.

Ed had fired one round, *ka-pung,* as if clearing his throat. In that pause before the lethal burst of three, Jim said, "I have a SAM activity light."

The burst never came. Ed asked, "You kidding me?"

SAM was death.

"Are you kidding me?" Jim shouted. "Damn. I have a SAM activity light!" The scope display on his radar homing and warning unit indicated that our slow-moving, four-engine gunship was being tracked by a missile launch site. "Turn to a heading of two-seven-zero," Jim said and locked unblinking eyes on the RHAW gear.

Ed turned to the heading, which put the launch site behind us, then rammed the airspeed up to 180 knots, and said, "Are you pos—"

"I have a SAM ready-to-launch light," Jim announced. "No shit."

Aboard the gunship, everyone froze for a moment.

The surface-to-air missile employed in Southeast Asia was the Soviet-built SA2 (NATO code-named Guideline), which, once it got humming, reached twice the speed of sound. The missile was guided by ground radar (NATO code-named Fan Song). The SA2's three-hundred-pound high-explosive warhead detonated upon impact or upon command of the Fan Song operator.

The SA2 had been designed for use against high-performance aircraft, fast movers. A lot of speedy F-4s and F-105s had outmaneuvered SAMs, however. But a lot of them also had watched the goddamn SAMs eat their lunch. Our turkey was no match for missiles. Our predicament was the same as drifting along in an old South Sea steamer and suddenly being attacked by a torpedo-firing nuclear submarine.

Everyone knew that North Vietnam was wall to wall with SAM launch sites. However, to that date—2 March 1971—no SA2s had been reported in Laos. United States Air Force Intelligence publications declared that the Guideline had "poor cross-country ability and would not be expected to be deployed in forward areas." Based upon past experiences with Intell we should have expected the SAM sooner.

In order to hear everything that was happening, I pulled out all the control buttons on my intercomm box. At once I heard the high-pitched rattle, nearly a whine, of the ground radar that was homed on us.

During training I frequently had heard tape recordings of ground-radar activity. First came the short, midrange squeaks, several seconds apart, of the normal three-hundred-sixty-degree radar searching sweeps; each time the radar beam passed over the airplane, the RHAW gear picked up and converted its energy to light signals for the BC and to sounds for the other crewmen. When radar was made to track the airplane, its sweep was narrowed to a few degrees and it painted back and forth across the target; in the airplane, the RHAW-gear squeaks became higher pitched and more frequent, occurring every second. When the ground radar scan was narrowed to approximately one degree for aiming the missile, the RHAW gear picked up a high-pitched rattle. The instructors had likened the sound to a rattlesnake's warning immediately before it struck.

"I have a SAM launch light," Jim said loudly and clearly. The signal indicated that a missile had been fired at the gunship.

"Ohhhhh," somebody moaned over interphone.

Stretched on the ramp, Master Sergeant Otis Birdwhistle searched in the blackness of the night. A moment after the "SAM launch" call, he reported, "I saw a flash, six o'clock. Six to eight, maybe ten miles." Held by his thin safety line, Birdwhistle leaned out of the gunship until he hung partially afloat in the aircraft's slipstream. "I saw another flash," he shouted over interphone. "Think it was separation." The SA2 was two stage, liquid propellent with solid fuel booster. Suddenly Otis clearly recognized the missile engine's fire. "I see it," he shouted. "It's climbing." He watched the flame for several seconds. "Turn right, sir," he said. Ed banked hard right and a moment later the missile turned after him. "It turned with us," Otis said. "Left, break left, sir." Ed rolled hard to the left and again the missile turned with him. The Fan Song operator definitely had his radar locked on us. "It's leveling off, headed this way. You better dive."

"Hang on," Ed said. "We're going down."

There have been great moments in sports when the man transcended the moment by calling his shot. Remember? The Babe pointing to the stands before belting a homer to the exact spot! Broadway Joe predicting Super Bowl victory and then producing it! Those feats birthed immortality. But no such feat ever related to cheating death, calling the shot with premeditated certainty. And that was what Ed Holcomb was about to try. He was going to snatch thirteen souls from the gates of hell exactly as he once had told us he would.

From an altitude of ninety-five hundred feet, he rolled the gunship into a 135-degree bank, practically upside-down, then arced the nose earthward in a four-thousand-feet-per-minute dive. The maneuver was like turning over a dump truck and then expecting to steer it. Our turkey wasn't designed for such a feat. Yet Ed did it. Maintaining a positive one-gravity load on the creaky, antiquated airframe, he plunged downward in open defiance of several laws of aerodynamics.

Tapping the attitude indicator, I looked at Juan and grinned. The technoviolent microscope had been reversed: we now were under the glass.

Over interphone the soothing voice of Dick Kaulbach informed: "Maximum terrain elevation is thirty-one hundred feet." A literary bitch once wrote "A rose is a rose is a rose." Had she described Kaulbach, she would have said "Cool is cool is cool." Acting as if he *knew* there was a tomorrow, he calmly read the altitudes as we vertically flashed through them: "Eighty-five hundred feet . . . eight thousand feet . . . seventy-five hundred . . ."

"It's coming straight at us," Otis said. He later stated that he had read accounts by fighter pilots who described Guidelines as "the size of telephone poles." Nose to nose with one of the big white bastards, he agreed: The missile was huge. "It's coming straight at us. Dive. Dive!"

The gunship was at its maximum rate of descent. Ed Holcomb silently watched the altimeter unwind.

Pulled back into the right rear corner of the booth, I looked across the narrow center aisle and saw Juan Sueno throw up his hands in resignation. "Don't give up yet, Johnny," I shouted. I didn't know what he thought, but I put no faith in my words. I found it difficult to believe that we were doing what we were doing. I tapped the attitude indicator again. The airplane did not have ejection seats. There was nothing to do but wait.

Ed's maneuver was termed a "split-S." He had explained its use one morning over breakfast when we were playing "What if . . ." Thinking the unthinkable, I'd asked, "What if they launch an SA2 at us?" Without hesitating Ed had said, "I'll dive and turn into it. The maneuver works for fighters. No reason it can't work for us." He had been irritated when we laughed at his answer. "I can do anything with a one-thirty that you can do with a jet," he had claimed, "only I do it

lower and slower. And tighter. I can escape from a SAM."
He had called his shot. And now he was doing it—maybe.

Momentarily fixated on my unwinding altimeter, I wondered how many men had sat in exactly the same manner,
expecting to be hit by a missile—ground-to-air or air-to-air—
and unable to do anything except wait it out. I decided that a
lot of guys had died that way. Right before it happened, they
probably had thought exactly what I was thinking: This could
be the end . . . Seconds passed like minutes. It seemed as if
Jim had made his warning calls hours earlier. I looked at Juan
and grinned, but my gut felt hollow. The altimeter unwound
in slow motion, but its numbers weren't registering in my
mind.

"Dive, please, dive," rear scanner Birdwhistle suddenly
begged. Because the smoothly coordinated split-S maintained
a normal one-gravity load on the airframe and because he was
prone on the ramp, Otis Birdwhistle's inner ear lied to him.
Furthermore, because of the blackness of night, Otis lacked a
horizon for visual reference (actually, he had eyes for only the
missile). As a result, Otis felt almost no sensation of diving.
"Dive, Major Holcomb. It's coming . . ." His voice went up
an octave. "It's coming right in the ramp." Then Otis
commanded, "Break hard left."

Ed snapped the huge airplane to the left and willed it to
hold together. Beyond tolerable airspeed, beyond all aircraft
limits, he had flown into an aerodynamic world of his own
creation.

There was a long silence.

Involuntarily I hunched my shoulders, contracted my neck,
lowered my head. After long moments I became aware of my
reactions and looked up. The three others in the booth had
struck similar expectant poses. They were motionless. I
realized I was holding my breath and wondered about the
others. I expected death but, at the same time, wasn't afraid
and felt death wouldn't arrive. I didn't hope or pray.

Ed broke the silence. "Otis? You see it?"

"No, sir," Otis said softly. "I think it went over top of us."

Somewhere that big, deadly son of a bitch was still chug-
ging along in the dark, I thought.

Easing the rate of descent, Holcomb gently pulled the

gunship's nose above the horizon and started a climb back to ninety-five hundred feet. He had outflown the most fearsome threat: the sparrow had escaped the hawk. "Missed," Ed said convincingly. "Nice work, Sergeant Birdwhistle. Very nice work. And you too, Major Ballard. You too. Great work." He spoke to Dick without calling him by name: "Think you can find that last convoy again?" Dick instantly gave him a heading. Ed said, "What do you think, gang—want to finish off those trucks?" It was a rhetorical question.

Juan said to me, "We shouldn't be working around out here any more tonight."

I shrugged. Never pass up a piece . . .

"That had to be an SA2," Jim said.

"Affirmative, sir," said Otis. "It looked just like the pictures."

"How long did that take?" Dick asked.

I said, "About forty-five minutes."

Lee corrected me. "More like forty-five seconds."

"Seemed like an hour and a half to me," I shouted to Juan, and I meant it.

Juan waved a hand irritably. "How come you were grinning like that? You think it was funny?"

"No," I said, "except for when we all hunched over . . ."

"What?" Juan said.

"We should be coming up on that intersection," Dick said. "You see it, sensors?"

"IR has it."

"TV has the trucks. TV tracking."

"Put in TV," Ed said. He rolled into a thirty-degree left bank, intercepted the firing orbit, opened fire with a 40-mm cannon. Rounds impacted near the last truck in line.

I said, "You hit—"

"Good God," Jim shouted. "I have another SAM activity light. Turn to three-zero-zero."

I looked at Juan and tried not to grin, but I couldn't control my face. "Here we go again," I said. Juan said something I didn't hear and tightened the leg straps on his parachute.

The next part of the mission was impossible to comprehend —even today, even if I lived to be a hundred, I wouldn't understand it. What made us go back? Gallantry? Arrogance? Ignorance?

Holcomb turned to Ballard's new escape heading and Ballard went through the same sequence of events as during the first attack: "Ready-to-launch light," then, "Launch light."

Birdwhistle reported, "I have *two* flashes, eight, maybe ten miles." His voice was in the upper registers. From that point, however, he narrated the flight of the two Guideline missiles in a dull monotone and I wondered if he was in shock or if practice made perfect. Ed executed the same evasive maneuver.

"You believe this shit," I shouted.

Sueno answered, "I don't like any of it." He had bags under his eyes that would have qualified as two-suiters.

Although events followed the same pattern, the actions took place more rapidly, yet very slowly to my eyes. It was like sitting through a movie that I'd seen before. Somehow a feeling of reality was missing. I didn't feel as if we actually were doing it again. My mind tried to tell me that I was seeing a replay of the first time, or that what now was happening was a continuation of the first time. I suppose I couldn't believe that we had encountered—had stupidly walked into—the identical trap twice within such a short period. More than anything, I just wanted it to be ended. The outcome didn't matter. Yet I knew the outcome. I'd seen the movie before. My mind and central nervous system were short-circuited.

Both SA2s missed—of course. Tex Tyler saw them detonate in the distance, beyond us, out of range. Ed headed homeward to Ubon at low level.

Dick couldn't resist the chance: "Ed, what about those trucks?" It was another rhetorical question.

The booth became a crowded madhouse. The gunners dragged in Birdwhistle, beat on him and shouted with joy. Several times he said, "Those last two weren't guided very well, I don't think."

One gunner gave a Rebel yell over and over until Sueno threatened to chase him from the booth. Juan kept saying, "The odds against doing what we did, against doing what we did *twice* . . ."

We had been so fucking lucky that it was unbelievable, I thought, but luckier yet to have had Ed Holcomb at the wheel.

At Ubon we learned that, simultaneously with the first missile attack on our plane, Rabbit Ripple met a SAM head-on. Rabbit's Phantom escorts saw the hit. They assumed that the gunship's electronic equipment failed to detect the lock and launch. There were no survivors to question. The escorts reported that the gunship fell straight to the ground. No parachute was sighted, no rescue beeper heard. Shortly after the gunship splattered into the jungle, the escorts went into afterburners and hauled ass.

It turned out that following the initial SAM attack, Ed was the only pilot who opted to remain in Steel Tiger. The Airborne Command and Control Center had issued a SAM warning and everyone had elected to pull back and regroup.

The debriefing officer doubted that the missiles had been Guidelines. His Intelligence reports contained no indication of such weapons in Steel Tiger. He said, "You probably encountered some type of unguided rockets."

"Horseshit," I said. "Ask Otis. He saw them. Said they looked just like the pictures."

"What pictures?" the Intelligence officer asked.

"Pictures of an SA2. Any pictures . . ."

"Well, we have no verification of SA2s anywhere in Laos."

"You have verification now," I said. "We saw them."

"Did *you* actually see them?" the Intell officer asked.

"What the fuck is this, Philosophy 101?" Lee said.

I had all the nonrated bullshit I was going to take. I stood up and pointed at the debriefer: "I don't care what you believe. They're out there. The NVA snuck those fuckers down and your sources flat missed it."

"Before we can confirm anything—"

"Confirm this." I gave him a shake of the old gonads.

Lee and Juan walked away.

The Intell weenie never blinked. "Before we confirm anything, we'll have to give it more study."

"Yeah? Well, go study Rabbit. Maybe he got a glimpse of

the fucker before it tore his head off." I followed Lee and Juan. "Unguided, my ass!"

I seethed until we got to the O-Club. Then I let down. My upper body ached as if it had been worked over. I felt as if I had the flu.

Breakfast was the weirdest meal of the year. We ate and looked at each other and went back to eating. We had cheated death, twice. There wasn't much else to say. We knew how lucky we were to have Ed. The son of a bitch put the birds to shame. I paid for his meal and told him, "I think I owe you breakfast, for the rest of my life." Ed smiled. I said, "Thanks," and he smiled again.

Everyone was very mellow, smug, satisfied. We were higher than any airplane or drug could take us. In a way, my feelings reminded me of one of the few times I smoked hash. I had nodded off and had seen big orange objects. Goddamn, were they *orange!* I'd never seen anything that orange. And they were enormous. But I couldn't figure out *what* they were. They towered over me, yet were in the distance. I kept walking toward them—through snow, but it wasn't cold—and admiring the orange color. I've always wished I could get one more look at those big, beautiful orange things. I had been smoking with a lady and I heard her say, "You with me, baby?" I opened my eyes and saw we were fucking, sort of side by side. I hadn't known it. Then I was awash with sex. The entire experience was tremendously satisfying. And also puzzling. That was how I felt now.

By the time Dick and I returned to our room, we were coming down. "I about crapped when Jim said he had an activity light," Dick said.

"How about when Otis said 'It's coming right in the ramp'? I was going to open the booth door and let that big son of a bitch pass on through and hit you guys up front."

Dick smiled. "Right after that, when Otis lost sight of it, there probably wasn't a heartbeat on the whole plane."

"Otis was cool the second time."

"And Ed . . . both times . . ."

"And you, both times," I said.

We kept a bottle of Courvoisier brandy in the refrigerator for special occasions. We had tapped it twice: the night Ed showed Grizzly how big his balls were and the morning I found out I had been promoted. We took the nearly full bottle outside and sat on the grass in front of our room and waited for the sun to come up. We sipped from pony glasses, part of our ritual. I doubted that I'd last until sunrise. I needed a rub, but it was too much trouble to go downtown. I was filled with ambivalent emotions and there was nothing subtle about them.

I wanted to gloat because against impossible odds I was alive. However, I had done nothing to save myself. I owed my life to Ed Holcomb. Few men, maybe no other, would have acted so daringly unorthodox, twice. The knowledge that I easily could be as dead as anyone on Rabbit Ripple's crew made my survival sweeter. At the same time, the loss of Rabbit's crew irritated me. Intelligence was as guilty as the NVA for those deaths. I sipped the brandy and it was nectar. I pressed the cold bottle to my forehead and it felt heavenly. I loved being alive and again wanted to gloat. I wondered if Dick felt the same and said, "In Nam, I flew with this pilot, first thing every morning he said, 'Any day you get up is a good day.' After a while I started hoping he'd get hosed so I didn't have to hear it anymore. Then I realized, if *he* got hosed, *I* got hosed too. Now I know what he was trying to tell me."

Dick nodded.

I read nothing in his expression and said, "Poor fuckin' Rabbit."

"Yeah. I really liked him."

We took turns recalling Rabbit stories.

"Guy had no luck at all."

"None."

"Goddamn those Intell assholes."

We clinked glasses, drained them. Dick poured another and another until we fell asleep on the grass. The sun woke us and we crawled off to bed. We didn't attend the memorial service for Rabbit Ripple's crew the following afternoon.

* * *

Memorial services sucked. That was how I looked at it. There were other viewpoints, but they didn't suit me. To me, memorial services sucked. They were filled with bad vibes that made flyers in the audience start itching: "Hey! That could happen to me." In-theater was no place for that type of thinking: it made a flyer play "Cover Your Ass" and stop taking risks, and then the job didn't get done. It was better to forget a man had been killed, to pretend he went home early. Good guys never died. Rabbit would be talked about forever.

The chaplains pushed memorial services. It was their chance to grab the limelight. Ubon had chaplains of several faiths and, unanimously, they were worthless. There was little call for them from Spectre. To my knowledge, they visited the squadron twice during the dry season, both times at preflight briefings. The first time, being polite, the aircraft commander asked the Protestant chaplain if he "cared to say a few words for the benefit of the crew." Being equally courteous, the chaplain said, "If nobody objects." FitzHugh was there and said, "I strongly object," then eyeballed the Prot and asked, "You want a list of reasons?" The chaplain backed off and that settled it: there was no prayer to carry that crew to combat.

. The second time, Chaplain Joseph O'Connor quietly entered one of our briefings and sat in the last row of the room, far behind our crew. He went unnoticed except by Ed Holcomb, who finished the checklist items, then asked if anyone had anything to add. Lee Schmidt stood, stretched, and said: "Yeah. What say we go kill a truckload of those little non-Christian fucks?"

Several men said, "Amen."

Father O'Connor quietly departed.

Ed said, "I think that request may have failed to meet higher authority approval" and smiled at our puzzlement, then explained the chain of events.

"We should've sung Father O a hymn," one of the gunners said.

From my experience with Spectre and in Vietnam I concluded that the old belief "There are no atheists in foxholes" was wrong. Or doesn't a cockpit equate to a foxhole? Among the men I knew, religion was not a topic for discussion. Every person seemed to have made peace with whatever cosmic thunderer he favored and then put the issue on stand-by. If God wasn't dead, he was at least abandoned in another hemisphere.

Morality wasn't a topic either. The only air force officers who debated whether or not we were doing the proper thing in SEA were groundpounding staff types who never took fire. What the aircrewmen did they accepted and lived with. They were beyond the bounds of conventional morality. That too had been left behind in another hemisphere.

Remember: What a man does overseas doesn't count.

Were we controlled schizos? Who knew for certain? Who cared?

To me, enjoying combat was like enjoying drugs. Both were acceptable if a man knew how and when to use them, recognized them as games, and never surrendered to them.

Many men returned from SEA and declared they couldn't cope because of what they saw or did in the war. Bullshit. People who said they got fucked up in Vietnam were more than likely fucked up before they went there. They knew that few civilians would dare to question their declarations. If pressed, they fell back on the "I'm not ready to talk about it yet" routine. The saddest part about their claims was that a number of those men never saw sustained action. They were mortared once or twice and saw one or two dead or chewed-up bodies and, as a result, couldn't work forever. Anybody who said he got fucked up by combat or by drugs was more than likely fucked up before he was exposed to them. Combat and drugs were ready-made excuses for surrendering self-control, for quitting life. The bad-trip scene was a bullshit rap.

Of all the men who went, there were damn few heroes in Vietnam. I worked it out statistically. It required ten support troops for each man in the field. At the peak of the war, there were 550,000 GIs in Nam; therefore, in any one year, 50,000 saw action. The other half million were on base or in camp holding each other's dicks and running from the BX to the swimming pool to the theater and all that other State-side shit. I saw them! I was into every airstrip in Nam, nearly every army camp. And all 50,000 who saw action weren't exactly *trading fire day in and day out.* There's a big difference between crawling around on the ground while being shot at and standing up to shoot back. Probably ten thousand Special Forces types and some other crazies like the goddamn marines did ninety fuckin' percent of the fighting. And the majority of that group probably loved it.

We once hauled six soldiers from Dong Ha to Da Nang. I spent some ramp time with them. The six had been filthy laterite red dustsuckers from Day One and they loved it, doted on it. They had finished their year-long tour with three months on the DMZ and they didn't resent the assignment. They had been with marines who spent an entire year there. They were laughing because they had copped two weeks early. Children reborn from laterite red ghosts.

"Poor fuckin' marines," one troop with "Son of Rosemary's Baby" boldly printed on his helmet cover said. "When we got to feeling sorry for ourselves, alls we did was look at them poor bastards."

"Dylan" said, "They get the shittiest duty everywhere."

"Those fuckas wallow in it. They love it," said a lean, sullen, unshaven redneck type. He smiled from half of his rotten-toothed mouth. On the back of his flak jacket it said "Born to Die" beneath a naked Satan throwing snake eyes, a work of art, muscular life drawing reminiscent of Michelangelo.

"Dago" was partially unshod. The sole of his left boot flopped loosely, like a circus clown's prop. I offered to trade boots. My life didn't depend on walking. Dago thanked me, adding, "The older the shit, the luckier."

"God Sucks" said, "Don't mean nothing now."

The group's only black had nothing written on his gear. "We're all's left from our original squad," he said matter of factly—no big fuckin' deal.

I admired those six men because they had lived in shit for a year and had eaten artillery for the last three months, and they didn't feel sorry for themselves. There hadn't seemed to be a trace of bitterness in them. They had survived and were better men for the experience.

Years later I wondered what atrocities they had been caught committing in order to be punished by spending their last three months on the DMZ. Three from their squad were KIA up there.

We went back into Steel Tiger the night after Rabbit's crew was lost. The North Vietnamese deployment of Guidelines into Laos turned out to be a one-time tactic. However, it caused doubts and puckers among air force crewmen during the nights that followed.

The NVA reinforced those feelings with another surprise. Shortly after dark on that very next night, in the center of Steel Tiger, a single missile of an unknown type shot straight up to twenty thousand feet and exploded into a massive white-and-orange fireball that probably was visible as far away as both Hanoi and Saigon.

Aircraft in Steel Tiger raced back to Thailand.

We had just crossed the Mekong River en route to our assigned target sector when the explosion lit up the sky in front of us. Stan Briscoe said, "That can't be the sun already." Minutes later, still headed east and target bound, Ed passed AC-130s and F-4s going in the opposite direction. Briscoe tapped Ed on the shoulder. "They are going that way, sir." He pointed aftward with his thumb. "And we're not." When Ed didn't reply, Briscoe added, "Ah, major, sir, you aren't going to fight the war single-handed again, are you?"

In one of his rare outbursts Ed Holcomb laughed loudly. He reversed course and, after orbiting the Mekong for an hour, called our escorts and said, "Let's go do it." He led the parade of gunships and fighters back into Steel Tiger, and he told Briscoe, "Somebody has to be first. If it's any consolation, remember that I'm in front of you."

We destroyed only one that night. For some reason the trucks weren't there.

Following the mission, while on his way to the Officers' Club for breakfast, Ed Holcomb ran his bicycle into a dry klong. The accidental maneuver was an eight-foot fall onto concrete. It took thirty-some stitches to close the gash in Ed's head. He also suffered a brain concussion which grounded him indefinitely.

On the way to preflight briefing the next evening, Juan and I visited Ed in the dispensary. Great Frankenstein stitches ran across his partially shaved skull. "You look like you won the Battle of Laos single-handed," I said.

Ed smiled.

Juan placed a pile of magazines on the foot of the bed. Ed thanked him, then explained, "I'm not supposed to read for a few days."

I couldn't take my eyes off the stitches. "Nice sewing. Who did them, Rajah?"

Ed smiled.

There was an embarrassing pause. Except for flying together, we had nothing in common. Beyond the demands of the mission, we were strangers. The relationship wasn't unusual, especially on a large crew overseas for a short time. The pause lengthened. Here was the man, Steady Eddie, who a couple days before had saved my life and now I had nothing to say to him. Jesus . . .

Ed was glassy-eyed. "You look like you need to rest," I said. "We'll see you again in a couple days. OK?"

Ed said, "Thanks anyway for the magazines."

"Need anything else," Juan said, "let us know."

"By the way," I said, "before we go, you ought to know that Juan and I flipped and I won. If you don't pull through, I get your bike."

Ed smiled. Obviously the fall had affected his thinking: he shot me the bird.

Chapter 18

Happiness Is a Warm Gun

DURING FEBRUARY AND March of 1971, American and South Vietnamese soldiers drove into southeastern Laos in Operation Lam Son 719. On 6 March they captured the crossroads town of Tchepone, which controlled east-to-west-oriented Route 9. The main north-south line of communication, Route 92, was thereby severed and the North Vietnamese Army was denied truck movement to termini in South Vietnam. The invading forces also tore up approximately three hundred meters of an NVA pipeline which was capable of carrying four hundred tons of fuel per day to the south, or the equivalent of fifteen tanker trucks.

In response to the attack, the NVA increased its volume of supply inputs down the trail. Truck sightings jumped from one thousand to two thousand per day, with the traffic concentrated on the seldom-used westward roadways leading into Cambodia. The change in routing was a boon to the gunships: double the number of targets were compressed into half as great an area. Traffic jams resulted. Convoys backed up on each other. In the eyes of the Spectre sensor operators, it was lovely chaos. Nightly, at least one gunship crew destroyed 25 or more vehicles, well above the truck-kill rate per sortie of 9.72.

Shooting was spectacular to the point that Ed Holcomb insisted on flying every night. "Chance of a lifetime," he told us. "This offensive could change the course of the entire war." Dick and I exchanged sleepy looks. "We've finally taken the initiative," Ed stated. During February he couldn't get enough shooting to satisfy him. When five minutes passed without finding a target, he hassled everyone. "Dick, you certain this is the best place to hunt? Call TFA again, see what's the latest. Hal, where're you looking?" The pilot had a display which monitored the sighting elevation and azimuth of each sensor. "You've been looking at that one spot for a long time. What're you looking at?" Before he got an answer, it was "Lee, you're scanning awfully slow. Do you have something?" After several seconds of silence, he said, "What's going on back there? Let's find something. We know they're out here. Jim, you certain the BC's working, no malfunction or anything? Let's go. Find something." The ludicrous part of the situation was that Ed Holcomb was the leading truck killer two out of three nights. Furthermore, we desired to destroy the enemy as much as he did.

Following a week of periodic harassment, Ed became insufferable immediately after decimating his second convoy of the night. "Come on, come on," he urged. "Five minutes and I haven't had a shot at anything. Let's go back there."

In the booth we looked at each other in frustration. Then I said, "Hey, fuck it, Ed. Tomorrow night, right after takeoff, we attack the base motor pool. They have plenty of trucks there. That way we don't waste time driving out here and raking through the weeds. OK?"

I could have saved my breath. Ed calmly said, "Trucks are out here too, Hal. Thousands of them. And I want only ten an hour. Now find them."

The gunships' advantage increased when, for the first time, the NVA was unable to keep up with the destruction inflicted upon its transportation system. Individual hulks remained untouched for days. Bottlenecks developed where convoys piled up in ruin. Moving vehicles were forced to weave around wreckage scattered along the roads. Juan Sueno observed, "Maybe our army captured the Great Laotian Junk Eater."

During that time, we came across a driver nearly as wily as the daredevil who escaped from us weeks before. The new man relied on speed and knowledge of the trail network. While Ed pounded the main road ahead of his truck, the new driver slipped down bypasses and along multiple parallel routes or hooked back onto spurs. Lee Schmidt said, "This guy is Son of Thunder Road."

"Son of a bitch," I said.

"He's good, but he doesn't have the moves of his old man: the spin-outs, the reverses," Lee said. "And he's nowhere as fast."

Ed fired when I told him to and we kept the quarry moving. We came closest to clobbering the truck when the driver momentarily stopped and was forced to back up after overshooting the second of two adjoining U-shaped switchbacks. "That was dumb," Juan said. "He could have bypassed both of those." Juan reminded me of a psychologist who was watching a rat run a maze.

"Maybe he wanted to get over on that other road," I said, "and that was the only way."

"Maybe he's showing off," Juan said.

Lee warned us, "He's coming up on a village."

"Six huts? That's no village," Juan said.

Lee said, "According to the ROEs—"

"Fuck the ROEs," Juan told him.

"That's what I thought you'd say."

"What's the matter, Lee," I asked, "you see a cop out here or something?" We were our own police force, I thought. Then, on second thought, I reached over to Juan's console and turned off the videotape recorder. We shot at the truck as it passed the huts.

With the recorder running again, we shot at the truck when it crossed a shallow ford ("Looked like he didn't even gear down for the water," Lee said in praise); we shot at the truck when it pounded uphill and when it freewheeled downhill; we shot at the truck as it raced ever southward.

Ed said, "Dick, the drivers usually know only a part of the trail, say a twenty-mile stretch. How far we chased this guy?" Waiting for an answer, he said, "The trucks go all the way, but the drivers rotate."

"He should be running off his turf any time," Dick said.

"We found him fifteen miles back. He's been headed in the same general direction the whole time."

Suddenly the driver whipped onto a narrow trail and slowed enough so that Ed got off a burst of four that hit ten feet in front of the truck. The driver made a hard right turn and took off into the jungle. Only the IR was able to follow the truck's heat signature beneath the foliage. "He's off the road," Lee informed Ed. "According to the ROEs—"

"You hang on to that son of a bitch," I told him, "or get out of the seat and give me the IR."

"Relax. I'm tracking," Lee said.

"I have him on BC, Hal," Jim said. "He won't get away."

The truck emerged along what was no more than a footpath. After fifty feet, it met a dead end against a rock bluff. "Tough break," Juan said.

I placed the TV crosshairs on the vehicle and Ed blew it apart. Before we left the truck, Lee said, "The driver had plenty of time to get away."

Of course, it was during Lam Son 719 that the NVA sneaked the SA2 Guidelines into Steel Tiger and blew away Rabbit Ripple and his crew.

As soon as the American and South Vietnamese soldiers pulled out of Laos with twenty-five to thirty thousand NVA infantrymen in hot pursuit, the volume of traffic across the eastern section of the Ho Chi Minh Trail leaped to above the pre-incursion level. Radio Hanoi called Route 9 "the cemetery of helicopters and armored vehicles." After hearing the report, Lee said, "They forgot to include their trucks."

"And Rabbit's gunship," I added.

Jim Ballard said, "There are times when I wonder about all of you. Morbid!"

For a week the gunships continued to have field days; then the NVA resumed its orderly road-and-vehicle maintenance and the gunships again had to work for what they got. In retrospect, the American commanders described Lam Son 719 as "an offensive limited in time and space and designed to disrupt the logistic supply flow." After reading that statement, Lee said, "They disrupted it, all right, and beat all the kinks out of it. Now, it's back together and working better than ever. Which only goes to prove we can fly until our buns turn blue, but there has to be troops on the ground to shut them down."

"In that case, next time we're over there, why don't you bail out," Jim Ballard said, "and be a one-man Lam Son 720."

Lee looked forlornly at Jim and asked, "When did you start getting hostile?"

"Send anybody but Lee," Juan said. "He'll let all the fancy drivers and little cars go free."

I nodded. "For sure. Pussy."

Lee Schmidt shook his head and said, "I search out and destroy one thousand trucks—one thousand!—and do you guys say 'There goes Pierre, that big truck socker'? Nooooo! But let Pierre suck *one cock . . .*"

During Lam Son 719 the wealth of vehicles influenced Spectre crews' attitude regarding damage assessment. According to the criteria, a truck was considered destroyed if struck by one 40-mm shell. Despite the rule, in December and January when targets were scarce, most crews hit a vehicle with several 40-mm rounds in hopes of making it blow or burn; half the time they succeeded. Nearly as decisively, those trucks which did not blow or burn nevertheless did sustain multiple hits before being classified as destroyed.

The large number of truck sightings during Lam Son 719 caused a shift in tactics. Crews spent less time on each truck in order to strike more trucks. The single-hit criterion was liberally applied. As a result, crews blew or burned only one out of four or five targets.

Spectre's March totals were 3,361 vehicles destroyed, 819 damaged.

The dry season totals climbed to 7,200 destroyed and 2,000 damaged.

After Ed Holcomb partially scrambled his brains, Major Billy Killeen, a tall, rawboned Oklahoman, was assigned to pilot our crew. Ed never returned to us on a permanent basis.

While he had his head in a sling, Colonel Godolphin appointed him operations officer ahead of numerous persons who outranked him. "That move definitely confirms my suspicion," said Lee, "that brain damage is a prerequisite for command."

"In that case," Billy Killeen told him, "you should make air force chief of staff."

Lee stared at me and asked, "Did *you* request him as our AC?"

Godolphin explained Ed's selection: "Using Major Holcomb in a staff position while he is unable to fly is the maximum utilization of personnel." Both then and later when Ed was again cleared for flying but remained at the desk job, Godolphin refused to discuss the matter with officers whom he bypassed.

After Ed's discipline, we enjoyed Billy Killeen's happy-go-lucky attitude. It was like a day of vacation to be led by him. For a man with only a master's degree from the University of Oklahoma, Billy was pretty clever. At the preflight briefing for our first mission together, he told us, "I expect to be treated with warmth. I can't stand rejection from people I don't respect."

Billy had our respect. The minute we learned that he had inherited us, we sat around and dredged up stories from his past. My favorite was the night over Steel Tiger when Billy's left outboard engine got tired and overheated. In accordance with the AC-130 Flight Manual, Section III, Emergency Procedures, he shut down the engine. The *Aircrew Operational Procedures* dictated: "When an emergency engine shutdown is required, a flight may proceed on three engines to destination providing two engine capability exists." Billy computed that the aircraft gross weight was such that he could get to Ubon on only two engines, if necessary. The fact that he was in the middle of creaming a ten-truck convoy also influenced his thinking. Deciding to remain on target and finish the job, he disregarded the *Aircrew Operational Procedures* line that read, "If an emergency shutdown is required during a combat mission, the combat mission will be terminated."

Billy polished off the convoy, then returned to Ubon and greased in on three engines. He didn't bother to declare an emergency, which also went against procedures.

Colonel Godolphin totaled the violations and met Billy face to face. "I don't know if I should write you a DFC or write you a reprimand."

"Shitcan both ideas," Billy said, "and write me a four-day pass to Bangkok."

Later at the bar, relating the confrontation, Billy said, "Killing the trucks saved my scalp. Grizzly admitted that. But he spelled it out regarding my future. Three more strikes and I join Fitz in Da Nang."

Billy Killeen was loose to the point of exasperation. After a few missions with him, Lee said, "Ed split his head open and tightly packed brains ran out. If you split Billy's head, nothing but a whole lot of tiny little pussies would come running out."

Billy spoke whichever idea floated to the top, regardless of the situation. Legend had it that moments after a 57-mm shell blew a three-foot hole through the left wing of his gunship, he said, "This is challenging. And just plain fun. Reminds me of the morning my wife was cooking breakfast, kids all over the house, and I scored a quicky from my sister-in-law. Never forget it. Standing up in the closet. She said, 'Kiss me, kiss me.' I told her, 'Kiss you? Hell, it's bad enough we're doing this.'"

With our crew, Billy frequently told stories. One night while working over a convoy near Attopeu, he stopped firing and said, "I was almost late for briefing today. I went downtown for a scrub-and-rub this afternoon and the alarm didn't go off."

"But I'll bet you did," Lee said.

"Don't encourage him," Juan Sueno told Lee.

"TV tracking, Billy," I reminded him.

Billy Killeen asked, "Did I ever tell you about the time I screwed this English broad in the back seat of a taxi while riding through Hyde Park?" and then fired several rounds.

"Every time you fly with us," Jim Ballard said.

"I thought that was part of the crew briefing," said Dick Kaulbach.

"You hit him," I reported. "You got a burner, Billy."

"Good. Find another one," Billy Killeen said. "Listen, let me tell you about the time I screwed this Spanish broad in the back seat of a donkey cart while riding through Madrid."

Juan Sueno said, "Anybody bad mouths Spanish women gets decked as soon as we land."

"In that case," Billy Killeen said, "let me tell you what I did to the donkey."

In the gunship's left seat, Billy Killeen displayed the style the crew admired. Ed Holcomb had a rhythm with the 40-mm: one, one-two-three. Billy Killeen had a "Golden BB." When Billy fired it, Juan said it was like being in "The Twilight Zone." Otis Birdwhistle thought "The Vacuum" was a better name. When Billy went into the gunsight, it was as if he stepped through the looking glass: the real world went away. Of course, he took on the same air when he entered a bathhouse and looked through the window . . .

Digression. Dressed in short white smocks, bathhouse girls sat on tiered benches behind a one-way picture window and occupied themselves by reading, crocheting, manicuring nails, or chatting. Each wore a numbered badge. From the bathhouse lobby, a customer looked them over through the window, told the mama-san the number (or numbers) he desired, then paid the price before the girl was paged over a loudspeaker. One night we walked into Sabithong's and sitting among the dollies, with hairy legs crossed and foot bouncing, wearing a smock and a number and crocheting as if his life depended upon it, was Rabbit Ripple. Nobody gave that crazy son of a bitch the satisfaction of having his number called, but we laughed our asses off. Rabbit never died.

The whole crew felt it when Billy Killeen went into the gunsight for a Golden BB—one shot directly on the nailhead. "Everything stops," Briscoe said, "just before he presses the trigger." Otis agreed. "On the ramp, the slipstream goes away. It gets calm. There's no feeling of moving. It's spooky." In the booth, we loved his style. "He flies perfect orbits, as if there's no wind to contend with," said Juan. "Once you kill the drift on the crosshairs," Lee said, "they stay right there."

The love feast was out of control. We felt it was justified.

The problems of being burdened with a poor shooter were more than we had ever discussed.

We had been in the target sector for an hour without making contact. "Anybody know what time it is?" Lee asked.

"Nearly three quarters past the twentieth century," I said. "If that's not close enough, ask some mortal."

Lee said, "I meant, how long we been on target?"

"Then why didn't you say that," Jim Ballard told him. Jim was turning into a smart-ass.

"Too long without finding anything," Billy Killeen said. "I'm tired of sitting up here, thinking off. Even Tex is beginning to look pretty good." He must have studied his watch because he then said, "Five after midnight. New day! Happy Easter, guys." I tried to remember what we had done on Christmas and New Year's Day but drew a blank. Billy said, "Let's kill a Commie for Christ."

Not ten seconds later, Jim Ballard said, "BC has a mover."

"Es un milagro," said Juan.

The trucks were at a ford. Two had crossed to the other side. Two were in the water. Eleven were backed up, waiting their turns.

"Un milagro grande," Juan said.

"Watch it, Juan. Remember what happened to Fitz," Jim said. He was becoming a real Jack Benny.

It was a clear, moonlit night. "I can almost see them," Billy Killeen said. "Put Hal in the computer. You know, this reminds me of the time—"

"Aw, come on, Billy," I snapped.

Billy Killeen laughed deeply. "All right, gents, let's earn our money. You tracking, Hal?"

I also laughed. "Yeah."

Billy Killeen lined up and commenced firing. Without a word, in seven orbits, a period of fourteen minutes, he destroyed the fifteen trucks. One truck attempted to escape after Billy Killeen blew up the leader. I slued onto it. A burst of 40-mm rounds ripped through the bed of the escaping vehicle and shattered the rear axle. The truck ground to a stop. Its rear tires rolled off in different directions. The feat was another marvelous combination of luck and skill.

"You *could* drive nails with this machine," Jim said.

Lee said, "Juan boresighted the airplane this afternoon. Didn't you, Juan?"

Boresighting was a procedure by which the bores of the gun barrels and the sight lines of the sensors were physically aligned. The procedure required a painstaking series of sextant sightings, mechanical adjustments, and repeated cross-checks. For most men, close usually was good enough and the computer was depended upon to do the remainder. Most were satisfied to reduce computer corrections to low numbers. Juan was one of the few FCOs who worked until the systems zeroed out and no computer corrections were necessary.

"Didn't you?" Lee asked again.

Juan Sueno saw that I was watching him. He puffed on the fingernails of his right hand, rapidly buffed the nails against the sleeve of his flying suit, held them at arm's length and examined them; then he grinned: "Yeah."

We located twelve other trucks in groups of three, four, and five and dispatched them with the same efficiency as the first fifteen. I was aiming at specific spots on the vehicles and Billy Killeen was hitting those spots. "In the engine, in the engine, in the engine," I reported following one burst. After moving the crosshairs a sixteenth of an inch, I said, "Wipe out the dash and we'll go to the next truck." Billy Killeen put two of the next three rounds into the driver's compartment.

Although it barely accommodated us, the entire crew, thirteen warm bodies, filed into the Photo Intell debriefing room. "Standing room only," Juan said, "a sellout."

"Best shooting I've ever seen," Lee said. "Even if Hal was tracking. Wait 'til you see it, Dick."

"I couldn't believe your calls," Dick said. "It sounded like you were making them up."

The gunners cheered when the fifteen trucks appeared on the television screen. Billy Killeen was heard to say, "All right, gents, let's earn our money," and the screen turned to snow.

"Looks like a recorder malfunction," Lieutenant Marconi, the photo interpreter, said and fast-fed the videotape through the reviewing machine. The remainder of the tape was blank.

"No malfunction was indicated on the control panel," Juan said accusingly.

Lieutenant Marconi shrugged and said, "Beats . . ." He looked over and saw me glaring at him. "Wait a minute. It's not my fault," he said. "I haven't touched that roll."

"What the hell," Billy Killeen said, "nobody would have believed it. They would have thought it was trick photography."

"Who needs pictures?" Lee said. "If it's not in here . . ."—he tapped his head—". . . and in here . . ."—he tapped his chest, near the heart—". . . it doesn't count."

I knocked Lee's cap off his head. Jim kicked it out the door. Dick pushed Lee off his chair and onto the floor and we pummeled him, gunners included. Billy Killeen declared, "Asshole sentiment like that buys breakfast."

Chapter 19

Let It Be

OUR TURKEY WAS sick. It was a turn-around bird, meaning it had flown an early mission and was scheduled to go out again after being rearmed and refueled. Along the way, however, it developed a few aches and pains that the ground crew was now trying to relieve. As usual, Briscoe was helping them and the rest of us were sprawled on the ramp, waiting and talking.

"Colonel Z, did you know Bishop caught the clap five times from the same snatch?" Technical Sergeant Rusty Brown asked. "I think her name is Cheetah."

"Only *four* times," Airman Ross Bishop, a nineteen-year-old gunner, said. "And her name ain't Cheetah."

"OK," Brown said, "only four times. Did you know that, Colonel Z? Major Killeen? Major Kaul—"

"Quit it!" Ross Bishop said. "At least I didn't catch the drip the last time I was with her."

Brown raised his eyebrows in surprise and then looked skeptical.

"That's right," Ross Bishop said. "I only got strep throat."

Like a crash of thunder that came without a warning flash of lightning, Billy Killeen nearly ruined the entire concept of ramp time. "You gunners have a line-of-sight philosophy of life," he said. "At a given moment, anything that feels good or looks good is good enough for you. You lack aesthetic sense. You have a limited concept of lasting values and of the future. To you, tomorrow will take care of itself." Billy frowned deeply. Rusty Brown appeared as if he were entering shock. Billy continued. "That's a shallow life, a very shallow life. You exist on the fringe of society." He looked at each gunner individually, then said, "Believe me, I know what I'm talking about. I'm the same way. But at least I recognize it."

Color returned to Rusty Brown's cheeks. "For a minute I thought you were serious, sir," he said cautiously.

"I am serious," Billy said.

"Then I guess you don't want to hear about Briscoe's latest," Rusty said sadly.

"He can put on his headset if he doesn't want to hear," Lee Schmidt said. "I want to hear."

Billy laughed. "Me too, Sergeant Brown."

Rusty Brown came fully alive. "Remember Harpo?" Harpo was a curly haired, platinum-blond gunner about eighteen years old who had flown with us several times. "He passed out at his champagne party, last night at the Ubon." A champagne party was a celebration immediately following a man's final combat mission. Usually his closest friends and fellow crewmen treated him to all the champagne he wanted, and usually the celebrant got totally faced. "Well, Harpo passed out about the time Briscoe showed. That Stan can sure come up with the ideas."

"Like Torquemada," Juan said.

"Who?" Rusty asked.

"Skip it," Juan answered.

"Well, Harpo no sooner hit the table when Stan and the gunners carried him downstairs to the beauty parlor and had half his hair dyed black. Parted it down the middle. The right side was platinum-blond and the left side was coal black. They had the women in the beauty parlor do the same to the hair on his chest, under his arms, and his pubics! The kid is going back to the States that way."

Another gunner said, "Harpo thinks it looks shit hot. He can hardly wait for his mother and his girlfriend to see it."

"Godolphin see it?"

"Yes. This afternoon."

"What did *he* say?"

"He said, 'Oh, shit! That fuckin' Briscoe!' Honest to God, those were his exact words. I heard them."

"I don't think dying the kid's hair is as bad as the time that gunner—Ingram?—passed out downtown and they shaved him," Juan Sueno said, "all over. Head, eyebrows, pits, crotch, arms, legs, you name it."

Dick Kaulbach laughed. "Is that what happened? I always thought he had some medical problem." He laughed again. "Now that's funny."

"More of Briscoe's handiwork?" Billy asked.

Rusty Brown nodded emphatically, proudly.

I said, "When I was at Tan Son Nhut, I saw an RF jock pass out at his champagne party. The other jocks propped him up at the head of the table and kept his glass full. When there was a toast, they threw a glass of champagne on him. When dinner came, they unzipped his flying suit and dumped it on his chest: spaghetti, sprinkled a little cheese, salad, oil and vinegar, garlic toast, butter, the works. Then they zipped the flying suit over it. At the end of the night, they carried him off to bed."

"Can you imagine waking up to that," Jim said.

Lee replied, "Sure. Breakfast in bed."

"Fuckin' Rabbit never got a champagne flight," I said, then laughingly added, "His whole life was a champagne flight."

Jim sighed: "Keep it clean."

Lee Schmidt said, "You know, my father flew F-80s in Korea. He told me about a time when he was low-level and his wingman took a hit and flipped inverted. He said the plane headed into the ground upside-down and just before it crashed the pilot said, 'No controls, Shoo. Looks like the sons of bitches got me.' You like that, Hal, grammatically correct right to the end?"

"Shoo? That your dad's nickname?" Juan Sueno asked.

"Yeah. Short for Shooter."

"I like Shoo better. Shoo Schmidt. Neat!" Juan said.

Billy Killeen said, "Before I went to pilot training . . ."

"Did you really go to pilot training, Billy?" Dick asked.

". . . I was a combat controller . . ."

"You mean you jumped out of airplanes when they weren't

on fire, or ready to crash, or anything?" Lee said. "You nuts?"

Billy Killeen ignored them. ". . . and we had a guy on our team named Roscoe who was Mexican . . ."

"This is a made-up story, man," Juan said. "No Mexican was ever named ha-Rrrrroscoe."

". . . and who was also a notorious late-puller. We were at HALO school, jumping from twenty thou, and most guys would pull around twenty-five hundred feet. Not Roscoe. He never pulled above a thousand feet. After a while the school commander got pissed and had Roscoe fitted with a barometric device to open his chute at twenty-five hundred, along with everyone else."

"If the barometer malfunctions and Roscoe splatters, I am going home," Jim Ballard said.

"Just listen. The next jump was our graduation jump. I was already on the ground when Roscoe's turn came. We were watching through binoculars. Roscoe's string of six jumpers exited at twenty thou. They free fell in a perfectly spaced oblique line. It was beautiful. At twenty-five hundred, one chute blossomed, then two, three, four, five. Number six man just kept coming, streaking by the others, headfirst, aimed for the ground. I put the glasses on him. It was Roscoe: he had his hands locked together behind him, *holding the back pack closed* so that the parachute couldn't deploy. At six hundred feet, he let go, hit it . . ."—Billy Killeen snapped his arms away from his body and arched his back—". . . and the chute popped open behind him. He oscillated twice and touched down while the other five jumpers were still up around a thou. Last out, first down. I looked at the school commander and he was deliberately watching something about twenty miles in the other direction and ignoring the shit out of us."

"Can't beat a commander who knows when to look the other way," Dick Kaulbach said.

"Grizzly's like that," Billy said. "He doesn't sweat the small stuff. I'll tell you, I've seen some poor fucking squadron commanders, compared to him. I remember one donkeyhole in SAC who was nuts about keeping the telephone recall roster up-to-date. He'd phone people at home, in the middle of the day or night. You'd answer the phone or your wife would answer the phone and he'd say, 'This is Colonel Moore. Have you had your telephone number changed recently?' And he was serious. He lasted about two months.''

"Talk about A-hole commanders," Juan Sueno said, "right before Tet in '68, the Tan Son Nhut base commander decided to beautify the place by painting the sandbags pastel colors. The grunts were actually painting the bags blue and pink and green when the VC attacked."

I said, "Goddammit, John, I told you that story."

Juan frowned. "You sure?"

"The VC also leveled a brand-new chapel that was waiting to be dedicated the following Sunday," I said. "I always think of that as Buddha 1, Christ 0."

Lee said, "Like Ohio State National Guard 4, Kent State 0."

Dick said, "Once I looked out of my hotel window and watched a tank roll down the street, pull up onto a sidewalk, swing its cannon around, and level a building at point-blank range. Right across the street from my room."

Jim said, "Were you in Saigon?"

Dick smiled. "I was in a hotel in Detroit."

There was a lull in the conversation.

"Billy told a long story," I said. "Now I get to tell a long story."

Lee said, "Let's vote on that."

"Don't make me pull rank," I said. Lee grinned. "Right after Tet in '68—April—we were dropping supplies around A Luoi in support of Operation Delaware. In the A Shau. Christ, that was Lam Son 216."

"All those fuckin' Lam Sons," Billy Killeen said.

Lee sighed. "Seen one, seen 'em all."

"First morning, everything was cozy," I said. "That afternoon, those little fucks were ready. We were lead and took some small arms. Then it got shitty out. Number Two had an engine and wing tip shot off. He was in the valley at five hundred feet, well below the ridge lines on both sides. It was a shooting gallery. The VCs had Twenty-threes plus a lot of smaller stuff on the ridges and they were firing *down* at the planes. Steve Lowe was flying Number Three. They shot away his entire tail section. He made it to the DZ, but he couldn't control it. He tried to crash-land near A Luoi. By then, they were too low to bail out. He hit some trees and fireballed. He was carrying twenty-five thousand pounds of ammo. That ended the drops for that day. We saw Number Two back at Da Nang. Intell weenies were walking around it and saying, 'There's a Twenty-three hole,' and 'That's definitely AK47 work.' Assholes! A crusty little major, pilot of Number Two, kept saying, 'I always wanted to see a firepower demonstration, but I never wanted to be the *target* at a firepower demonstration.'"

The major's line got a better laugh than when he spoke it, but he hadn't meant it to be funny.

"That night," I continued, "B-52 strikes went in on both sides of the valley. The next morning, it was very friendly. Chopper gunships were over both ridge lines. We were tooling down the valley, getting ready to drop, when an F-4 with wall-to-wall ordnance pulls up off our right wing. The F-4 jock was wearing a bright red scarf and a bright red helmet with the fucking visor down. He flashed the Winnie sign to us. Our co, Roger the Lodger, came up on fighter freq, gave him the finger, and said, 'How come nobody woke you yesterday when we needed help?' The jock said, 'Fuck you very much,' and hit AB. As the F-4 pulled away, Roger—being really original—screamed, 'Your scarf sucks!'"

"The worst I ever heard on the radio was up in the Barrel," Dick Kaulbach said. "A Nail FAC kept asking Moonbeam for ordnance and Moonbeam kept telling him to stand by. The FAC finally came up and said, 'Moonbeam, you motherfucker, I've been taking fire for forty-five minutes waiting for you to get off the pot.' He said he had about two hundred bad guys holed up for a while, but they decided to walk. They were marching down a road and waving at him. He said they were probably monitoring his freq and knew he wasn't getting a thing. He told Moonbeam, 'You run a shitty war.'"

Lee laughed. "He really said all that? What did Moonbeam do?"

"Sent him ord," Dick said.

I said, "Let me tell the rest of what happened."

Dick said, "When Hal says long, he means *long!*"

I plowed ahead. "Lowe, the guy who got shot down, he and

his wife had five kids. After he was killed, his wife started getting phone calls and letters telling her that he got what he deserved. The letters called him a warmonger and a killer and all that. Lowe was one of the most gentle guys . . . The wife couldn't take the cards and letters that kept pouring in. She gave up the will to live and died less than a year after he was killed."

"Fuckin' civilians," Rusty Brown said.

"People are worthless," Lee said. "He wasn't killing anybody flying Trash Haulers."

"Except himself," said Billy Killeen. "Life's a bitch."

"Anyhow," I added, "an air force family adopted all five kids to keep them together."

"I don't believe it! Hal told a story with a happy ending," Billy said. "Too much." He stood up. "Is that rampsucking airplane ever going to be ready to fly?"

"They can't fix it tonight," Jim Ballard said. "We were scrubbed."

"What? When?"

"About ten minutes ago. And there's no spare available. That's why Briscoe and the gunners left," Jim said.

"I thought they went for Cokes," Billy said. "Why didn't you say something?"

"It's too late to go anywhere," Jim explained, "and I was enjoying the stories."

Chapter 20

Satisfaction

APRIL TURNED OUT to be another Spectre spectacular: 3,064 destroyed and 743 damaged. Those figures pushed the dry season totals to 10,319 destroyed and 2,733 damaged. The numbers were double those of the previous season. The reasons were logical: twice as many airplanes, heavier firepower, better sensors. Surprisingly, nobody bothered to figure out who got Number Ten Thousand.

Along about mid-April, however, Intelligence started recomputing the number of trucks the North Vietnamese owned. Intelligence figures for the previous season, 1969–1970, claimed the NVA had fed sixty-eight thousand tons of material into the trail network and had twenty-one thousand tons reach final destination. For 1970–1971 Intelligence claimed the input ran the same but estimated only ninety-five hundred tons would get through. The answer was logical: twice as much destruction, half as much success. By working the problem backward (throughput, support requirements, destroyed and damaged vehicles, input), Intelligence determined the number of trucks required to accomplish the task.

Dick Kaulbach took the numbers game seriously. "I read a USAF Intell report from last dry season that claimed the NVA had six to eight thousand trucks. Another report written at the start of this dry season said eighteen thousand.

Now, Intell says between twenty-three and twenty-five thousand."

At the mention of the word "Intell," I was listening to refute. I said, "Another typical cover-your-ass Intell guesstimate—pick a number from pi to infinity . . ."

Dick said, "The report claimed the NVA already asked Russia and China for twelve thousand new trucks for *next* season, nine from Russia and three from China. That makes our totals for this year look pretty good. The report said some of the trucks from Russia are produced in Czechoslovakia and East Germany."

I had a delayed reaction: "Did you say twenty-five thousand? Jesus . . ."

Dick was into the problem: "Supposedly the NVA needs only nine to twelve percent throughput to maintain an offensive in South Vietnam and Cambodia. If the NVA pushes through ten out of seventy thousand tons of input, that's fourteen percent. Twenty-nine percent of the input supports trail operations. And about six percent is stockpiled. That means we destroyed fifty-one percent . . ."—he smiled weakly—". . . and failed?"

"That's what I need, Dick, more numbers. Jesus . . . Yesterday, Tex Tyler comes to me with a diagram showing how a truck's vital parts—you know, the engine, the drive shaft, whatever other shit there is—that all takes up only nineteen percent of the truck's surface area. Isn't that wonderful information? We destroyed more than a thousand trucks without knowing that and I'm supposed to be impressed with his drawing, on graph paper yet." Dick laughed when I added, "And I'll bet he traced it." I also laughed. "I studied his drawing for a while, then told him he forgot to include the spleen. He looked at me like I was a lunatic. No sense of humor. Fuck him. Fuck Intell too. Those assholes word every report so that you can read whatever you want." I often thought that the ostrich approach, head buried in the sand, was the best approach to life for anyone who put his ass on the line day after day. "Reading Intell reports always makes me feel doomed."

"I hate to admit it," Dick said, "but I think we're going to lose everything over here. It's a matter of time."

I tried to sound as if I was joking, but inwardly I was irritated by the idea that we had destroyed half the 559th Transportation Group without accomplishing anything. "What do you expect from forty-year-old men shooting thirty-year-old guns out of twenty-year-old airplanes?"

April was easy. After averaging twenty-five missions a month until then, I flew only twenty times. Our crew had good flights with Billy Killeen. On most of them we destroyed trucks numbered in the high teens. As good as Billy was, however, he never matched Ed's single-mission high of thirty destroyed (and nine damaged), the only time I was with a pilot who totaled thirty in the first column.

Spectre's one-mission high for destroyed trucks was fifty-one by Aguilar. The number included few burners. Aguilar's sensors found two large groups within half a mile of each other. To prevent trucks from escaping, the crew worked over both groups at the same time, hitting one for several orbits, then switching to the other. The crew had fuel enough only to strike each vehicle once, which, in accordance with the criteria, classified each as destroyed. The following morning a recce OV-10 found no trucks at the two locations. Situations like that disturbed staff personnel at Seventh Air Force Headquarters. When related to the problem of determining the size of the North's truck fleet, cases such as Aguilar's were used as a basis for second guessing. Staff officers asked questions that were accusations: Did the crew actually hit fifty-one vehicles? Were the targets trucks or something that looked like trucks? If the latter, what were they? If they were trucks, where did they go? The staff officers ignored obvious questions: Did the recce bird overfly the correct spot? Did time enough elapse for the NVA to sweep up thoroughly? Why did Seventh put faith in visual reconnaissance when Aguilar had videotapes of the kills?

In such cases, the integrity and ability of the crews were at stake. Among air force staff officers there was an unwritten rule: first verify crew integrity before delving deeper into a problem. Whenever results were questionable, staff officers wondered if the crew was telling the truth or covering its ass for failing to do the job properly. After integrity, ability was questioned. To staff members, crew duties were menial work, but, they also believed, crew members were too stupid to execute them correctly.

From the perspective of most staff officers, a man of intelligence would not remain at the crew level, the lowest spot in the combat chain of command. I agreed that crew duty was situated at an extreme end. I often said, "All the shit flows until it hits the crews. Then it piles up there and they sort it out." In SAC, crewmen said, "We'll win the war, despite the staff's plan." Reasoning dialectically, I placed crews at the top of the hierarchy. We were the knights who rode to battle. Without us, nothing came to pass. We were the reason everyone else had a job. As Mao wrote: "Some comrades in the army have become arrogant and high-handed in their behavior toward the soldiers . . ." In SAC, I once heard a staff officer declare, "I am too intelligent to be a crew member." Several crewmen were within earshot. We were in the O-Club bar. That staff officer left soon after several faces offered to punch his off. As Mao concluded: ". . . the army must endeavor to eradicate these faults."

O-Clubs in SAC were like the old Madison Square Garden: there was a main bout every Friday night. The crews possessed all those awesome megatons of power . . . lived on a short leash . . . never got to kill a fucking thing. We blew off steam by fighting each other.

Tim FitzHugh raved at length on the plight of combat flyers. On a night when Juan and I flew with him, he announced at dinner, "Combat pay is an insult."

"Here we go again," Major Dave Wine, his aircraft commander, said.

"It's like giving whores a subsidy because they're exposed to VD," said Fitz, "when exposure is part of the job."

"This whore can use the money," Juan said.

Fitz didn't join the laughter. He said, "The amount! That's the biggest insult. Sixty-five dollars a month for being shot at. Two dollars a day!" He sneered. "The whole system is fucked up. Look at flying pay. Uncle teaches you how to fly and then turns around and pays you extra for doing it."

"I'd accept extra pay for shitting if I could get it," Juan said. "Of course, I'm a natural; nobody had to teach me how."

"Just where," I said.

"Fitz, if combat pay and flying pay are such insults," Dave Wine asked, "why don't you do something about it?"

"I have. I don't accept combat pay."

Dave Wine squinted for several seconds, adjusted his glasses, then shook his head. "No way. The squadron certifies you; finance pays you."

"Not anymore. My combat pay accrues in my record. I never have to accept it." Fitz grinned. "You should have seen the finance office come unglued. According to them, nobody ever refused pay before. Even the finance officer got into it. He wouldn't go along until I showed him where it's spelled out in the finance regs. He was pissed. He wanted to know when I intended to collect. I told him, 'Never. Pay it to my next of kin, in about fifty years.'"

"Going to miss a few dollars interest on that money," Juan said. "You have stronger principles than I do."

I smiled. I guessed Fitz felt it was worth the price to hassle Finance.

"Fitz," Dave Wine asked, "are you now going to tell us you also refuse flying pay?"

Fitz lowered his eyebrows and shook his head. "That's two fifty a month. Even *my* principles have limits."

I laughed. "The pragmatic martyr."

"You guys never learn," Fitz said with a smile. "The mission of the air force is to fly and fight. But Uncle pays extra to people who do it. Therefore, it must be pretty important. Or is it the risks you're paid for? If that's the case, there isn't enough money for what you do and—"

"A lot of guys would fly without flight pay," said Juan.

"Exactly!" Fitz said. "Because flying is glamorous. You can't put a price tag on that. And they'd fly combat without combat pay too. That's the most glamorous of all." He made a long face. "And in the air force, nobody dies." Rabbit was still alive then. "You fly off to work and never return. No mud, no blood. Everything goes right, you're in your own crematorium."

222

Dave Wine said, "Save that shit for when I'm finished eating."

Fitz ignored him. "There's one big bonus for flying: you get commissioned and that gives you status. It also hides the fact that you're a grunt. Think about it. You're a grunt. In the army and marines the average rank of a casualty is PFC. In the air force it's captain. Does that tell you grunts anything?" He looked challengingly at the faces around the table. "And there aren't many wounded air force troops walking around. Of course, that's the way it should be. We fucked up the subliminal purpose of war when we started allowing the vegetables to survive. A man should emerge from combat either whole or dead."

Dave Wine said, "You fucker, you're a bundle of fun."

I grinned and slapped Fitz on the back. "Spectre's own Mr. Sunshine. You're fucking beautiful, Fitz."

"Yeah, Fitz," Dave Wine said, "*if* we get back, let me buy you a toadstool omelet for breakfast."

Seventh Air Force never directly accused anyone of anything in regard to counting kills, or perhaps specific issues never reached the crews, for a change. Several weeks before the end of the dry season, Colonel Godolphin initiated one rule change that made it obvious he was being pressured: no pictures, no score. Until then, if a videotape recorder malfunctioned, the crew's word was good enough. Before announcing the rule change, Colonel Godolphin cornered the tech reps and maintenance personnel and told them, "For the remainder of the season, the BDA recorders *will* operate with one hundred percent reliability." And they did.

The staff members at Seventh Air Force Awards and Decorations helped create the maelstrom which eventually surrounded the truck-kill figures. Based upon data from the previous season they declared that a gunship crew that stopped twenty-five trucks (a total of destroyed and damaged) on one mission and encountered at least a moderate amount of triple-A (say, two hundred fifty rounds) would be awarded a Distinguished Flying Cross. In Spectre we got hosed by at least that much trip-A every mission; therefore, half of the criteria was automatically satisfied.

Twenty-five trucks was a good night and for the first half of the season few crews attained the figure. During Lam Son 719 the total of twenty-five became a joke. Each night at least one gunship crew *destroyed* that many, or more. Spectre crews won a bunch of medals, in the thousands.

By regulation, medals were presented in a formal ceremony. The merit of the award determined the rank of the presentation officer. For example, a Silver Star had to be presented by a commander of a numbered air force (in Spectre's case, General Hunchworth); a Distinguished Flying Cross or Air Medal could be presented by any full colonel (in Spec's case, Colonel Godolphin sufficed). A man received a medal with his name engraved upon its reverse only on the first occasion that he won it. Subsequently, he was awarded the right to add a bronze oak leaf to the ribbon from which the medal was suspended. Five bronze oak leaves converted to a silver leaf. In oak leaf ceremonies, a token medal decorated with the proper number of leaves was pinned on the recipient but returned afterward.

By the time a man received a third or fourth DFC the award lost much of its significance. Spectre had crewmen with up to twelve oak leaf clusters on a DFC. Flyers also received an Air Medal or oak leaf after every fifteen combat missions, "for attendance." Following the initial presentation of an award, by unanimous mutual consent Spectre crewmen accepted the certificates and citations for oak leaf clusters through their distribution boxes, a sort of squadron mailbox. The personal satisfaction of having the gong pinned on by Grizzly wasn't worth the long standing around while everybody else trooped across the stage.

When a crew earned a DFC every man aboard the airplane received the award. General Hunchworth made that decision. In a letter, he explained, "A gunship crew is a team on which every member is equally vital and on which every member faces equal danger. Therefore, each crewman deserves an equal reward." Spectre's enlisted men loved the general's decision. The F-4 pilots who escorted us resented it.

The escort jocks believed their contribution to a gunship's

success was at least equal to, for example, what the flight engineer provided. Following Lam Son 719 one F-4 squadron commander submitted paperwork requesting that his pilots receive awards identical to those earned by the gunship crew they escorted. Already deluged by the unforeseen flood of paperwork from Spectre, Seventh AF Awards and Decs summarily disapproved those and future such requests from the fighter squadrons. The Spectre enlisted men loved that decision too. It proved once again that "If you ain't Spectre, you ain't shit."

As discussed previously, when there were few targets Spectre crews tried for blowers and burners; when targets were abundant the crews resorted to the single direct hit criterion. In late April, with undertones of doubt in the background, the scoring system of many Spectre crews became perverted. In a sort of mass atonement for suspected wrongs, many crews claimed as destroyed only what blew up, burned, or was hit numerous times. In the last half of April, strange after-battle reports were filed. On one mission we destroyed twenty-three (blowers, burners, and multiple hits) and damaged eleven (single hits and near misses) but claimed none of the damaged. Therefore, we did not qualify for a DFC. Lee and I spent a couple hours convincing Lieutenant Marconi that we did not actually come close to the trucks that we hit or came close to. When we finished, Marconi said, "Sir, no disrespect meant, but you Specs are cracking up. The Swine Brothers were here earlier and pulled the same crap."

On another mission, we drove Dave Wine batty. "Right on," I called when he hit the lead truck in a convoy; it didn't burn.

"Destroyed?" Dave asked.

"No."

"You said, 'Right on.'"

"I did? Oh—I meant 'Close.'"

"Then it's damaged?"

"Not that close."

"Shit," Dave said. He fired a long burst and hit the truck again. Nobody in the booth spoke. "Well?" Dave finally asked.

"Close again," I said.

"But not close enough?"

"Keep firing. I'll tell you when you hit it."

"What the fuck's going on?" Dave asked.

"Keep shooting," Juan urged.

Dave poured it out and hit the truck again and again and again. After the seventh hit, I said, "Hold it. That one is damaged."

"Severely damaged," said Juan.

"*Very* severely damaged," said Lee.

"You mean I didn't hit it once?" Dave asked. "What the fuck . . . ?"

"TV tracking the last truck in the convoy."

"Let me know when I hit this one," Dave said.

"Sure," I replied.

"Come on, Dave, you can do it!" Lee shouted across the booth. We laughed as one.

Dave Wine pounded the life out of the truck, but it didn't blow or burn. Some trucks were stubborn that way. "Another very seriously damaged truck," I told him.

"Another hit and it should be damaged beyond repair," Lee said.

"You said 'Hit'! I did hit it," Dave shouted.

"He meant another *close hit*," I explained. I moved the crosshairs to a different truck. "Just keep shooting."

"What the fuck . . . ?"

"Dave, you wearing your glasses?" Jim Ballard asked.

Dave figured it out. "I'll see the destroyed trucks. Am I right?"

"Right," Juan said. "Usually they burn."

We ended the night with pictures of seven destroyed and sixteen very seriously damaged. When the tape ran out, Juan didn't bother to replace it in order to record another four that we damaged. On the way home Juan said, "Only twenty-three. Too bad, Dave. No DFC."

"I thought I counted twenty-seven," Dave said. "Seven and twenty." He thought about the numbers. "*Twenty* damaged?"

"I counted twenty-seven," Dick said.

"Tape don't lie," Juan said. "Maybe next time, Dave."

"Maybe next time," Dave said, "I'll bring a flamethrower."

A sensor team couldn't play that game with somebody who was a weak shooter. Dave was one of the best. And a good sport too.

The next day, a picture of a truck was on the squadron bulletin board. In the picture the truck's tires were off, its cabin was smashed flat, its bed was mangled. It was a total wreck. However, the truck had not been gutted by fire. A grease-penciled caption read: "One of Zorn's slightly damaged trucks."

"Wonder who put that up?" Juan said.

"I don't know," Lee said, "but he sure knows what he's talking about."

"Had to be a pilot," I said. "The message is printed, and in crayon."

Chapter 21

I Am the Walrus

THE RAINS CAME on the first of May, and throughout Thailand communities welcomed the new season. With parades and parties they celebrated Nature's gift to grow crops for another year. In recognition of the rain, Thais flicked droplets of water on each other in greeting. Those who paraded willingly were splashed with pails of water and joyfully soaked by the end of the march.

The Americans delighted in the old Thai custom and splashed each other. What started in the O-Club with a spoonful of water playfully tossed across the breakfast table quickly escalated to a fire-hose washdown of the entire club. Water War was declared: flying squadron against flying squadron. No place was safe. People were hit with buckets of water at their desks, in bed, at the barber shop, anywhere and everywhere they happened to be. Before noon, flyers were soaked several times over. The Water War expanded. Nonflying support personnel on their way to lunch were attacked and drenched without warning. Bands of men in wet flying suits and armed with buckets of water roamed the streets of the base and doused anyone who was dry—man, woman, or child. A Spectre crew on an afternoon mission bombed the base with water-filled condoms before heading to the Basket.

The war ended after an over-zealous group of disguised

raiders swamped the wing commander while he was busily signing papers at his desk. The Man didn't see the humor in the attack. By late afternoon, air policemen patrolled the streets and issued warnings to cease water.

That evening after everyone was dry, Lee Schmidt was sitting alone, reading a book in the O-Club dining room. Juan and I saw him before he saw us. Without a word, we backed from the dining room. "You're not really thinking what I'm thinking?" Juan said. We hurried to the kitchen's back door. We signaled the Thai cooks and waitresses to go about their business. After half-filling a twenty-gallon stock pot with shaved ice, we put it under a faucet. We were giggling, and the head chef and waitresses giggled along with us. I held a forefinger to my lips in the universal signal for quiet and the chef giggled louder. It seemed to take forever to fill the pot. Juan scurried back and forth to the kitchen doors to make certain Lee remained facing away from us. Juan pointed out the victim to the chef.

The filled pot was heavy, difficult to control. Juan and I, each gripping a handle in both hands, staggered to the door with it. The chef made things easy. He parted the swinging doors, kicked wedges in place, then put both hands under the pot. Juan and I took two fast side steps into the dining room and the chef upended the pot. I had to hand it to Lee. He was stolid. The water was near freezing, but he didn't flinch or make a sound. Still seated, soaked completely, he exaggeratedly licked a forefinger and carefully turned to the next soggy page. The chef howled with delight. "He number one GI leader."

"I have five months to get even," Lee said. He looked first over his right shoulder, then over his left. "You'll never know when or where you're going to get it."

The rains came on the first of May and the southwestern monsoons rolled low clouds across Laos. Trucks continued to move because the rains did not instantly turn the dirt roads to quagmires. B-52s and F-4s made radar, computer, and LORAN-controlled bomb drops through the clouds on coordinates provided by TFA. They continued the drops on into June.

Spectre had a difficult time. Frequently sensors found a vehicle but, before the pilot attacked, a cloud layer drifted into the picture and the truck escaped. The IR, which could sense heat through thin foliage, was washed clean by clouds; the IR picture turned a dirty gray. The TV also was useless against clouds.

Late in May, the Black Crow on Pete Angelino's crew located a mover and, when the IR and TV were blocked by clouds, on a whim the BC suggested shooting with guidance from his sensor. Like a wife, it was better than nothing. On his cathode-ray tube, the BC centered crosshairs on an imaginary midpoint of the bouncing and shifting dancing green dot cluster generated by the truck's engine. The BC's erratic guidance data fed through the fire-control computer. In the pilot's gunsight, the electronic display representing the BC sensor's line of sight bobbed and weaved. After several futile attempts at superimposing his fixed gunline reticle on the BC display, Pete Angelino switched to a less refined tactic. Whenever the gunline reticle passed near the BC display, he squeezed off a long burst of 20-mm fire. The procedure was as haphazard as a blind man washing a car by hosing water from an altitude of a mile while another person guided him by honking the car's horn.

On Angelino's third long burst, Buddha must have stepped out for tea: a bright flash illuminated the clouds from below and the dots disappeared from the BC's CRT. Moments later, through the cloud layer the IR faintly detected a hot spot where the BC had been sighting. The truck's loss of vital signs was positive enough to satisfy everyone: Angelino's crew was credited with the first truck killed off BC guidance. The BC tech rep was so delighted that he treated Angelino's crew to dinner and drinks.

After that, when the IR and TV were blanked out, every crew rained gunfire down through the clouds off BC guidance in hopes of winning a free meal. Billy Killeen crept along the top of cloud decks, around five thousand feet, and buzzed away at six thousand rounds per minute with the 7.62-mm machine guns. "We're safe," he said. "We can't see them; they can't see us." Of course, *they* were safe too. Except for

Angelino's lucky burst, using BC nobody hit anything but the ground.

Coming off the dry season high, I guessed the NVA gunners were desperate for a little excitement too. Every so often they launched a big unguided rocket at nobody in particular. The NVA probably got a good price on them as leftovers from Chinese New Year's. The fireworks displays lasted about a week. The most our crew saw on a single mission was four. When one of those speeding shapes spitting sparks and flames ripped upward out of the undercast and exploded with enough energy to light half of SEA, Billy rolled into geometry and sent a string of 40-mms earthward. With boring predictability Jim Ballard said, "Chalk up another destroyed cloud," and Lee said, "Looked only damaged to me," and Juan and I said, "Fuck it."

Jeff Scott's crew held the record for sighting unguided rockets: fourteen in one night and the closest missed by only half a mile.

As May progressed TFA reported a steady decline in truck traffic, and gunship sorties were reduced proportionately. We logged ten missions that month. Before the fifteenth, we totaled six destroyed and seventeen damaged; after that, two and fifteen. The trucks we found were either empty or carrying nothing that would explode.

During the month only twelve hundred AAA shells were fired at our crew. Nevertheless, Jim Ballard continued to wear his combat gear, as he had on every flight during the dry season. The dressing habits of other booth dwellers ran in cycles. Juan and I knew from experience that the booth was penetrable. Following harrowing experiences we wore our equipment. At those times Juan said, "I wish we had flak socks too." Then the passage of time dimmed our fears and we succumbed to the cozy *feeling* of safety provided by the booth, that "big womb in the sky." At such times, parachutes became backrests (we reasoned that, if things got hot, we could slip into them in a second . . . or three). Flak helmets were replaced by headsets that were lighter, cooler, more comfortable. We draped our survival vests over the backs of our seats so that we could slip into them at the same time we put on our parachutes. A flak vest? If I didn't wear it on the NOD, I certainly wasn't going to wear it in the booth.

Only Jim Ballard wore his combat gear every day. Into the wet season he faced away from us while putting it on. When dressed, he looked out of place (". . . like some fuck from Mars who caught the wrong bus," I muttered to Juan) and he acted guilty about wearing the junk. I finally told him, "Jimmy, don't be ashamed because you wear that shit." To prove my point, I too put it all on. I searched the cargo compartment until I found a spare flak vest and put it on too. After an hour, laded to my psychological and physiological capacities, I let out a comic book "Aaaaarrrrrgh!" and piece by piece tore off the equipment and flung it around the booth. Then I began taking off my clothes too.

On the spur of the moment, Juan and Lee also undressed. Boots, socks, flying suits, underwear sailed through the air. We popped a spare parachute and draped the enormous canopy inside the booth, like some sheik's tent. Stark naked, Lee shouted, "Nothing in moderation." I agreed: "I'd rather be sorry than safe." At that point, nobody wanted to be a pussy and make the first gesture to dress. Wearing only headsets, we turned the booth lights to red and sat around with our balls out to air. Then, of all fucking people, Tex Tyler walked in without knocking. He had been on his way aft to piss. Nobody offered to explain our configuration to him, and he backed out without asking. Of course, Jim Ballard was still dressed to the teeth. We probably confirmed a lot of Tex's suspicions that day. But, Jesus . . . we were bored.

Lieutenant Danny Dashout broke up our boredom the day he flew in Ballard's place. I had hardly seen Dashout since he rammed me in the chest with Herky. The way Dashout acted, once every six months was enough. The night he accompanied us, Steel Tiger was socked in solid below and in the booth we were grabbing Zs. Suddenly Dashout shouted, "This is BC. I . . . ," then quickly mumbled, ". . . don't . . . ," before he roared out, ". . . have a missile ready-to-launch light." The words that registered were "launch light." I came wide awake. My pulse accelerated into triple figures. For a two-beat the gunship was quiet as death. Then Killeen spoke: "What? What? Say that again." Dashout muttered, "I said . . ."—he knew by then that the joke wasn't funny—". . . I have no ready-to-launch light." His humor was like shouting "Fire!" in a packed auditorium. Juan Sueno glared blackly. He leaped out of his seat a step ahead of me, glided forward, and slapped Dashout's helmet with a force that cracked like a pistol shot. Lee Schmidt was already eyeball to eyeball with Dashout: "You imbecile, that's not funny." Juan didn't speak for an hour. I finally saw the humor in the situation, about two years later.

The rains came on the first of May, and I used the privilege of my rank to move into a two-man trailer which had private rooms separated by a bath. Now that we were flying less often, Dick Kaulbach spent most of his time downtown. The new room privileges were more than I expected. The second day I was there, while I was reading, my slim Thai housegirl walked up beside me, ran her fingers through my hair, then pulled my face into her belly. Fifteen seconds later she was spread on the bed, holding me with raised arms, and I was one millimeter from penetration. She looked into my eyes and said, "When you leave, can I have your radio?" It was a Zenith Trans-Oceanic. I laughed and told her, "Yes. You can have everything." Minutes later I thought, *Welcome again to the East.* Her name was Mei and she was a little bit better than excellent.

Billy Killeen's promotion to lieutenant colonel became effective and, when the adjoining room was vacated, he moved in as my trailermate. Some late afternoons, we and Mei engaged in what we called the Orgy Hour. During the postcoital interludes, Billy Killeen and I chatted while Mei showered and dressed, then tidied the room before going home to her parents. Of our many conversations, there was one that I was unable to forget. "At the bar one time," Billy said, "I heard a group of aircraft commanders complaining to Grizzly about the way you throw shit at everybody. They thought you were crazy and wanted him to send you to a shrink."

Surprised, I told Billy about meeting with Colonel Godolphin over *Quotations from Chairman Mao Tse-Tung*. By then I had given away the little red book. One hot afternoon on the ramp, I left the crew, walked to a group of Thai construction workers, and presented the book to the tallest laborer. I saw only the dusty man's black irises and pupils set in bloodshot yellow. The man was dressed like an open-hearth shoveler: wide-brimmed hat, head coiled by a rag that hid all but the eyes, shirt-sweater-and-coat, gloves, pants clipped at the ankles, but—below it all—bare feet. I told him, "You need this more than I do." The man studied both front and back of the bright red cover, gestured to make certain the book was intended for him, then brought his hands together in front of his face and in gratitude slowly bowed lower and lower until he was squatting with his chin touching his knees. The other laborers stopped working. He held the pose for many, many seconds. Nonplussed, then chagrined because I thought the laborer was overreacting and attracting unnecessary attention, I broke my own mood by saying to the man, who obviously spoke no English, "Sure, we're friends now, but when you've taken over this country will you remember who gave you the book?" Afterward, Billy said my gesture was so sweet that in my next life Buddha would probably bring me back as the Tooth Fairy.

Now, sitting in my room, Billy said, "Grizzly doesn't care about stuff like Mao's book. He probably agrees that the complainers suck. You flew your missions no matter what, and, when you weren't scheduled, you volunteered for more. That's all he wanted. He told those ACs at the bar that he needed a dozen more crazy navs who were willing to fly as much as you." Mei walked by Billy. "How 'bout that, Mei?" he said and patted her backside. "Good flyers all crazy?"

"Hey, GI, watch you' hands. Fun time gone." She giggled and bent over and pressed her cheek against his.

"What about Fitz?" I asked. "He flew all the time."

"Fitz fucked up when he took his problem outside the family. He shouldn't have gone crying to a stranger, least of all to a general, before he talked it over with Grizzly. Fitz challenged Grizzly in public and Grizzly couldn't let it pass. Put yourself in his place. In private, man to man, Grizzly doesn't care what's said. People don't understand that. Anyhow, you and Fitz are different cases. You flew with Ed Holcomb."

I questioned what he meant.

"Flying with Ed gave you special dispensation. To Grizzly, Ed is unequaled. Hell, he made him ops officer ahead of everybody. He let Ed do anything he wanted to do, especially after that one night . . . Why do you think Ed never got a sick airplane, even when maintenance had four down with battle damage? Why do you think you always found trucks?"

"Not *always*," I said.

"More than anybody else," Billy said. "Ed was allowed to pick the airplane he wanted, the takeoff time he wanted, and the target sector he wanted. And that was practically every time he flew. Ed figured it out. At TFA he researched every record and history he could get his hands on. He recognized patterns of where the trucks would be and when they'd most likely be there. He even tied it to phases of the moon. Why am I telling *you* this? Weren't you with him at TFA?"

"No. I mean, yeah. I mean, we all went. But we made a gee-whiz tour of the building and headed downtown. It was a wasted day. Ed stuck around base, but that's how he is: he never goes downtown. He never told us . . ."

Billy frowned in thought for a while, then said, "You all were busy flying with other crews. On those days, Ed must have planned the missions you flew with him." Billy smiled. "That Ed! He'll be a general some day. He probably never told you what was going on because he wanted you all to think you were doing it. Things always are better when you work for them."

Ed Holcomb had used us, I thought. He'd used all of us: Dick, Lee, Juan, Jim. He had used the airplanes, the squadron, TFA. Godolphin had permitted him to do it. Why not? Ed had all the answers. And we had never suspected it. I smiled to myself. *The clever son of a bitch,* I thought admiringly. Who was I to complain? Ed had taken good care of me, good care of the whole crew. Without him we would be dead. I looked at Billy Killeen. We both smiled broadly, I said, "Fuck me!"

"No. No more today," Mei said. "We do again tomorrow. I go home now."

Chapter 22

You Can't Always Get What You Want

THE RAINS CAME on the first of May and while the NVA truck drivers slowed down, Seventh Air Force second-guessers shifted into high gear. They analyzed Spectre's dry-season performance with a list of questions:

How often had Spectre crews restruck and recounted vehicles that had been struck and counted earlier the same night by a different crew?

What percentage of Spectre targets were hulks of previously destroyed vehicles which the NVA had strategically parked to attract gunfire?

How often had Spectre crews been fooled into thinking they had destroyed a vehicle as a result of decoy explosions? Smoke grenades? False fires?

In the mistaken belief that it was a truck signature, how often had IR attacks been made on flare pots or similar decoy hot spots?

How often had Spectre scored a single hit on an armored truck and scored it as destroyed?

Colonel Godolphin called in Ed Holcomb and the navigators from our crew and showed us the questions. After reading the list, I said, "Those are loaded questions."

"Yes, but the assumptions are interesting," Colonel Godolphin said.

237

"Nothing we didn't already think about," Lee Schmidt threw in, instinctively playing cover your ass.

"Seventh wants us to analyze our results," Godolphin stated.

"If they're not satisfied with what we've done," said Jim Ballard, "why don't they go back and review the tapes?"

Colonel Godolphin reminded him that most of the tapes had been erased.

"Oh?" Jim said it as if it were the first time anyone had told him. Sometimes BCs were in their own world. "What about 'The Best'?" he asked.

"That's nothing but a commercial," said Juan Sueno.

Godolphin nodded. "Its name condemns it. 'Best!' What about the other ninety-nine percent?"

I asked, "Why did they wait until now to start this?" but I knew the answer. We all knew the answer. Nobody had expected Spec to rack up over thirteen thousand trucks. As a result, a larger issue was at stake: How could Tactical Air Command program managers justify huge expenditures for sleek "advanced" multi-purpose jet fighters when a lumbering cargo plane accomplished interdiction on such a grand scale?

Godolphin told us, "Answer the questions and verify the destroyed and damaged totals the best you can. If it's any consolation, you're doing it for General Hunchworth, nobody else. He happens to be on our side. Whatever you come up with goes directly to him. Take a hard look at the big picture. Tell us what you see."

Lee said, "The big picture was flushed down the tubes. If we had the tapes . . ."

Godolphin was patient. "General Hunchworth understands that. And he regrets it. Do the best with what you have."

With the evidence destroyed, it now was up to us to prove the deeds had been done. George Orwell would have loved our predicament.

We trashed Seventh's list of questions and struck out on our own. The only things we had to work with were the mission reports coupled with our intuition and experience. We decided to do a hatchet job on the squadron. If the results turned out to be too embarrassing, then we jokingly agreed we would lie.

Dick, Lee, Juan, Jim, and I went through more than two thousand mission reports, one by one, the entire 1970–1971 dry season. If nothing else, the exercise proved that navigators are outstanding bookkeepers, CPA quality. The sensor which made initial contact, the sensor which provided firing guidance, the Greenwich Mean Time of start and stop attack, the geographical coordinates to the minute (within one hundred feet) as taken from LORAN readings, and the results (blower, burner, etc.) were logged for every target. The forms were a statistician's dream.

We determined that of the ten thousand trucks claimed as destroyed (10,319 to be exact):

—Twenty-eight hundred burned.
—Twenty-two hundred exploded in some manner.
—Fifty-three hundred suffered at least one direct hit by a 40-mm shell (and, of this total, one thousand could have been restruck vehicles).

Of the twenty-seven hundred trucks damaged (2,733 to be precise):

—Seventeen hundred suffered from near misses by 40-mm shells.
—One thousand were struck by 20-mm shells.
—Of the total, five hundred could have been restruck targets.

We were harsh in our judgments. The slightest indication of duplicated effort put the truck into the restruck category. That is, if on the same night two trucks were logged within a thousand feet of each other by different airplanes, we called one restruck. There was no way to account for decoys, or for armored vehicles, or for trucks that were damaged, repaired, redamaged, re-repaired, redamaged . . .

We also came up with figures that showed fifty-four percent of the vehicles were initially located by the Black Crow, which indicated they were live targets—the engines were running. From February through April, the microphones and seismic sensors of Task Force Alpha provided leads that resulted in thirty-five percent of the BDA, again proof of live targets. Unable to resolve duplication between the BC and TFA, we concluded that from fifty-four to eighty-nine percent of the targets were valid.

As we saw it, five thousand trucks definitely had been destroyed. Sixty-five hundred had been damaged to various degrees. The other fifteen hundred (eleven percent of the grand total) we chalked up to experience, or inexperience. It was easy to see that the measure of success depended upon the degree to which we had damaged the sixty-five hundred.

Shortly thereafter, along with Colonel Godolphin, our crew made a trip to Tan Son Nhut Air Base, outside of Saigon, and met with General Hunchworth and a staff that overflowed a large conference room's seating capacity. The meeting was short and to the point. General Hunchworth told everyone to pay attention and then talked only to the sensor operators.

Once again, his attitude made me feel as if he was working for us as much as we were working for him. I doubted that we told him anything he didn't know or hadn't already guessed. Still, he listened.

We said that from our experience we believed that:

—Crews relied upon the single hit with a Forty criterion mostly for expediency.
—When time was available, crews tried for burners and blowers.
—Crew errors were honest mistakes. (It was possible to attack a hulk or a decoy. It was possible to be faked out. As in any work, experience reduced errors.)
—If it didn't burn or blow, a vehicle probably wasn't destroyed with a single 40-mm hit.

* * *

On 12 May 1971 we took our show on the road. At the crack of dawn Colonel Godolphin piled our crew aboard a gunship piloted by Ed Holcomb and took us back to Tan Son Nhut to meet with General Hunchworth. The general appeared to be tired and looked like a man with problems, but he had a smile and greeting for each of us. He thanked us for our research, then said, "We may be working the problem backward, but the truth is all that matters. At the start of the dry season, we took ASD's word on how much damage the Forty would do. Perhaps we made a mistake. Now, I want to see for myself."

A staff officer briefed us. We learned that in the afternoon we would strike trucks parked near a set of coordinates north of Bien Hoa. We received a takeoff time and a radio frequency on which to call for further instructions after we located the trucks. That was it.

Following the briefing, Colonel Godolphin had only a few moments to talk to us before he went to lunch with the general. "The trucks are on a firing range. We'll be observing you from a bunker about a thousand yards away. Go get 'em, tigers." Then he was gone.

"Did you know about this?" Dick asked Ed.

"Sort of. I picked the crew." And, obviously, the airplane. We had the same bird we flew on Easter, the morning Billy Killeen drove nails.

Ed hadn't flown with us for two months. I wondered if he still had his touch. I would have felt more confident with Billy Killeen. We recognized that we were representing the entire squadron for the whole year. If we failed, Spectre may as well have claimed zero destroyed for the season. It seemed unfair. After proving ourselves so often in combat, we had to prove ourselves and our airplane one more time before the eyes of our critics. We had little to gain.

At least there wouldn't be triple-A.

Dick headed us to the coordinates. About five miles out, Jimmy picked up engine signals on the BC and said, "I smell trucks." Ed rolled into geometry on BC guidance. Eight trucks were parked on an S-shaped portion of dirt road, out in the middle of nowhere. The first six were thirty to forty feet apart, staggered left and right of the center of the road. The last two were a hundred yards farther back, around the second curve, near a clump of trees.

Lee and I looked over the area, searched the road in both directions, checked out the roadsides. A long, grassy field abutted one side of the road. At the far end of the field was a bunker topped with grass. I had the uneasy feeling that this mission meant more than all the combat sorties we had flown.

"This must be the place," Lee said. We both slapped crosshairs on the lead truck. "IR tracking."

"TV."

"Put TV in," Ed said.

"In," said Dick.

Tex Tyler made a call on the assigned frequency. General Hunchworth answered: "Affirmative, Spec, we have you overhead. How many trucks have you found?"

"Eight," I said.

"Eight," Lee agreed and Tex Tyler relayed the answer.

"According to the BC," the general asked, "how many engines are running?"

"Three," Jim Ballard said and his answer was relayed.

"According to the IR, how many engines are running and which ones?"

"Three," Lee said. "Numbers one, three, and seven in line." They produced the brightest heat signatures. "Eight looks like it shut down not too long ago."

There was a pause following Tyler's relay; then General Hunchworth laughingly said, "My aide tells me that's right. We had trouble finding a suitable eighth truck and it arrived only a little while back." He told us to strike the first six trucks with 40-mm fire and the last two with 20-mm.

"TV tracking the lead truck."

"Give me a Forty," Ed said.

"You got it, sir," said Rusty Brown.

Ed and I couldn't find each other. I hadn't felt one-tenth as nervous on our first truck kill together. I had never been as rough. The tracking handle felt like a roll of salami to my touch. Ed wasn't smooth either. We chased each other, overcompensated, anticipated, and made mistakes we had never made even as beginners. I caught myself waiting, expecting the gun to fire at any moment, practically flinching in advance. Then when it didn't fire, I started hoping it would fire, anything to get off that first shot. We went around twice, four minutes that seemed like four hours, with the droning engines making the only sound.

General Hunchworth came up on the radio. "You're clear to fire, Spec."

"Affirmative. Thank you, sir," Tex Tyler said.

My hand was slippery on the tracking handle. I was soaked with flop sweat. I looked at Juan and he had an unsympathetic expression, nearly a look of disgust. I felt sick to my stomach. Hating myself and forcing myself to mentally blanket my ego, I was about to ask Ed if he wanted to try shooting off the IR when the Forty fired. I nearly leaped out of my seat. . . . *ka-pung, ka-pung, ka-pung* . . . It wasn't Ed's normal tempo. Instead it was one long stream of fire. . . . *ka-pung, ka-pung, ka-pung* . . . I looked at the TV. The crosshairs had drifted into a roadside ditch. What the hell was I doing? . . . *ka-pung, ka-pung, ka-pung* . . . Jesus Christ! I slid the crosshairs onto the hood of the lead truck and killed the drift without thinking about my actions. Parallel to the lead truck, rounds exploded in the ditch. "Five low," I said automatically. Ed was still firing. Like an old fire horse reacting to a bell, I had been galvanized to action by the cannon's report. Tracking tight, on the edge of my seat, I felt cool as ice. . . . *ka-pung, ka-pung, ka-pung* . . .

Ed's stream of shells walked out of the ditch, arced across the road, and smacked all over the lead truck.

"Beautiful," Juan said.

It was the most impressive opening number I had seen. Round after round now smashed into the lead truck.

"Dork," Juan muttered. He had forgotten to turn on the video recorder. Nobody was perfect, I thought.

Except maybe Ed.

If you took away his bike.

Ed was in his groove, a groove beyond his groove. On his deathbed Ed would be in his groove. Ali move over. Ed was the greatest.... *ka-pung, ka-pung, ka-pung* ... From seventy-five hundred feet he plastered the lead truck with direct hits. Covered with goosebumps, I had the crosshairs frozen on the target. The truck didn't burn.

"Spec, enough, enough," General Hunchworth said. "Try the second truck."

I moved the crosshairs; Ed resumed firing. Three direct hits and the truck blew and burned. Thick black smoke rolled up toward us. Two minutes later we set number three afire. *What a command performance*, I thought and felt a kind of omnipotence, like Genghis fucking Khan, a power rush I hadn't experienced since some of our early kills.

We beat on number four but it wouldn't burn.

Hunchworth asked which sensor we'd been using. Tex told him and the general said, "Switch to IR for the last four targets. On trucks five and six I want you to cease fire when you consider the trucks damaged."

I was finished for the day! Pumped up to my eyeballs with adrenaline, I sat and bounced while Lee led the attack. Why had play suddenly become more exciting than the real thing?

Firing one round at a time, Ed planted a shell about ten feet from the fifth truck. We talked it over. Ed wasn't satisfied. He put another round four feet in front of the target and we agreed it was close enough to classify the truck as damaged.

Ed accidentally hit the sixth truck with the first round. "Sorry, sir," he called.

"Good enough," the general said. He sounded pleased.

Ed split the load of 20-mm rounds equally between the last two vehicles. Sparkles danced over both trucks but neither blew or burned. Out of ammo, Ed called, "Winchester, sir."

"Using dry-season criteria," General Hunchworth asked, "what would be your score for the day?"

"Five destroyed; three damaged."

"Come on down and let's look at them," Hunchworth said.

By the time we landed, then drove to the range, the high-ranking spectators were gone. Trucks two and three had burned because each had been carrying three barrels of fuel. We had hit the barrels, set them on fire, and in turn torched the trucks.

Trucks one and four had six-to twelve-inch-wide holes all over them. The 40-mm shells had penetrated the hoods and torn into the engines. On one, the driver's cabin was demolished. Oil and hydraulic fluids dripped from both trucks.

Trucks five and six were disappointments. Near-misses had flung shrapnel through the sides of number five. Its tires were flat, as were the tires of the first four vehicles. Likewise, most glass was punched out or shattered. Once the tires were replaced, however, it looked as if number five would be operable. The keys were in the ignition.

Dick climbed aboard, started and raced the engine. It sounded healthy. He shifted the truck into gear and drove fifty feet on flat tires while I wished the vehicle would die.

The sixth truck upon which we had scored a single direct hit was unharmed except for a nine-inch hole through its quarter-inch corrugated steel bed. Even the tires were intact. That truck could have been driven to Hanoi.

The trucks were American, heavy steel brutes. "Think the Commie trucks are this well made?" I asked Dick.

"Not quite," he said. "Same size, but lighter weight, thinner metal. These are old trucks. Our new ones aren't this heavy either."

The ground around the last two trucks was strewed with unexploded 20-mm HEI shells. From seventy-five hundred feet many of the rounds tended to tumble in flight before reaching target. Fist-size dents covered the trucks like vehicular pockmarks. A few shells had gashed the hoods without producing visible damage to the engines. With new tires, both trucks might have been operable.

I wondered what the results would have been had we used misch metal rounds. As I saw it, we definitely destroyed the two burners, damaged two so that they required major maintenance and would be out of commission indefinitely, damaged three that probably could be repaired and returned to duty within a day or two, and barely touched the other. I was disturbed by that last one, the single hit with a 40-mm shell. Using the dry-season criteria, it would have been logged as destroyed when actually it was the least damaged of the lot.

After examining the trucks, we gathered before the least-damaged one. "Somewhere in the back of my mind, I always suspected this," Dick said.

"Me too," said Lee.

Juan kicked a tire. "Asi es la vida."

"And que sera sera," Jim added.

We had risen above shattered idols before . . . Santa Claus . . . the Easter Bunny . . . God. Now, it was the Forty Millimeter Cannon. We could rise above it again.

Colonel Godolphin was ecstatic when he met us at the gunship for the flight home to Ubon. "A marvelous, marvelous demonstration," he told Ed. Working his way between Lee and me, he threw his arms around our shoulders. "Marvelous. You cleared the crews once and for all. There's no doubt about what the gunship can do."

I wondered if anyone remembered the miles of videotape.

"You should *hear* the guns from the ground. We were a thousand yards away, but when you fired in our direction, they *boomed*. The flash suppressor must funnel the noise. They sound amplified. It has to be ten times worse when you're directly under them. I don't know how the drivers stand it. And the Twenties! They growl like they're about to eat you alive. A marvelous demonstration." He grinned from ear to ear. "Ed, when you walked that first stream of Forties out of the ditch and right onto the truck, the skeptics nearly fell over. General Hunchworth was delighted. He's been on the crews' side from the beginning." Godolphin patted Lee and me on our backs. "I'm damn proud of you, all of you." He looked off into the distance. "I just wish you could *hear* those guns . . ."

When we were airborne, the rest of the story came out. In the future, no matter what it was hit with, a truck had to burn or blow up before being counted as destroyed. Crews were expected to hit trucks more than once in an effort to make them burn. "General Hunchworth has no complaints with the crews," Godolphin explained, "but he is irritated with ASD for selling the wrong criteria."

Later he told us that the dry-season figures would stand as they were. Exact numbers were impossible to recompute, although General Hunchworth thought the statistics from our research had validity. Trying to explain a change would be too difficult, too controversial. Instead, the gunship mission would be played down in public reports. Besides, officially there was no war in Laos.

We were permitted to keep our medals.

Chapter 23

Under My Thumb

COMMON SENSE TOLD a person that if he screwed around in a war zone long enough, eventually *friendly* fire would mistakenly zero in on him. It happened in every war novel. To my way of thinking, when my own people started shooting at me, it was time to call it quits and go home. Over Laos we weren't concerned with that threat: there were no friendlies on the ground; the closest guys in the sky were our escorts; every airplane was a buddy.

My first time under *enemy* fire was at the start of the 1968 Tet Offensive. I was caught in the open, out in the middle of the Tan Son Nhut aircraft munitions loading area, when rockets and mortar rounds crashed into the base without warning. For the next few minutes my mind and my body weren't synchronized. Rather, they were engaged in independently solving the common problem of survival . . .

At the first explosion, finding myself with neither helmet nor flak vest, I expected to be killed on the spot. Jesus, my mind thought, I was helpless to protect myself. My resigned mind cursed its luck: A journey halfway around the world . . . to come to this . . . stupid . . . I was going to die . . . and I had volunteered for it . . . doubly stupid!

Meanwhile, my body had reflexively thrown itself to the ground, was suctioning itself to the tarmac, straining to be absorbed by the impervious surface. It seemed to be the most natural act in the world. Finding it impossible to melt into the ground, however, the body bellied across the paving in search of greater protection. Adapting instantly to its primordial instinct for slithering, the body located a depression an inch or two below the surrounding surface, then nestled into it. The Grand Canyon couldn't have provided a greater sense of security.

Curiously, my resigned mind found occupation with analyzing events outside itself. It observed that the rockets overhead were sailing in from the north, making soft, sibilant sounds in flight—*sssss-swwwww-swswswswsw.* Doppler effect, the mind said. The rockets were crashing into the aircraft parking area, far across the runway: *ka-kwack!*—a sharp, evil sound.

The sons of bitches weren't aimed at me, I happily decided but in the same instant reflected on the one inevitable round that accidentally would fall short. Well, nothing I could do about that, the mind said. As long as I heard the rockets swishing overhead I was safe.

Almost unnoticed, mortar rounds had been impacting modestly: *whumph*—a muffled cough of death. Through the ground my body felt the mortar rounds' deep concussions, nudges of high explosives compared to the rockets' slash of scalpel shrapnel.

Pretty much at ease by then, I decided that, after all, it would take a direct hit to kill me, as low as I was and everything. I estimated the chances of a direct hit at around fifty thousand to one . . . at least . . . probably more . . . definitely more . . . much more. After all, *they weren't aiming at me!* That thought reunited mind and body. I confirmed to all parts of myself that most likely I wasn't going to die, at least not then and there.

Crawling onward to a drainage ditch, I located a truly secure spot and watched the conclusion of the bombardment. It was anticlimactic. I felt disappointed that the explosions weren't more colorful, more long-lasting. Most of the rounds missed worthwhile targets, failed to wreak meaningful destruction. It certainly wasn't Hollywood, where a single bullet destroyed any foe, my mind said.

Not too many weeks later I decided that my initial reflexive fear was best. That type of fear was justified. Danger came out of nowhere, without warning, grabbed one by the throat and jerked him clear out of his boots. The body reacted. The experience ended. Everything was open, on the up and up. That was good, honest, wage-earning fear.

Sudden fear was void of the subjective buildup of foreboding, lacked the intellectually motivated, gnawing feeling of impending doom that usually accompanied the unknown. That sort of fear—insidious fear—was a royal motherfucker, an element that should be purged from mankind's periodic table of emotions.

Insidious fear stalks, sneaks up from behind, wraps a silk noose around the heart, and slowly strangles life.

I learned the mind-warping power of insidious fear the day Steve Lowe's C-130 was shot to pieces in the A Shau Valley . . .

Our crew was scheduled for the first resupply drop on the following morning. That night, insidious fear crept into my Saigon room, silently crawled into my bed, pressed its clammy body against mine, and wrapped a silk noose about my heart. Its touch told me that tomorrow *I was going to die.* Rows of guns, barrages of piercing steel awaited me. Never had I felt such dread. I fell into the hopeless sleep of one fatally damned.

In the morning, premission briefing held the climate of Death Row when an execution was imminent: sullen resignation filled the air. I wasn't alone in my feelings: pilot, copilot, flight engineer, and loadmaster were strictly business, each wrapped in private thoughts and duties. (Everyone pretty much controlled his feelings except the engineer, who checked out a steel helmet and, somehow, performed the impossible feat of forcing that metal pot *over* his headset prior to the descent into the valley. His action was completely out of step: nobody wore a steel helmet in an airplane. Looking back on it, the act had been ridiculous enough to break the tension. At the time, however, I'd failed to see the humor because I had no clear idea of what danger lurked in the valley.) Nobody had a clear idea of what lurked in the valley, a valley of death into which we were to lead the way. The previous day, the last C-130 had been shot down, the one before it shot up. Although on the previous day we had sneaked through untouched, today we expected fate to even the score.

The briefing officer provided one avenue of escape. "You don't have to enter at the southern end and fly yesterday's route down the length of the valley," he said. "Today you can follow any route you want. All you have to do is make good on your drop time at A Luoi." Reprieve? We didn't have to crawl the Last Mile; we could leap into the execution chamber through a side door! For a moment the noose stopped contracting.

At the airplane, pilot and copilot read checklists as if searching for points of appeal in a capital punishment trial transcript. Gloom was the order of the day.

Since the briefing, I'd been obsessed with alternate routes to the DZ. At one point, dive-bombing sounded reasonable. The noose again was tightening. A deeply imbedded premonition told me that we were going to be hit hard—very, very hard.

From entry point at the southern mouth of the A Shau Valley northwest to the DZ at A Luoi was a distance of thirteen miles, straight up Route 548. A C-130 needed six minutes to fly that far. Six minutes sounded like six years to me. I decided to sneak into the valley near Ta Bat, only four miles from the DZ. That way, we'd be exposed to the waiting destruction for only two minutes. My plan seemed sane: burst in, get hit very hard, dump the load, run for our lives.

When we arrived over A Shau, the area was covered by a cloud deck with tops around five thousand feet. My chart showed a valley perpendicularly intersecting the A Shau two miles south of Ta Bat. That looked good enough for me: slither down one valley and into the other. Without hesitating, I told the pilot to descend. I didn't brief him on my plan because I knew that no pilot liked to fly between hills while inside clouds.

Trustingly, he started down. "Where we going?"

"Into the valley," I said. Using radar, I guided him through the cloud deck, around the rocks. We were heading primarily southwest.

After a minute or three, the pilot said, "Hal, if we're going to the DZ, shouldn't we be heading northwest?"

By then we were clear of the ridge. "Correct," I said, "take a ninety degree right turn."

"What's going on?" the pilot asked.

"Don't worry. Take a ninety right. Hurry! That'll line us up with the valley, with the DZ."

As he banked into the turn, we punched out of the bottom of the cloud deck and found ourselves a thousand feet above the landscape. When we rolled level, the panorama that met us was forever locked into a prime-time channel of my memory:

We were perfectly aligned with Route 548, the landing strip at Ta Bat directly before us; four miles beyond sat the strip at A Luoi. Yellow smoke blossomed from the DZ. To the left, batteries of friendly arty busily chunked rounds in the direction of Laos. Several gunship helicopters prowled both sides of the valley, hunted the hillsides. The setting looked as safe as any State-side training range. Regardless, *I wanted out of there*. The silk noose was crushing me.

By then we were below the ridge tops and I felt trapped, claustrophobic. With jungle closing in from both sides and clouds pressing down from above, there was no exit. We were flying in the shadow of death, following the track that had led Steve Lowe's crew to destruction. Then, off to the left and short of the DZ, I spotted the charred skeletal remains of Lowe's Hercules. The noose drew tighter than ever. I raced through checklists, signaled for the drop, called, "Green light!"

The pilot pulled up the C-130's nose. The co saw I was far too early and, for a moment, waved in disagreement; then he dropped his hand and muttered, "Forget it."

The load landed on the road, *six thousand feet short of the DZ*. The cargo was recoverable but the poor groundpounders would have to manhandle the dozen one-ton bundles of ammo and C-rats an extra mile, I thought.

We were still climbing, banking right now, topping the ridge. The pilot found a hole in the overcast, bumped through, and we were in clear blue.

I'd managed a final glimpse of Lowe's wreckage: a scattering of blackened metal along a devastated tree line, the burnt bones of the wings of a dead bird. Then I forgot, slipped free of the noose.

Making light of my fear-induced error, I said, "Knowing how the grunts operate, they'll probably shoot up and eat up the load right where it landed." Nobody in the cockpit seemed to be listening.

For days afterward, I kicked myself: I remembered my perfect drops at Khe Sanh when it was under siege and the DZ was a postage stamp, a square 150 feet on a side, one-sixteenth normal size. Day after day the weather at Khe Sanh was absolute dog shit. Murk hugged the ground and a C-130 let down on guidance from the portable Ground Control Approach or from the navigator's airborne radar whenever the GCA was under attack or temporarily blown away, which was nearly always. During GCA letdowns, the gooks shot into the clouds: by monitoring approach frequency, they heard range calls and, when an airplane reached a known distance from the field, they put up a steel curtain at that point in hopes of getting lucky. Sometimes it worked.

When a Herky finally slipped out the bottom of a cloud deck, hurling along at a hundred thirty knots (losers averaged faster than that at Indy) and three hundred feet above the ground (within bow-and-arrow range), then the gooks who had trenches up to the perimeter of the tiny base and who actually stole CDS bundles from off the drop zone because that was how close they were, then those little mothers really opened up with the crossfire.

From low altitude in daylight, a flight crew had difficulty seeing small-arms tracers fired at it. At Khe Sanh, ground observers made certain the crews knew what was happening with encouraging radio calls, such as, "Charley is really hosing your ass. Solid streams! I can't believe you're not taking hits. Goddamn! You should see this!"

There was no such thing as evasive action: it screwed the lineup and ruined the drop.

A navigator had no time to worry about ground fire. After the plane broke out of the clouds, a nav had less than two minutes to move forward and verbally aid the pilot with final lineup, return to his desk to check drift and ground speed and to recompute timing while reading final checklist items to copilot and loadmaster, then rush to the copilot's side window to find a predetermined landmark from which to start timing for the drop.

Despite every obstacle, on ten missions to Khe Sanh I stacked bundles on the lilliputian DZ, one right atop the others, like an A&P display. And then, at A Luoi, I panicked and missed by six thousand feet—*panicked when the whole world was on my side*. My failure was enough to make any navigator worthy of the title fall onto the points of his dividers in disgrace.

Of course, I had watched others visit Choke City.

On one delivery to Khe Sanh, we broke out of the murk too late and too far right for any chance at lineup. It was obvious that the pilot would have to make a low-level go-around while we ate ground fire. Oh, well, what the hell, I thought, nobody won them all. Taking a second glance out the front window, I was startled to see that the pilot was boring straight toward a peak north of the base.

About then, Major Jerry Prager, who was copilot, asked, "Sir, you see that hill?" After several moments passed without the pilot answering, Prager pointed and said, "There is a hill there, sir." By then I was hanging over Prager's shoulder and also pointing. The pilot, a crusty old LC, continued to stare blindly straight ahead.

The plane was ten seconds from becoming a permanently implanted monument to inertia when Prager boldly announced, "I have control of the airplane." He cranked the wheel hard left and banked away from the peak; then he flew the plane back across the base, lined up aimed at the DZ, and said, "You have it, sir, if you want it."

Coming out of his trance, the pilot said, "Yes. Thank you." From there we went in and made a perfect delivery.

The old LC never explained what went wrong. Nobody ever asked. Every man was entitled to one mistake, I decided, and, if lucky, he got away with it.

* * *

About a year later, back in the States, I was marched in front of a three-star general to receive the Distinguished Flying Cross. Normally, trash-hauling was second-string work. Herky crewmen got Air Medals and that was about it. However, at the squadron commander's direction, the awards and decorations officer selected what he considered to be each individual's best mission and wrote it up for a DFC, a little bonus for the year if Seventh Air Force approved.

As I stood tall before the general, memories of Khe Sanh flooded my mind, produced a lump in my throat. Khe Sanh had been a high point of the war, forever memorable, even if controversial. And I had played a small role in that drama. I smiled at the general and whispered, "Khe Sanh."

As he prepared to pin on the DFC, his adjutant read "... distinguished himself ... near A Luoi ... in support of a major offensive underway in the A Shau Valley. Flying through mountainous terrain under extremely adverse weather conditions ... unerringly navigated his aircraft ... exposed to heavy hostile ground fire, Zorn calmly directed his crew in the highly successful delivery of their essential cargo ..."

Once again I felt the silk noose tighten. That time it choked my vanity.

Amazingly, within a month the dry season seemed never to have happened. I had helped to destroy more than a thousand trucks—1,084, to be exact—and in my memory they now appeared as an unscheduled series of selected short subjects.

I likened the operation of my mind to that of a cantankerous television receiver. When I tried to tune in the details of a specific show/mission, I frequently received only a test pattern, or static. Then, at times when I wasn't the least interested in watching television, the set flipped on by itself and a graphic selected short feature beamed through to me as vividly as the original action.

Mainly, only the sensational remained.

For example, while reading in the base library, I suddenly recalled blowing three tanker trucks that were in the middle of a shallow stream. It was as real as if it was happening right

255

then. Chief Bender was the pilot and, when the third tanker exploded in flames, he let out a tremendous war whoop. "Fucked again by the white man's magic," he shouted into the night.

The three fires expanded in size and merged into one. Flames reflected off the water and made the stream glisten from bank to bank. Reflected brightness illuminated the steep bank toward which the tankers had been headed and revealed to me a long line of tanker trucks snaking up the hillside. The trucks, still on the road, were hidden far under the trees. On TV they were visible from only one quadrant of the orbit and, without light from the raging fire, they easily could have remained undetected because the IR was inoperative. I was lucky to spot them.

Chief Bender used the misch metal and within half an hour the stream bank was an inferno. I first shot the vehicles highest up the trail, which switched back on itself. In that way, flaming gasoline poured down the hillside and ignited things below. The chief whooped with every new explosion. To top it off, there wasn't a round of triple-A. We simply flew circles and burned two dozen gasoline trucks, turned the stream to a lake of fire.

Afterward, Chief Bender treated the crew to breakfast because twenty-four destroyed was his highest score of the war.

In June I flew three times: one sortie down into the Basket, one up into the Barrel, and a final trip to Steel Tiger. It remained that way until I went home in September: two or three trips each month into Commando Basket or Barrel Roll in support of friendly troops. Mostly, however, we inspected cloud tops and qualified for flight pay, and for combat pay without being shot at. Simply flying over certain areas was enough to be certified for combat pay. Fitz probably would have argued that, in our case, that too should have been waived. Every Spec had enough trip-A backlogged to qualify for combat pay until he retired, Fitz might have said.

Only a couple of the missions are worth talking about. One was the farewell trip to Steel Tiger in late June . . .

* * *

Through a gap in the cloud deck we found two vehicles at a road intersection northeast of Saravane. Different targets which were always the same, I thought. On the NOD, I was lending experience to a crew that had been with Spectre less than a month.

In order for crews to fly an uninterrupted dry season, the greatest turnover in Spectre personnel took place during the wet season. A few crews were rotated into theater during the dry season as replacements in the event of combat losses, such as when Rabbit's crew bought the farm.

Back on that late June night, we fired away trying for burners. We weren't wasting time. The new pilot, a captain, showed class with the Forty. "You hit the one closest to the intersection again," I reported.

"Seventh hit on that one," the navigator said.

"Lucky seven," said the pilot.

"He's never gonna burn, sir," a gunner said.

"You're probably right," the pilot said, "but there's not that much out here tonight. What say we hit them one more time. Sound OK to you, Colonel Zorn?"

I was in hunchbacked pain from bending over the NOD. I too doubted that the trucks would burn, but it was good training nevertheless. "Sounds perfect. But let's have the IR track for a while."

"IR in," the table nav said.

The pilot said, "Then let's also switch to the other Forty. Complete change of luck. Maybe with it we can—"

A geyser of flames appeared near the intersection.

"Jesus . . . one of those—"

The first yellowish-orange explosion was followed by another of equal force. The fountains of fire weren't centered on the trucks but appeared beside them. Instantly, in line with the first two, a third explosion spurted upward.

"There's a—"

"What the—"

In three distinct rows, explosion after explosion erupted inside the orbit. Blossoms of equal size, evenly spaced, advanced toward the gunship. Recognition of a bombing pattern overrode my astonishment. "Arclight," I shouted. Spectre was circling in its path. "Break right," I called.

I suddenly was racing across the broad gulf between fear and terror.

My mind focused on a single desire: to escape the falling bombs that produced the inferno below. "Break right," I called and felt my stomach turn hollow. Knowing that the sky was alive with iron, I practically felt air and earth vibrate and shudder beneath the weight and impact of the indiscriminate target-hungry bombs. In a perverse reversal of roles, I had become a target.

I knew at once that the situation was hopeless. I knew the power of an Arclight strike. The gunship would not escape the cascading death that filled the blackness of space above, would not escape the iron waterfall of manmade destruction. My scrotum contracted. My throat clogged.

Arclight was the code name for B-52 Superfortress area bombing. During my first tour of duty in SEA, at night from the roof of a billet in Saigon, I often had watched and heard and felt the power of Superfortresses dropping mere conventional weapons, so-called iron bombs, the instruments of limited war. A freight train laded with destruction, each B-52 was weighed down with 500-and 750-pound bombs crammed into its twin bomb bays and suspended from pylons strung beneath its wings. One B-52 carried 108 bombs in all, a total of sixty-seven thousand pounds of destructive force.

Basically, B-52s operated in threes, a delta of terror. Coasting six miles high in V-formation, like an aluminum cloud dense with explosives, three Superfortresses rained over one hundred tons of iron in a pattern that saturated a coffin-shaped area three kilometers long and one kilometer wide. At ground level nothing survived whole.

The bombers' muted performances had been awesome when I watched from the billet roof in Saigon, miles and miles from target areas as far away as Cambodia. First, sporadic yellow and red flashes flared from the darkness beyond the horizon to the west. Then an aurora of copperish gold arose, the pinkish glow of Thai gold faded into view, hung along the distant skyline. A luminous band of sunrise, out of time and place.

Muffled thunder built slowly, grew in volume like the

rumbling tattoo of bass drums crescendoing. Responding to the beat, the earth came alive to the tempo, made my building tremble and sigh, then groaningly sway in synchronization to the pulse of ground shock waves. Doors fluttered a rat-a-tat and window panes vibrated, hummed in sympathy, tinkled like wind chimes to the tempo of shock and to the wordless song of overpressure. A concerto of pain flowed from one tortured nation to another.

I also had overflown areas punished by B-52 strikes. Overflying the boxes, I felt adrift in the middle of nowhere, feared being trapped by the unheralded reappearance of indiscriminate destruction that already had preceded me.

Above, the apparently empty sky waited to be cleaved with long slashes, trailing wounds that healed themselves instantly, waited to be cleaved broadly by heavy, plummeting iron released silently from invisible airships guided by compartmented, oxygen-breathing robots. B-52s dropped their weapons upon command of an earthbound controller, a man in a radar site designated MSQ, pronounced "miscue." A mistake? An error?

To anyone on the ground, the exploding bombs seemingly appeared from nowhere, could have sprung from the soil as easily as fallen from the sky.

Below, gaping, unhealed terminal points of the six-mile-long slashing air wounds testified mutely. During the rainy season hundreds of pools, thousands of pools, reflected chalky sun and steel sky. In dry times the landscape stared back with a pocked barrenness, the laterite ghost of a deceased alien planet.

And now I was trapped on such a planet.

"Break right," I pleaded.

The pilot twisted the airplane into a steep right bank. Flung off-balance, I slammed against the NOD, rolled off to the left, banged my flak helmet and shoulder on the side of the NOD opening, then crashed to my hands and knees. I clawed the deck until I found a chest-pack parachute.

Hugging the pack, I snapped its right ring into the right clip of my harness but failed to align the left ring with the left clip. When I missed I was surprised, felt more vulnerable. I had practiced the hookup flawlessly hundreds of times with eyes closed. Now frustrated, a touch embarrassed, I slammed the left side of the pack against my chest, failed once more, then slammed it again and again with irrational madness. I suddenly understood that if I didn't connect the left ring to the left clip I was going to die. The parachute was my sole salvation. Struggling to my feet, I continued slamming the parachute pack against my chest as if I were a malfunctioning automaton. Never looking or feeling, I depended upon luck alone to accomplish the hookup in the dark.

Throughout my struggle and while the pilot was performing a breakaway maneuver, the table nav gushed words that denied reality, sounded worse than any sick joke. "We're not in an Arclight area," he stated. A daily schedule of proposed Arclights was posted at Intelligence; the navigator was responsible for the knowledge. "We didn't receive a warning call. It can't be an Arclight," he declared. Ten minutes before a drop the Airborne Command and Control Center broadcasted a set of coordinates and warned aircraft to avoid that location by ten nautical miles. "Somebody really messed up," the navigator insisted. "If there isn't—"

"Break right again," the rear scanner shouted. "That stuff's following us."

My initial breakaway call hadn't cleared the gunship from the bombs' relentless stream. It merely had headed the plane downstream in line with the flow. The pilot horsed the airplane into another steep turn while my mind calculated wildly: one-fifty knots for the gunship against four-fifty for the bombers . . . that made overtake time of the bombs . . . Jesus, 324 bombs! . . . what was density of coverage? . . . forget that . . . what was overtake? . . . would the answer be in time or distance?

No answer came to me. My mind shut down and I was helpless: unable to work mental problems, unable to physically clip ring to harness, unable to bail out the NOD hole because of the spinning left inboard propeller, far too far from the ramp. Everything was against me.

Sweat ran coldly down my rib cage and I shivered. Why this? Why now? There were no answers. I gave up trying: forgot the problems, stopped struggling with the parachute. Closing my eyes, I saw everything clearly. I was nothing. I was a dead man.

"That stuff's going off under us," the rear scanner said.

I visualized the bombs slashing downward. Any one bomb was capable of obliterating the gunship. Trembling, I pressed my arms tightly against my chest. I was nothing. I was helpless against the world, as helpless as those I had consumed. Hadn't I known that?

Absolute justice blazed into my darkened sight. The creator of a thousand holocausts was to be devoured in the all-consuming flames of an airborne crematorium.

Opening my eyes, I felt as if I were a newly born infant who, upon emerging from the blackness of the womb, immediately recognized that someday he would possess the capacity to intellectualize, perhaps to understand the meaning of life; yet in the same instant he knew with dialectic certainty that he was dying, was about to be killed in the very instant of his birth of insight. For the first time I knew for certain that *I did not want to die.*

Hate burst from me. *What a stupid-goddamn-fucking way to die,* I thought. After all I had been through, I was going to die a meaningless death. Killed by those cocksucking robots in the B-52s! Had I possessed the power to strike them dead or to knock them from the sky, I would have used it without hesitation. Yet against them I was helpless. I was nothing. It wasn't fair.

Whatever animal resided within me grew mad with a lust to kill. I went insane with a rage to kill one more time before I perished . . . to kill anything . . . anything I could get my hands on . . . kill . . . destroy! In desperation I attacked the NOD, rammed a shoulder into it again and again, tried to break it off its mount, wrestled it with all my might, snapped it left-right-up-down to tear it loose. But it was stronger than me. The son of a bitch!

With icy terror transformed to incandescent rage, I was drenched with sweat, blinded by the salt of my body.

261

Wrapping my arms around the NOD, I strained to uproot it, strained until I trembled with fatigue, strained until saliva flew from my grimacing lips. Sweating and drooling and panting, I took a new stance and a new grip and heaved anew, heaved upward, lifted with every muscle contracted, heaved until my thighs popped, muscles tore, and I screamed in agony.

Lame, staggering in pain, I sobbed and swore at the NOD, but I wasn't finished. I attacked once more, slapped, kicked, punched until my fists ached, then butted with my helmet, hugged the NOD and beat my head against its deathless metallic form. "I am nothing," I whispered through pain and tears.

"You can roll out on this heading," the rear scanner said. "Them bombs passed us." After several seconds, he added, "Looks like we're safe."

Interphone was silent. I leaned backward against a bulkhead, closed my eyes, and snapped the left parachute ring to the harness. So easy . . . I undid the ring and snapped it in place again. My arms trembled. Unclipping the chest pack, I dropped it to the deck. My head throbbed, pulse pounded in both temples. I realized how tightly my jaws were clenched, wondered why my teeth hadn't crumbled. I ached all over, was without strength, arm weary, hobbled, weak-kneed, dripping with sweat. I leaned into the chilling slipstream and a shiver ran the length of my hollow body. I was a shell, totally empty within. The fire was gone.

Was a single stroke from the chilling finger of naked terror enough to mark a man forever, to inscribe a permanent remembrance of mortality?

The navigator spoke first. "My fault. I misplotted the Arclight area. I heard a warning about ten minutes ago but thought we weren't near it. I misplotted the coordinates." He breathed heavily. "I'm sorry, I . . ."

I sat on the deck, gritted my teeth. Pain was my only companion. Would my body ever heal? A rubdown seemed futile, distant . . .

The copilot said, "I monitored that call. I should have double-checked."

Somebody said, "Jesus fuckin' Christ, what're you two doing . . ."

There was a long silence before the pilot asked, "Now what?"

I voiced my thoughts and surprised myself. "Fuck it. Let's go home."

And we did.

Chapter 24

The Last Time

FOR A GUY who seldom dreamed, I suddenly had more than enough of a sweaty, technicolor, recurring nightmare.

Always I was in the gunship, trapped at the isolated NOD position, surrounded by a yellow cocoon of fire. I waved my arms to fend off the flames but instead my gestures seemed to hug the flames to me until I was set ablaze like a strawman, made to jig in a halo of painless fire while my exposed face was seared to an ebony crust, turned from flesh to ironwood. With gloved fingers I touched my ironclad face, produced no sensation of agony, felt only a rigid, icy grimace.

In desperate, futile escape attempts, though I had no parachute, I ran aft and leaped off the gunship's ramp. Was I fleeing from the airplane or from myself? Expecting to fall like a stone, I instead floated like an ember on the cold night—a faint spark of life.

Overhead, the gunship was a flaming torch, radiated the energy of infrared and radar and radio waves—a growing electromagnetic nova amid black isolation.

The nova turned to a waterfall of standing yet falling flames that cascaded down upon me, passed through me as much as washed over me. The falling yet stationary fire filled the night with the brightness of daylight, revealed a landscape of war as remote and as alien as a lost planet.

After a few nights, I recognized the fiery events as a dream, recognized my mind's tricks as a lucid nightmare beyond control. I understood that within the dream I was fated not to die, that despite the yellow flames I would not follow my inevitable path from ashes to ashes. My incinerations were nothing more than symbolic rituals designed to leave my face charred, hardened into a living ebony death mask for the world to see.

Near the end of the dream I was miraculously transported to a familiar setting—the O-Club dining room, or the squadron briefing room, or a bathhouse—where I slinked along walls, gravitated to corners, turned my face so that others could not see the shame of my disfigurement.

But someone always saw me—my father, or a forgotten girlfriend, or my daughters, or dead mother—persons out of time and place, out of context—and when they failed to recognize me but nevertheless recoiled in horror, then I wept in self-pity for my lost identity.

One afternoon over a sandwich, I described my nightmare to Dick Kaulbach. He nodded as if he understood every word. He finished his sandwich before he smiled and said, "Dreams are bad habits we learn as children."

Following that conversation—or was it a confession?—my nightmare vanished. My sleep grew as cold as the ashes of a fire that long ago had warmed me during the cruel winter of war.

At the same time, I no longer was the same person, no longer considered myself a solitary man. I felt a constant dread of something vaguely ominous about to happen. Had I been infected with the dreams and anxieties of everyman, a waking rather than a sleeping curse?

One last flight worth describing, a trip into Cambodia, wrapped up the year. The flight wasn't my final combat mission but it should have been. I no longer deserved to fly.

In a small clearing in the middle of the jungle directly west of Pleiku, I located seven huts. The setting was like an illustration for a story by Kipling: through a break in the clouds, huts neatly circled a large bonfire.

"TV tracking," I said and the pilot rolled into orbit.

The bonfire's intensity overdrove the camera beam current and momentarily blacked out portions of the television picture. I had the wide-angle camera display on my small monitor and telephoto on the large. By jiggling the cameras I elongated the blackened spots into streaks and made the scene appear as if ghostly figures were racing between the circled huts. Shadows cavorted. What the hell was going on, I wondered. Were the people who lived down there insane?

By then, the IR operator, Dennis Kohler, was describing the huts for the crew's benefit. Practically on sight I'd been irritated by Kohler, an overweight captain who also was overly fawning. I'd grown angry after I'd explained a search technique that wasn't written anywhere, a technique only Schmidt and I used, and Kohler had accepted it without asking its origin. *A blind follower*, I'd thought and had been tempted to make up another technique, something totally wrong and asinine, to see if Kohler would buy it.

Before I could say anything about the huts, the table navigator was on the radio to Moonbeam, the Airborne Command and Control Center, with a request to validate them: friend or foe? Schmidt and I had always made our own decisions, I remembered. Weren't the huts in Cambodia?

The gunship circled, awaited Moonbeam's reply.

It was a little after two in the morning, I noticed. What was going on down there in the huts? Was what I viewed the aftermath of some feast, some ritual? What was the date? July something . . . no holiday I knew of. Now, there was no sign of activity. Earlier, had I seen shadows or people? Any sane person was in bed, I thought. Or had the people run away? Had they heard the gunship prowling overhead? Did they know its lethal power?

What if they were drunk on home brew, passed out, had carelessly left the fire burning, figured they had nothing to fear or didn't know any better? I wanted to shout, "Are you all insane? How have you survived this long with that attitude?"

A Moonbeam controller called back. "We have no friendlies at those coordinates. Anything there can be considered hostile."

After validating the message, the navigator said, "We're clear to hit them."

"IR tracking," Kohler said softly, then looked over his shoulder at me. His eyes begged approval. I stared back. *I had found the huts and they were mine.*

"Who you want in the computer?" the table nav said. Was he asking me or the pilot?

Silence bred consent, I knew. Within the gunship, silence sealed approval on group actions. No single man was guilty. Through mutual consent each man became part of the relentless machine, part of an arrogant force infinitely more powerful than any individual. Yet couldn't an individual, particularly a sensor, master that power? Wasn't one man's strength enough to halt the machine? Did stopping the machine require greater courage than any of us had displayed thus far?

"Wait a minute," I said.

After a silent ten-count, the pilot asked, "TV, you want to hit them?"

Kohler said, "Looks good to IR."

"Hold it," I commanded. They had waited for Moonbeam and now they could wait for me, I decided.

With his bulk turned sideways in his seat, Kohler watched me. Squeezed into a flak helmet, Kohler's fat, red-lighted face appeared gluttonous despite not yet having tasted what it was offered. Studying Kohler's pig face, I felt as if I understood everything while understanding nothing.

None of my sensors, none of the airplane's technological miracles could have given my present view into myself. With a distinctness beyond the capacity of manmade devices, I centered the vision of my inner eye on the core of my being.

Did the war really matter? Did its outcome have consequence for me? Hadn't I returned to Southeast Asia because I'd wanted to be omnipotent, because I'd wanted to get even, to kill? Hadn't I come for the excitement, for the danger, for my own glorification? Or had I come because I had been bored, because I'd had no idea of what else I wanted from life? Had I come because I possessed a death wish, sought an honorable escape from life?

Now I had done those things: used power ruthlessly, killed,

faced the danger, earned more medals. And now I was bored again, a boredom predicated upon resignation, remorse, and a sense of self-inflicted defeat. I felt the psychological weightlessness of a kind of eternal homeless desolation that one might feel if marooned alone in space with no place or no one for comfort. I realized that now I more than likely would not die, would not be killed. The dangerous days were behind me. All that remained was to live.

The huts revolved on the television screens before me, my confined world.

Let the innocents down there survive another day, I told myself. The thought that sooner rather than later those careless creatures were certain to be blown away made my stomach churn. Helpless, I wished that I could provide them sanctuary forever, grant them an Eden within the war.

During the year I had seen that there were limits to fury. Now I discovered limits to compassion. And, if there were limits to compassion, I wondered, were there also limits to atonement? When did a man become totally lost? When did he reach the point from where there was no return?

At the time, my imperfect reasoning could not comprehend that a man could choose not to destroy in hopes of gaining salvation from his own destruction. Was it wrong to want to live? Wrong to want others to live? In later years I gave a name to such compassion. Redemptive insurance, I called it.

"Nobody's down there. Nothing's going on," I announced.

"We could waste the buildings," Kohler suggested like a fanatical voice from my pitiless past.

I stared icily at Kohler, then said, "Pilot, let's go somewhere else, find something worthwhile."

"Roger that," the pilot said and broke out of geometry. "Heading, nav?"

Kohler gave me a short, snappy salute before turning to his console. Was he agreeing with me or mocking me? Did it matter?

But then, in the next instant, I knew Kohler was wrong in

not insisting that we strike the huts. Would Schmidt or Sueno have permitted such a decision on my part? With a jolt I remembered the videotape recorder. I forced my guilty eyes to look at its control box. The tape wasn't running. My conscience felt clean.

Chapter 25

Time Is on My Side

YEARS LATER, THERE were times late at night when I was doing nothing more than nodding off in front of "The Late Show," times after I'd wasted an entire day, when suddenly I would come wide awake, keenly alert, and remember friends killed in plane crashes, in combat or in accidents, from years before. Steve Lowe . . . Rabbit . . . Board . . . Keith . . . Harlan . . .

What would they be doing if they were alive, had survived the intervening years? Would they now be as lethargic as I was? As contented to do nothing?

I imagined them resurrected, forced to spend the remainder of the night with me. Would they understand my ability merely to sit, to accomplish so very little in the course of a day?

I would have found it difficult not to gloat in their presence. Like a time thief, I possessed and wasted what they never had had, what was most precious: the future.

What would they do with a single night, a single hour back on earth, resurrected physically rather than merely spiritually from the womb of my mind?

Epilogue

For the 1971–1972 dry season the Spectre fleet was increased from twelve to eighteen gunships. Most important, however, the aft 40-mm gun was replaced by a 105-mm cannon which immediately became the star of the motion picture "AC-130 SEA Gunship Activity—The Best of the Week." When fired from an orbiting airplane, the big gun was a staggeringly awesome weapon. Its thirty-three-pound warhead emerged from the eleven-foot barrel at a muzzle velocity of fifteen hundred feet per second, less than half the speed of the 40-mm, and was visible on the sensor's pictures for several seconds during its downward trajectory. As if in slow motion, the warhead inexorably arced from slightly off-center at the top of the sensor presentation to the target in the dead center of the screen. The warhead in flight looked like a falling anvil attracted by some powerful, hidden magnet. The warhead exploded with a fierce flash followed by a blossom of smoke that lingered about the impact point. When the warhead struck a truck, the truck was torn open, ruined. The simile was completed: it looked as if an anvil had been fired through the vehicle.

Depressed from the horizontal like the other guns, the 105-mm cannon's huge barrel was so long that for takeoff and landing it had to be retracted to the recoil position. The big gun fired with a loud *whoom* that resembled a gigantic rush of air more than an explosive report. With the gunship banked in orbit, the gun recoiled upward for a distance of four feet along a heavy steel sleigh assembly and then slowly counter-recoiled back to the battery position. Compared to the 40-mm, which was bolted to the cargo compartment floor, the movement of the big gun in that confined space was frightening. "That fuckin' sleigh ever fails," the gunners agreed, "the whole gun'll go clean out the top of the airplane." In gory detail they speculated about what would become of anyone who happened to stand in the path of the recoiling mass of metal during normal operation.

The 105-mm cannon proved equal to what designers at the Aerospace Systems Development laboratory had anticipated when they modified the model M102 for use in the airplane: a single direct hit really did destroy a vehicle. Regardless, Seventh Air Force Headquarters retained the criteria that ruled vehicles had to blow up or burn in order to be considered destroyed.

(Author's Note: In the fall of 1971, on a range at Eglin Air Force Base, Florida, I participated in live-fire missions similar to the one Holcomb's crew flew for General Hunchworth. We test-fired the 105-mm cannon at vehicles, tanks, and other assorted military hardware. From the results I saw, I conservatively estimated that there was no more than a twenty percent chance that a truck would be operable after being hit with a 105-mm round.)

Statistically the 105-mm warhead was far superior to the 40-mm. It weighed 32.85 pounds and produced more than three thousand pieces of shrapnel, in sizes up to six hundred grains (the weight of one and a half silver dollars). The shrapnel traveled at a speed of four thousand feet per second (twenty-seven hundred miles per hour) and had a lethal radius of forty feet against vehicles and two hundred feet against personnel.

The ASD laboratory also perfected a trainable mount for the 105-mm cannon and thereby eliminated the need for precision flying to align the guns with where a sensor was aimed. Instead, the pilot merely flew a bank angle based upon the aircraft's altitude. Then, electro-hydraulic gun mountings allowed the sensor operator to move the 105-mm barrel as much as fifteen degrees in any direction. In essence, the sensor operator sighted the gun from a stable platform maintained by the pilot. An electronic symbol on the sensor display showed where the gun was aimed; when satisfied with the alignment, the sensor operator depressed a "consent" button and the gun fired. The modification brought spectacular results: the average time spent in hitting a vehicle at least once was reduced to three minutes.

By the 1971–1972 dry season, the Ho Chi Minh Trail had been expanded to twenty-seven hundred miles of roads compared to eight hundred in 1966. There was enough traffic to fill the network. Spectre's initial truck-kill rate was better than any previous season, more than twice as good as the previous year:

Nov/Dec	Destroyed	Damaged
1970	425	246
1971	780	1143

On 10 January 1972, a pair of SA2 Guideline missiles were launched at a flight of F-4 Phantom jets over Steel Tiger. The F-4s escaped unharmed. The following day USAF Intelligence confirmed the deployment of SA2s into Laos with coverage extending over the Demilitarized Zone and northernmost region of South Vietnam. Aircraft operations in those areas were temporarily curtailed.

The speed with which the series of events occurred made crewmen wonder aloud if higher headquarters had stashed away the missile information until forced to reveal it. "It's based upon a need to know," explained one of the F-4 pilots who had been fired upon, "and the crews don't need to know about all the crap that's waiting out there to zap them."

The AC-130 was not designed to go up against SA2 missiles, but Seventh Air Force planners continued to target the gunship into Steel Tiger. Spectre crews used a groping attack: each night they hunted trucks on the fringes of the trail and then worked inward toward the more heavily defended main arteries. However, at the first electronic indication of missile activity, they had Seventh's permission to run for their lives.

Despite the hazardous situation, Spectre's totals nearly

matched those of the previous dry season, although the percentage of destroyed vehicles was lower:

1972	Destroyed	Damaged
January	838	1,450
February	829	1,482
March	853	1,200

Everyone from the lieutenants in Intelligence up to the editor of *Aviation Week* had predicted a major North Vietnamese Army offensive in mid-February, but that month and the following month passed without significant action.

On 30 March the North Vietnamese Army swept across South Vietnam in what the news media labeled the "Easter Offensive." The previous night in Steel Tiger, ten miles southwest of Tchepone, an SA2 destroyed an AC-130 and killed its crew.

On 2 April, Easter Sunday, another AC-130 was downed by an SA2. The missile clipped off a large portion of the gunship's right wing but, miraculously, the pilot held the airplane level until the crew bailed out. Fourteen parachutists went into the jungle of western Laos and at daybreak fourteen crewmen were rescued by Jolly Green Giant helicopters, the largest SAR pickup in USAF history.

The loss of two AC-130s within a week caused Seventh planners to suspend gunship operations in Laos and in Military Region I, the area immediately south of the DMZ in Vietnam.

Spectre's role as the ultimate truck buster was ended.

The battle for An Loc began on 7 April 1972. In capturing Loc Ninh, district capital of Binh Long Province, the NVA routed South Vietnam's Fifth Infantry Division, which fled southward toward Saigon. When the fifteen thousand men of the Fifth Infantry reached An Loc, they learned that their avenue of escape along Route 13 had been cut ahead of them. Further retreat was impossible. They were surrounded. They decided to make a stand.

On 13 April, in a day-long assault, three thousand men and forty tanks of the NVA captured the northern half of An Loc. Two days later, Radio Hanoi claimed victory.

At that point Spectre entered the battle.

Seventh AF assigned Spectre the task of providing around-the-clock close air support to the beleaguered South Vietnamese in An Loc. Flying at altitudes above ten thousand feet in order to have time to react to shoulder-launched SA7 Strela missiles, Spectre crews still managed to place 105-mm rounds as close as across the street from friendly troops and made firing corrections as small as one meter. Within three days, the 105-mm cannons of the continually orbiting gunships leveled the portion of the town held by the NVA and forced its troops and tanks to flee to the surrounding countryside. The remaining nine thousand men of the Fifth Infantry Division at last had breathing room.

On 20 April, Spectre's big guns destroyed six Soviet-built T54 tanks during a short-lived encounter. A South Vietnamese relief column was reported to be fighting its way up Route 13. A glint of optimism appeared in what otherwise was a bleak picture.

Throughout the siege, the South Vietnamese forces at An Loc were supplied by C-130 Hercules airdrops. While making low-level daylight deliveries on 18 April, a C-130 was shot down and several others were seriously damaged by concentrated small-arms fire. The following day, a flight engineer was killed instantly by a bullet which struck him in the left temple when his airplane passed over the drop zone. That single bullet was the only one to strike that airplane.

Before the week ended, two more C-130s on low-level daylight drops were shot out of the air.

After the third C-130 and crew went down, a new high-altitude night delivery technique was put into use and proved eighty percent effective.

On 21 April the South Vietnamese Army abandoned its counterattack up Route 13. At An Loc the battle of attrition continued.

On 27 April, using its favorite 130-mm field gun, the NVA

artillery punished the remaining eight thousand An Loc defenders with a barrage of nearly twenty-three hundred high-explosive shells. Spectre crews orbited and watched the seventy-five-pound shells hammer the town. They were unable to locate the heat signature of the NVA guns. A Spectre fire-control officer explained the problem. "The NVA digs guns in separately rather than lining them up in nice straight ranks. It's not Waterloo. Each gun is at a different range and azimuth from the target. They fire sequentially whenever they want all the shells to arrive at the same time. They did it at Dien Bien Phu. They did it at Khe Sanh. And they're doing it here. That muzzle flash out there by itself lasts about a second. You blink, you miss it."

Throughout May the fight for An Loc was stalemated. The NVA kept the town surrounded and Spectre kept the NVA from overrunning it.

The siege ended in June, when the NVA pulled back its forces. One third of the original fifteen thousand men of the South Vietnamese Fifth Infantry Division survived.

During the siege of An Loc, Spectre crews encountered IR-seeking SA7 Strela missiles. Dozens of the shoulder-launched weapons were fired at gunships. The SA7's effective and absolute altitude were the same, around ten thousand feet. Only one Strela hit a gunship. The missile was passing well abeam of the aircraft when it suddenly veered hard left and homed on the 2KW searchlight which inadvertently had been left operating in the IR mode. The missile rode the beam until it struck the gunship. The fuselage suffered limited structural damage.

To counter missiles Spectre received wing pods which dispensed chaff to blind guidance radar, and an ejector system which launched flares with an IR signature that attracted heat-seeking warheads better than the gunship. Additionally, Spectre was repainted a ghostly gray to dim its IR image.

Following An Loc, and despite selective deployment, two more AC-130s were shot down before 1972 ended.

* * *

Spectre flew its final SEA combat missions in support of Operations Eagle Pull and Frequent Wind, the evacuations of Phnom Penh and Saigon, and by striking naval vessels during the SS *Mayaguez* incident.

Beginning in 1983 in the permissive arena of Central America, the sixteenth SOS began surveillance support to deny the dark to guerrillas in El Salvador. To cover areas that are of concern to the United States, the gunships operate from Howard Air Base in Panama. With the help of air refueling, missions last twelve hours or more, long enough to survey an area from sunset to sunrise.

Spectre's long-range capability and endurance have been unquestioned since a November 1979 exercise in which four AC-130s flew nonstop for twenty-nine hours and traveled from the United States to Guam.

With a smattering of Vietnam veterans and a bunch of new guys, the sixteenth SOS reconfirmed old truths and verified new concepts during the Invasion of Grenada in 1983.

Deploying directly from home base at Hurlburt Field in the Florida panhandle, three AC-130s flew nonstop to Grenada and then provided close air support throughout the day and night.

One gunship's initial sortie lasted fifteen hours, with eight and a half of those hours spent on call over the island. After the fifteen-hour flight, the crew landed, heard ground forces needed more assistance, and immediately refueled and relaunched to fly another five hours.

"On the way down we refueled twice in flight—no, make that three times," a Spectre crewman said. "I forgot one because I was asleep. We had augmented crews. Everyone got a chance to take a break." Each gunship carried six substitute crewmen.

Arriving over Grenada prior to dawn, about two hours before the invasion task force, the first Spectre gunship reconnoitered the Point Salinas airfield for the planned landing of follow-on MC-130 Combat Talon transports carrying U.S. Army Rangers. When TV and IR revealed vehicles and construction equipment parked on the runway, the Spectre crew warned the inbound Talons. The assault landing was changed to a low-altitude air drop.

Probing with sensors, the gunship crew also analyzed the antiaircraft threat, found 23-mm and 12.7-mm weapons. (Later, 37-mm cannons were found in storage on the island.) "The defense had been well thought out," a pilot said. "I didn't anticipate as much triple-A as we received." He estimated that three hundred rounds of 23-mm were fired at his plane.

With their array of cannons, Spectre crews had the appropriate firepower for each situation. "Surprisingly we fired a lot of 20-mm, especially against trip-A sites," a Spectre said. "The high rate of fire really cleared the crews from around the antiaircraft guns."

During the first day, at certain periods three gunships were over Grenada at the same time, stacked at different altitudes. In one instance, firing from opposite sides of an orbit, two gunships simultaneously struck enemy forces that had surrounded the Governor's House and provided instant relief to troubled friendlies.

Spectre crewmen recounted the following:

—In two instances when Rangers requested fire support around the Point Salinas airfield and the Spectre crew put down a single 105-mm shell as a marking round, the Rangers reported that no further firing was necessary because the accuracy of the marking round had made the enemy surrender. In addition to referencing with marking rounds, ground forces used signal mirrors to coordinate with the gunship crews.

—In an attack on three armored personnel carriers, a Spectre crew fired only four 105-mm rounds. All were direct hits.

—When U.S. forces came under fire from enemy troops who were holed up in the center building of a three-building complex, a gunship crew destroyed the enemy position without damaging the building on either side.

—Because of a solonoid malfunction, one Spectre crew was forced to fire its 105-mm gun manually. "It was like being in the field artillery," a Spectre weapons mechanic said. "The pilot would line up his display, then he'd holler 'Fire,' and we'd pull the lanyard." The man sadly admitted, "We weren't as accurate as when the computer does it all by itself."

—Pinned down behind a vehicle on the runway at Point Salinas, two Rangers were under heavy fire from a nearby machine gun. After they called for help, a Spectre crewman told them that they were so close to the target that they risked injury from the gunship's ricochets or shrapnel. One Ranger radioed back, "You shoot them or they shoot us. Take your pick." The gunship destroyed the machine-gun position and the Rangers walked away. (Author's Note: The ultimate sin in Spectre would be to fire on friendlies. To my knowledge, it has never happened. Precise navigation aids, high-resolution sensors, emphatic training, and disciplined crew coordination have kept the record clean. Each crew, however, never learns exactly how close to friendly troops it can safely fire until the situation demands it.)

—After an army helicopter was shot down near Point Salinas, the survivors came under fire. To get a navy rescue helicopter to the downed men, a Spectre crew cleared a path with gunfire while simultaneously guiding the rescuers with directions from its sensor operators.

—"Several times we put down fields of fire that kept the enemy away from our guys," a crewman said. During the first day and a half, the gunships fired more 20-mm and 40-mm ammunition than had been anticipated. "Carrying the larger guns, we sometimes forget how effective the Twenties can be," a pilot said. "We learned a lot of things that can be used to improve future operations." For example, a minor problem occurred on the first day when there was no ammunition available to rearm one gunship's 20-mm cannons.

After the first day and a half of operations, the Spectre gunships were limited to surveillance and selective firing. The change was not due to lack of ammunition, however. By then, supply problems were solved, but targets were scarce and fleeting. Flying throughout the nights, Spectre crews coordinated with ground patrols to enforce curfew. Surveillance also kept suspected enemy personnel contained in the Calivigny area. On the third day, the AC-130s followed navy fighter-bombers in a coordinated attack on a terrorist training camp.

During the first days of the invasion the gunships operated from Barbados. When the initial three aircraft were joined by three more, part of the fleet was dispersed to Puerto Rico because of a shortage of ramp space at Barbados' Grantley-Adams airport.

What had been planned as a one-day operation turned out to be an eight-day commitment for the sixteenth SOS. During that extended period Spectre provided either airborne or strip alert crews for around-the-clock coverage of ground activities.

When the island appeared to be secure and the AC-130 crews requested to redeploy, the Airborne Division commander delayed them. He told his joint task force staff that he would give up his offshore naval gunfire, his land-based artillery, and his helicopters before he would release the Spectres. He wanted their timely surveillance and instant, accurate firepower on hand as long as there were enemy soldiers unaccounted for. "Spectre is enough," he told his staff.